Jokes Cracked
by Lord Aberdeen

JOHN CAMPBELL
HAMILTON-GORDON

1st Marquess of Aberdeen and Temair,
Earl of Aberdeen, KT GCMG GCVO PC

Jokes Cracked
by Lord Aberdeen

The Friday Project
An imprint of HarperCollins*Publishers*
77–85 Fulham Palace Road,
Hammersmith, London W6 8JB
www.harpercollins.co.uk

This hardback edition 2013

1

First published in Great Britain by
Valentine and Sons Ltd, Dundee and London, 1929

John Campbell Hamilton-Gordon asserts the moral right
to be identified as the author of this work

A catalogue record for this book is
available from the British Library

ISBN 978-0-00-753235-3

Printed and bound in Italy
by L.E.G.O. SpA

INTRODUCTION

By John Finnemore

I suspect you have picked up this book for the same reason I did. I may of course be doing you a terrible injustice – it may be that you're a huge fan of Scotland's foremost late-Victorian aristocratic comic, and have been counting the days until this chance to revel again in some of his classic gags. However, I suspect that you, like me, picked up this book because the cover made you laugh. And I further suspect that the reason the cover made you laugh was because you couldn't imagine that his Lordship ever could.

I mean, look at him. That shaggy beard, that granite face, that forage cap. It's hard to picture the Most Honourable John Hamilton-Gordon, 1st Marquess of Aberdeen and Temair ever even cracking a smile, far less a joke. And it's that word 'cracked', I think, that makes the title so funny. These aren't just jokes he knew, or even jokes he told ... these are the jokes Lord Aberdeen *cracked*. Immediately, you picture a cavernous banqueting hall, moth-eaten stag's heads are gazing down at the shivering guests, glumly chewing their tatties … when, suddenly, a strange glassy look comes into the eye of their host. His moustache twitches. His wife, ever-alert to the warning signs, stifles a sob and flees from the room. The guests are not so lucky. With a wag of his finger, Lord Aberdeen alerts his ancient butler, who staggers over to ring the brass bell that has been installed for just this purpose. 'Pray silence,' he intones. 'His Lairdship wishes to crack a joke.' Lord Aberdeen rises to his feet, clears his throat seven or eight times, and says something like this:

'A young man had occasion to move from where he had hitherto lived, to another district. He had been associated with Presbyterians in his former abode, but it occurred to the clergyman of the Episcopal Church in the neighbour-hood that the young man might suitably be invited to become a member of that Church. This was accomplished; but not long afterwards it transpired that he was about to join the Roman Catholics. On hearing this a friend of the Rector, who, like himself, was a keen curler, remarked, "Man, you've souppit him through the Hoose."'

Yeah? Hello? Is this thing on? Oh, come on! He'd souppit him! Through the Hoose! Because, he *had been* associated with Presbyterians in his former abode, but *now* … oh, never mind. Tough crowd.

And, if that's what you're hoping for from this book, you will not be disappointed. You will find that joke on page 24, where even the editor at the time has

– presumably after staring at it blankly for ten minutes – entitled it 'For Curlers Only'. And I can't pretend it's the only one of his Lordship's rib-ticklers that is baffling, unfunny, or bafflingly unfunny. 'The Tandem Story' is a consummate exercise in taking one very, very slight glimmer of humour, and relentlessly beating it to death; and I don't even understand the *title* of 'Fact-Up To Date'.

Nor is the Marquess's tone that of a natural comedian. His Lordship is scrupulous about giving credit for his gags where it is due, which is very laudable, but does result in build-ups such as: 'A reminiscence concerning the late Dr. Campbell, Bishop of Glasgow, which he probably narrated himself, and which at any rate would be thoroughly appreciated by him was ...' I would not recommend this approach should you ever be invited to appear on *Live at the Apollo*.

Sometimes he goes even further in his desire to set the scene. One story begins: 'Some years ago at one of the Sir Walter Scott Anniversary Dinners in Edinburgh, I had the advantage of sitting next to Sir Arthur Conon [sic] Doyle. We were both to make speeches later, and perhaps this prompted me to mention ...' He then relates the joke he told Conan Doyle ... and that's it. There's no record of what Doyle thought of it, or replied – his only role in the story is to sit there, silently enduring Lord Aberdeen's joke. Perhaps there's a whole other book to be written there: *Jokes cracked at Sir Arthur Conan Doyle*.

So, yes, as you rightly suspected as you gazed into those sad and slightly wonky eyes, you are not in for a

laugh riot. But nor is he quite as bad as all that. There
are, I submit, funny jokes in this book, if you can look
past the natural distancing effect of the language. My
second favourite is this one:

> A lady remarked to a former Bishop of
> London on one occasion 'Oh! Bishop, I want
> to tell you something very remarkable. An
> aunt of mine had arranged to make a
> voyage in a certain steamer, but at the last
> moment she had to give up the trip; and
> that steamer was wrecked; wasn't it a mercy
> she did not go in it?'
> 'Well, but,' replied the bishop, 'I don't
> know your aunt.'

Now, come on! That's not bad! And surprisingly cruel.
Modernise the language and I reckon you could get a
laugh (from a tolerant audience) with that today. Which
is pretty good, coming from a late Victorian Governor
General of Canada.

My favourite actually made me laugh out loud when I
first read it. I mean, not much, we're not talking breathless paroxysms of mirth here, but definitely audibly. I
genuinely like it, especially the punch-line. I feel I should
let you come across it in the course of the book, but I will
just say it's the one with the unpromising title 'A Curious
Mistake'. Oddly, it also concerns the death of an aunt.
Every comic has a theme that brings out the best in them,

and for Lord Aberdeen, it would seem, as for P.G. Wodehouse, it was aunts.

The illustrations in this book are rather nice, as well. I like the Gothic up-lit quality the artist has given to the Bishop/Aunt story mentioned above, and there's an excellent horse on page 21. I also enjoy the chap who has fallen asleep in church on page 11, and whose beard and moustache are apparently taking the opportunity to scuttle quietly off of his face.

So, look. Like you, I picked up this book to laugh *at* Lord A, rather than with him. But having read it, and as someone who knows all too well what it's like to write jokes that aren't as funny as you hoped they'd be, I find myself oddly protective of the author. I like that he enjoyed cracking jokes; I like that despite being a Marquess and a former Lieutenant Governor of Ireland he didn't think it was beneath him to publish a book of them, and I quite like, ooh, at least six of his jokes. So, here's to John Hamilton-Gordon. Long may he have them rolling in the aisles ... or at least souppit through the Hoose.

(Speaking of which ... in curling, you want to sweep the ice enough to get your team's stone to the target, or 'House', but not so much that it overshoots. Meanwhile, the Presbyterians are an extremely low church denomination of Christianity; Catholicism is of course a very high church; the Episcopalians are somewhere between the two. By encouraging the new arrival to join his church, only to lose him to the Catholics, the Rector has metaphorically swept him through the House ... or souppit him through the Hoose! You see! It *is* funny! It is! Where are you going? Come back! I've got a great one about an aunt ...)

JOKES CRACKED BY
LORD ABERDEEN

THE MOST HON.
THE MARQUESS OF ABERDEEN AND TEMAIR,
P.C., KT., G.C.V.O., G.C.M.G.

Jokes Cracked

By

Lord Aberdeen

Illustrated by D. C. EYLES

FIRST EDITION, 1929

PRINTED AND PUBLISHED BY

VALENTINE & SONS, Ltd.

DUNDEE AND LONDON

Printed in Gt. Britain.

FOREWORD

N the realm of Wit and
Humour, Lord Aberdeen
is a name to conjure with.
All the kindly geniality of
the North comes out in his rich
repertoire of stories, and here the
Publishers have pleasure in introducing to a wider public a few Gems
from his collection.

CONTENTS.

✚

	Page
A Curious Mistake	33
A Few Sparks	36
A Misapprehension	28
A Question of Binding	35
A Recent Howler	27
A Repartee	34
A Satisfactory Will	30
A Small Crop	20
Advice	22
After-Dinner Speakers	26
An Irish Story	19
An Offender	14
Animal Food	5
Another Irish One	29
Blind on Sunday	6
Dinna Boast	12
Fact—Up to Date	20
For Curlers Only	24
Foreword	4
He Couldn't Say	25
His Time was up	11
Hotel Accommodation	35
In the Spirit Line	15
In the Wrong Train	28
Keep on Blowing	22
Longing for His Living	6

	Page
Mr Spurgeon's Diplomacy	30
No Blame of His	26
No Coward	7
Not So Black	32
Pinching and Pinching	31
Reservoir and Tanks	29
Something for Golfers	36
Something Funny	27
The Business Heads	34
The Capital of Scotland	12
The Doctor's Cure	33
The Effect of Nervousness	31
The Fool of the Family	9
The Invitation	10
The Monkey Story	16
The Pouthers	24
The Provost's Chains	32
The Red Herring	10
The Speaking Horse	23
The Tandem Story	17
They Tossed for it	13
Travelling under the Seat	14
Try the Empire	8
Uncut Books	18
Unsettled	8
Where the Jarvey Scored	21

ANIMAL FOOD.

A certain Scot was not very well, and the doctor was called in. On making enquiries the doctor found that the man was mainly depending on farinaceous food, living, as his wife admitted, on "porridge and milk and whiles brose and tatties," so he said : "I think your husband should take some animal food ; it will brace him up."

The wife seemed rather dubious, but replied, "Well, I suppose he micht try."

"All right" said the doctor, "I had better call again in a few days to see how he does."

And sure enough, in due course, the doctor arrived and on asking the wife how the new diet was suiting her husband, received the following reply :

" Weel, he manages middlin' well wi' the neeps ; and whiles the linseed cake, but oh ! doctor, he canna thole the strae ! " (he cannot stand the straw).

LONGING FOR HIS LIVING.

In the Scottish Presbyterian Churches there is a plan whereby a minister who, through advancing years, finds the burden of his charge too heavy, can be partly relieved by the appointment of what is known as an " assistant and successor."

In this way an element of permanence is secured for the assistant or colleague, since, humanly speaking, it is only a matter of time when he will have full charge, and the full stipend, such as it may be.

I remember that the late Dr. Marshall Lang, who was a Moderator of the Church of Scotland, and latterly Principal of the University of Aberdeen, when speaking on a subject which included the above arrangement, said that he had heard of an elderly minister who once said to his " assistant and successor : " " I suppose, my young friend, you are ' thinking long ' for my dying ? "

" Ah, no, sir," replied the younger man, " you must not put it so ; for it is your living that I desire."

BLIND ON SUNDAY.

Dauvid : " I didna see ye, Sandy, at the Kirk on Sabbath."

Sandy : " I noticed that, when I was takin' up the collection."

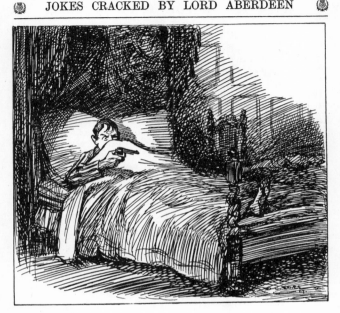

NO COWARD.

A young man arrived unexpectedly at the house of some friends in the country. Could they put him up for the night ? Well, they were about full—but, yes, there was one room still vacant, so he could use that. In due course the visitor was conducted to his room, the hostess remarking—" After we had taken the lease of this house we found that one of the rooms was supposed to be haunted ; but I daresay you are not superstitous about that sort of thing." " Oh, well, no," said the visitor, " I don't trouble about such tales." When alone, he surveyed the room. It seemed to him to be rather a gaunt sort of place and somewhat chilly. He began to ruminate as to why such a rumour as he heard should have existed, and he decided that in case there should be any humbug of any sort he would place a small pistol, which he always carried in his dressing-case, by the bedside. Soon he fell asleep ; but in the dim, grey light of early morning he awoke, feeling far from comfortable, and soon espied at the foot of the bed the appearance of a hand, in upright position. This seemed uncanny, and after a few moments he reached for his pistol, and then said very deliberately, " Now, I am no coward ; but if that hand is not removed when I have counted three, I shall fire—One, two, three—*Bang !*—Oh ! ! " And ever since that morning one of the toes of that man's right foot has been missing.

TRY THE EMPIRE.

A reminiscence concerning the late Dr. Campbell, Bishop of Glasgow, which he probably narrated, or which at any rate would be thoroughly appreciated by him was, that some English friend, once addressed a letter to " The Right Rev. the Bishop of Glasgow, The Palace, Glasgow." The letter was returned from the Post Office, marked, " Not known at the Palace—try the Empire."

UNSETTLED.

" I've seen better days, sir " said a tramp to an Aberdonian, who replied, " So have I—but I havna time to discuss the weather the noo."

THE FOOL OF THE FAMILY.

A retired naval officer had a son, a smart boy, who
joined the Navy. While the lad was with his ship
at one of the British Naval Stations, it occurred to
his father that as an old friend of his—a retired
Admiral of some note—was living in the neighbourhood, he would send to his boy a note of introduction
which he might present personally to the veteran
Admiral, and this was done. The note was opened
while the midshipman deferentially waited. The
old Admiral, though kind-hearted, was somewhat
gruff, outwardly, in manner. After reading the note

he said : "So you have joined the Navy : fool of
the family, I suppose—eh ? "
" Oh, no sir " was the respectfully uttered reply,
" they've changed all that since your time, Sir."

THE RED HERRING.

A Highlander looked into a village shop one evening
and asked for something which would do for his
supper on his way home. The shopman suggested
a red-herring. " But," asked the Highlander, " what
way would I cook it ? " " Oh," said the shopman,
" just give it a sight of the fire." The Highlander
took the herring accordingly.

The distance which he had to go was considerable.
Darkness was coming on and he was getting hungry.
It happened to be about Hallowe'en time, and some
boys had kindled a bonfire near the road. The
Highlander thought this would be a good opportunity of letting the herring see the fire, so he held
it up opposite the blaze ; but after a few moments
the string to which it had been fastened got loose
and the herring fell down. The Highlander groped
for it in the damp grass at the roadside and got hold
of what he imagined was the desired article and
immediately rammed it into his mouth ; but in
reality it was a frog, which naturally resented the
operation ; but the Highlander exclaimed " Kick
here, kick there ; ye hae seen the fire and doon ye
maun go."

THE INVITATION.

" Jock, will ye dine wi' me the morn's nicht."
" Aye, Sandy, I will."
" Guid ! Eight o'clock at your hoose."

HIS TIME WAS UP.

In most Scottish Churches it used to be the custom to take up the collection by ladle.

A man had on one occasion accidentally dropped a half-crown, instead of the intended penny, into the receptacle. This worried him very much—and the following Sabbath when the ladle was passed before him he pretended not to see it, and put nothing in. The officiating elder, who knew of the previous mishap, quickly sized up the situation and did not further obtrude the ladle. On the following Sabbath the same thing occurred, and after a while the elder practically ignored that member of the congregation; but he had kept note of the date; and on the thirtieth Sunday after the half-crown had been given, he held the ladel in front of the con-tributor, and whispered, "Your time is up now, Geordie."

DINNA BOAST.

A young woman who had obtained a situation in the South of England, was asked by the lady by whom she was employed: "Annie, I know of course by your tongue that you are Scotch, but you have never mentioned the part of Scotland from which you come. Which is it?" "I come from near Aberdeen, Ma'am," she replied. "Oh, indeed," said the lady, "but why did you not tell me before?" "Weel, I didna like tae dee that, Ma'am, because when I was leaving hame ma Mither said, 'Noo, Annie, be sure an' dinna boast.'"

THE CAPITAL OF SCOTLAND.

But the Scot, especially the youthful Scot, is not always so reticent. For I heard of a boy who on being asked, "What is the capital of England?" replied "Scotland!" "Indeed!" remarked his questioner; "and what would you say is the Capital of Scotland?" "Aiberdeen!"

12

THEY TOSSED FOR IT!

Two school boys, brothers, were invited by an aunt to spend part of their holiday at her place in the country, the aunt having indicated that she would be very glad to have one of them—she could not take both.

In due course one of the brothers arrived. On being asked how he and his brother had decided who was to come, the visiting boy said, "We tossed for it." "Oh, indeed," said the aunt, "and you, of course, were the winner." "No," replied the lad, "I lost."

TRAVELLING UNDER THE SEAT.

A party of young men were returning one evening from a football match somewhere south of London. One of them, taking off his bowler hat, inserted his ticket in the hatband, so as to make sure of producing it when required, and then relapsed into slumber. His companions observing this, quietly removed the ticket without disturbing him.

By and by, Vauxhall was approached and the cry "All tickets ready please," was soon heard. The sleeper was nudged by his companions and warned that he would have to show his ticket immediately. He hastily examined his hat and then his pockets.

" Any o' you chaps seen my ticket ? "

" Why, have you lost it ? "

" Yes, thought I'd put it in me 'at."

" Well," said the others, " you'd better look out, you'll be fined if you're caught travelling without a ticket."

" What d'you think I'd better do ? "

" 'Ide, man ; git under the seat."

Quickly this was done and in another moment the ticket-collector appeared. " Tickets, please," and all were handed to the collecter, who said ; " Why, there's only five of you gents. and you've given me six tickets ! "

" Oh, it's all right, ticket-collector, we have a friend here, but he prefers to travel under the seat."

AN OFFENDER.

On the way home from the Kirk—" Did ye hear Duncan snorin' i' the sermon ? "

" Aye did I ; it wis disgracefu' ; he waukened's a'."

IN THE SPIRIT LINE.

On one occasion a well - known Bishop travelled to a town about 45 miles from Aberdeen to perform some Church function; and when this was completed, there was still a considerable time to wait before the next train. Accordingly, he adjourned to the hotel. There he was welcomed by the proprietor who said : " I think your lordship should take a seat in the commercial room; there is a good fire there, and a comfortable arm-chair."

To this arrangement the Bishop at once agreed. There was no one else in the room at first; but soon

a little man bustled in, and after surveying the intruder for a moment, said : " Excuse me, Sir, but this is the commercial room—reserved for travellers."
" Yes," said the Bishop, " so I understand, but the proprietor was good enough to suggest that I should sit here."
" Then may I ask what line you are in ? "
" Well," replied the Bishop, after a moment's pause, " I'm in the spirit line."
" Oh, in that case," said the commercial man, " of course it's all right."

THE MONKEY STORY.

A certain man received from some friends in the East the present of a monkey. It had been well trained to perform various tricks, one of which was further developed by his owner, namely, the animal was taught to go to the front door when the bell rang, and when the plan was convenient, to lift the latch with his paws and open the door.

In due course the owner and his family happened to arrange to spend a summer at a place in the Scottish Highlands ; and in order to get a little extra fun from the monkey, they dressed up the animal in a kilt. Soon after arrival in the new quarters, one of the neighbours called. The occupants, in order to see what would happen, sent the monkey to the door while they meanwhile took up a position where they could see what happened without being observed. The door having been opened, the caller surveyed the small kilt-clad figure with surprise, and then taking out of his pocket a card, he handed it to the monkey, saying, " Will you give this to your father ? "

THE TANDEM STORY.

The late Mr John Gough, who in early life was ad-
dicted to drink, overcame the habit and for the
remainder of his life was the foremost Temperance
advocate of his time, and his fame as an orator was
widespread. I heard him give an oration at Exeter
Hall, London, under the auspices of the Y.M.C.A.,
to a vast assemblage of young men. In the course of
his speech, he had occasion to illustrate some point
(I do not remember what it was, but the illustration
was vivid). He described how the Curate of a Church
of England Parish started a tandem for a dogcart

(a tandem in those days of course applied only to horses and it was regarded as the most sporting style for a pair). The Rector, however, explained to his Curate that he did not think that this style was quite suitable for a Clergyman. The Curate, deprecating this view, remarked that the Rector himself drove a pair of horses, the only difference being that in that case the horses were placed side by side, whereas in the case of the Curate's dogcart, he merely put one in front of the other, and he didn't see much difference, " Don't you ? " said the Rector, " but position *does* make a difference. Do you see no difference between this ? (placing his hands together in an upright position) and that "—placing his hands, one in front of the other, with fingers extended.

This mode of indicating contempt, still not unknown, was at that time absolutely familiar to every man and boy in the country, and the dramatic manner in which Mr Gough displayed the action evoked a roar of laughter not to be forgotten.

UNCUT BOOKS.

A certain man had built and furnished a new house and was showing it to Cardinal Cullen, who was accompanied by Father Healy. In one of the rooms, on a shelf above the writing-table, there stood a neat row of books. Pointing to them, the owner said : " These, your Eminence, are my friends." But Father Healy chimed in " Yes, and he has treated them like friends ; he has never cut them."

AN IRISH STORY.

During the proceedings of a court on circuit, on a summer day with the windows of the building open, while Curran, a well-known Lawyer, was addressing the court, a donkey in an adjoining field happened to bray loudly. The judge intervening said " Excuse me, Mr Curran, one at a time please." Curran bowed acquiescence, and then proceeded with his speech. Later, when the judge was delivering his charge to the jury, the donkey again brayed; on which Curran rose and said: " I am sorry, my lord, but there seems to be such an echo that I can scarcely make out what your lordship is saying."

FACT—UP TO DATE.

During the latter part of August 1908, a generous American lady had been spending a few days with a friend in Dublin. Her next destination was Aberdeen. The Dublin friend accompanied her to the Station. On arriving at the gate to the platform, the travelling lady showed her ticket to the attending official who, after a casual glance returned it to her. The lady then said to her friend, " You'll come along to the train to see me off, won't you ? " " Oh, but " said the friend, " they won't let me through without a platform ticket ; I'll run and get one." " Oh, but," said the other, " there may hardly be time for that," and she added with a smile, " I'm sure the Ticket Inspector will let you through." On hearing this remark, the official said, " Will you please let me look at your ticket again, Madam ? " The ticket was at once produced. After looking at it for a moment, the official said, " Ah ! yes, just as I thought, ABERDEEN."

A SMALL CROP.

Some time ago there was a good deal of discussion about artificial manures, some of which had been greatly advertised as likely to be of enormous value to farmers. Someone declared that he had heard of a Scottish landed proprietor who said to his farm steward : " The time is coming, John, when I shall be able to carry in one pocket of my waistcoat, what will fertilise a whole acre of land." " Deed, sir, and I'm thinking maybe ye'll be able to carry the crap in th'ither pouch ! "

WHERE THE JARVEY SCORED.

The late Senator Kirchhoffer of Canada, well known and very popular, happened to stay for a few days in Dublin, and used to narrate with relish to his friends, the following characteristic repartee, at his own expense.

He had hired an outside car, and at the end of the trip, handed to the Jarvey what he (the Senator) knew was the full fare. The Jarvey, however, who of course had observed that he was driving a stranger, and also perhaps one from the other side of the Atlantic, suggested an increase, but the Senator remarked that he was sure the payment was correct, adding " I am not such a fool as I look," to which the Jarvey replied, " Indeed, yer honour, I wish you were."

KEEP ON BLOWING.

During a special Church service, in which the music formed a prominent feature, the organist when completing—with full force—a fine piece on the organ, was disgusted by finding that the wind had been allowed to fall short, and the disastrous effect can be imagined.

In those days hand-blowing for pipe-organs was the usual method ; and the organist seizing a slip of paper, wrote something on it with a pencil hurriedly, folded it up, and then beckoning to a verger who happened to be near, whispered rapidly a request as to the delivery of the note.

The verger did not hear distinctly what was said, but as the preacher for the occasion was just then ascending the pulpit he (the verger) assumed that, as often happened, he was intended to deliver to the preacher a request that some intimation might be given from the pulpit. Accordingly he succeeded in handing to the minister the little slip of paper.

The minister at once unfolded it and was astonished to find that it contained the following message :

" When once you begin to blow, keep on blowing till I tell you to stop."

ADVICE TO A YOUNG SPEAKER.

" Remember three things. Stand up; speak up; and soon, shut up.

THE SPEAKING HORSE.

The following conversation is supposed to have taken place between two Irish farmers.

" By the bye, Mr Cassidy, how is that little horse doing, which I sold to you a year past ? "

Cassidy : " He did very well at the first, but I am sorry to tell you he has lately had a pretty bad attack of the vernacular."

On hearing this, a bystander remarked, " Well, it's a queer thing, but I never before heard of a four-footed animal suffering from that complaint, saving only, Balam's Ass."

FOR CURLERS ONLY.

A young man had occasion to move from where he had hitherto lived, to another district. He had been associated with Presbyterians in his former abode, but it transpired that his views in Church matters were not of any rigid sort. It occurred, therefore, to the clergyman of the Episcopal Church in the neighbourhood that the young man might suitably be invited to become a member of that Church. This was accomplished ; but not long afterwards it transpired that he was about to join the Roman Catholics. On hearing this a friend of the Rector, who, like himself, was a keen curler, remarked, " Man, you've souppit him through the Hoose."

THE POUTHERS.

An old farmer had become a widower. A neighbour called to express condolence. The old man in gratefully accepting the assurance, said that he would like to tell his visitor the circumstances of the loss he had sustained.

" A while ago I wasna feelin' verra weel, an' I sent word to the druggist telling him what like the trouble was, an' he said he wid sen' me some pouthers ; but by the time the pouthers cam, I wis feelin' a good piece better ; so I jist put them past, thinkin' they micht be o' some e'es anither time ; an' then soon efter, the wife took ill, so I thocht she wad be better for the pouthers, so I gied them till her, but she didna improve ony ; and sune she jist slippit awa."

" Dear me," said the visitor, " how very sad."

" Ay," said the other, " it's terrible ; but man, isna it a maircy I didna tak' thae pouthers masel' ? "

HE COULDN'T SAY!

A lady remarked to a former Bishop of London on one occasion, " Oh! Bishop, I want to tell you something very remarkable. An aunt of mine had arranged to make a voyage in a certain steamer, but at the last moment she had to give up the trip; and that steamer was *wrecked*; *wasn't it a mercy* that she did not go in it? "

" Well, but "—replied the Bishop, " I don't know your aunt."

NO BLAME OF HIS.

A certain man had a wife who was unfortunately of a querulous disposition, and who was apt to lay the blame of any mishap upon her husband, whether deservedly or not. He, however, being a peaceably disposed person usually accepted this with philosophic calm.

After a while a shock of earthquake was experienced in the locality. It was not very severe, but it was sufficient, in the case of the cottage of this couple, to cause the crockery which was placed on the kitchen " dresser " to fall to the floor with a clatter and much breakage, This of course was very upsetting to the housewife.

After comparative quiet was restored, the husband remarked, in contemplative tone, " Weel, that's the first time in saxteen years, that I hinna been blamed for onything wrang in this hoose."

AFTER-DINNER SPEAKERS.

Some years ago at one of the Sir Walter Scott Anniversary Dinners in Edinburgh, I had the advantage of sitting next to Sir Arthur Conon Doyle. We were both to make speeches later, and perhaps this prompted me to mention to my neighbour the story of how, when a Shah of Persia visited this country he was entertained (amongst other functions) at a banquet in the City of London. Soon after the repast had commenced, the Shah, surveying the scene, as his manner was, through large blue spectacles, asked the chairman : " Who are those men who look so gloomy ? Are you going to cut their heads off after dinner ? " The chairman replied, " No, your Highness it's not so bad as that, but these are the men who have got to make speeches after dinner."

SOMETHING FUNNY.

A young lady meeting Father Healy one morning, greeted him thus : " Oh, good morning, Father Healy. Now, won't you say something funny ? "—to which came the prompt reply, " Well, I'm glad to see you : isn't that funny ? "

A RECENT "HOWLER."

In an upper class school in Glasgow the other day, a pupil was asked, " What is a *Centipede* ? "
Promptly came the reply,—" A *Centipede* is a man that has lived to be a hundred and can still walk upon his feet."

27

IN THE WRONG TRAIN.

Perth Railway Station is well known as an extremely busy place; and the traffic was not always so effectively arranged as it is at present. Sir Harry Brooke, K.B.E. used to tell of a man who had occasion to change his train at Perth. He had a good deal of luggage, which he entrusted to a porter with instructions to be sure to put it into the train for his destination, while he went to the refreshment room for tea. While he was there one of those nerve-racking bells clanged loudly. The passenger hastily left the refreshment room and proceeded to the part of the platform where a train was standing which he imagined was the one he had to take; but as it moved away, he observed with disgust his luggage still on the platform while the porter stood seriously surveying it. Irritated, he called out, "You silly fool, why didn't you put my luggage in?" To this the porter also now annoyed shouted back "Your luggage is nae sic a fool as yersel; you're in the wrang train!"

A MISAPPREHENSION.

A young American friend told me that when a friend of hers was going through a large Upholstery establishment, she was shown an apartment in which there were several very luxurious-looking couches and cushions, with every appearance of oriental luxury. The visitor remarked, "One feels as if these cushions ought to have Sultanas resting upon them," to which the attendant replied, "Well, yes, perhaps; only, that might attract mice."

JOKES CRACKED BY LORD ABERDEEN

RESERVOIR AND TANKS!

An Englishman, who was saying Farewell to a French acquaintance, and who wished to utter the appropriate expression, (though his knowledge of the French language was slender) said, " *Au reservoir* " to which the Frenchman, whose knowledge of English was likewise imperfect, replied " *Tanks.*"

ANOTHER IRISH ONE.

" An Irish Census Recorder on enquiring—" How many males in this house ? " received the reply— " Three of course ; breakfast, dinner and tea ! "

MR SPURGEON'S DIPLOMACY.

The late Principal Rainy told me the following story about Mr Spurgeon, the celebrated preacher.

During the zenith of his fame for eloquence Mr Spurgeon observed that near the entrance to one of the Galleries of his Church, (a vast building known as " The Tabernacle"), a group of young men were standing, and in order, apparently, to indicate that they had been attracted, not by the religious, but by the oratorical element in Mr Spurgeon's discourses, continued to wear their caps.

Mr Spurgeon adopted the following method of effecting an alteration.

On the following Sunday he spoke as follows :

" Before beginning my discourse, I wish to mention that recently, owing to a special occasion, I was invited to attend a service in a Jewish Synagogue. On entering a place of worship I was naturally about to remove my hat ; but an attendant courteously intervened, saying, ' Excuse me, we retain the head covering here.' and of course I complied at once with the usage." And then, turning towards the Gallery where the young men referred to were again stationed, Mr Spurgeon continued, " And I shall be glad if our young *Jewish friends*, whom I observe in the North Gallery, will kindly conform to *our* custom *here* in regard to that matter."

The caps were removed *instanter*.

A SATISFACTORY WILL.

"Did you hear that old so-and-so had died ? "
"No ; What was the complaint ? "
"No ; complaints ; all the relatives are quite satisfied."

THE EFFECT OF NERVOUSNESS.

In a certain country district, interest was aroused by the announcement that there was to be an addition to the little community by the arrival of a lady, said to be wealthy, who had taken a place in the locality. Her name was Mrs Broadwood.

One of the neighbours, who had been introduced to Mrs Broadwood, asked a friend who would be likely to know, whether Mrs B. was connected with the well-known piano manufacturers.

" Yes " was the reply, " and I fancy that is the source of her income. But it appears that she does not care to be recognized as directly connected with a commercial undertaking."

" I'm glad you told me," said the other, " because I am asking her to tea, and I shall be careful to avoid allusions to pianos ; indeed, to any sort of musical instrument."

The tea duly took place. All went well, until the guest said, " I think I must be going : would you kindly ask for my carriage ? "

The hostess rang the bell, and when the servant appeared, said to her " Please send for *Mrs Broadwood's piano*——Oh !— I mean carriage ! "

PINCHING AND PINCHING.

A clergyman expounding to one of his parishioners the importance of parents being prepared to make sacrifices for the sake of their children, said, " In order to send my son to college I had to pinch like anything, but I managed it." " Ah, yes, sir," said the parishioner, " but my husband is too much afraid of the law to do anything of that sort."

THE PROVOST'S CHAINS.

Kintore, a small town, about fifteen miles north of Aberdeen, is one of the Royal Burghs in the north-eastern part of Scotland. The railway station is also a junction. In the former days (I am almost inclined to call them the "good old days") of the Great North of Scotland Railway, now part of the L. & N.E.R. when things were done in a more leisurely manner than now, a tourist passenger in a train going North, observing that Kintore did not seem to be a very busy place, asked a porter who was standing on the platform, "Why are we stopping here?" The porter replied, "Ye *maun* stop here, it's a junction ye ken; and forbye Kintore's a Royal Burgh."
"Indeed" said the tourist, becoming interested, "and have you a Provost and Magistrates?"
"Ay, surely," said the porter.
"And does your Provost go about with a chain?"
"Na, he jist gangs aboot loose."

NOT SO BLACK AS HE WAS PAINTED.

A certain man who had "a good head of hair"—jet black—of which he was rather proud, discovered, with chagrin, that grey hairs were beginning to make their appearance. He accordingly took steps to obliterate the colour of these intruders, so as to maintain the uniform colour throughout.
A friend remarked to another as he passed one day. "Doesn't he bear his years well—no signs of grey hairs?" "Quite so" was the reply "and he is a man of whom it may truly be said that he is not so black as he is painted."

A CURIOUS MISTAKE.

About fifty years ago, two ladies, sisters, were living at their home in Scotland. They had an Aunt to whom they were much attached, who was staying for a time with friends at St. Petersburg.

After a while the sisters received unexpected tidings of their Aunt's death.

They felt that the interment must take place in the Homeland, and accordingly arranged with the Russian Authorities that their Aunt's body should be embalmed and sent to their care.

In due course a coffin arrived——but when the lid was removed the ladies found, to their surprise and distress, that the coffin contained, not the body of their Aunt, but that of a Russian officer clad in uniform, with all the insignias of high Military rank.

Immediately a telegram was sent to St. Petersburg, intimating that there had been a mistake, and begging that the body of their Aunt might be sent on without delay. To this message the following reply was received :

" Your Aunt has been buried with full Military honours. Do as you like with the General."

THE DOCTOR'S CURE.

A Doctor on being called in to see one of his patients informed the good lady of the house :

" What your husband wants is complete rest ; and so I have prescribed a sleeping draught."

" Very well, doctor, and when shall I give it to him ? "
" Oh, don't give it to *him* ; take it yourself." he replied.

A REPARTEE.

On the occasion of a Social evening Party at which a Minister—a friend of the family—was expected to be present, some of the younger folk with whom the Minister was popular thought they would like to have a joke at his expense. There was a consultation ; and then, when a suggestion had been made, the others said " Yes, that will do nicely." Soon the Minister appeared " Oh ! Minister," said one of the youthfuls, (with mock seriousness) " there is a certain matter which we don't quite understand, and we would like you to explain it to us ; it is this, ' what is the difference between the Cherubim and the Seraphim ? ' " " Ah, yes," said the Minister, " 'tis true, they did have a difference ; but they've quite made it up now."

THE BUSINESS HEADS.

Perhaps the most judicious, and in some degree unconscious, tribute to nationality, was that which was given by a young man connected with a Scottish business establishment who was sent up to London by his employers on a business mission.

After his return home, some of his family circle asked him to give them his opinion of the English, and to this he replied, " Well, as a matter of fact, I didn't come very much in contact with English people, because my interviews were usually with the Heads of Departments at the various business houses where I called."

A QUESTION OF BINDING.

A successful auctioneer having decided to retire from business, found that he had an accumulation of books, of various sorts, which, from time to time, he had bought in. Wishing to make some use of these, he applied to a bookseller as to having them bound in good style. The bookseller remarked, " I think I quite understand ; you wish to have them bound in a shape which would look well on shelves in one of your rooms ? " " That's just it " said the auctioneer. " Very good," said the bookseller ; " but I must ask whether you would prefer to have the books bound in Morocco or in Russia ? "

" Well, I 'm not particular as to where the work is done," was the reply ; " but could'nt you find some place nearer at hand ? Why not the city of Glasgow ? "

HOTEL ACCOMMODATION FOR SCOTSMEN.

Two Scotties arriving in Dublin to see a " Fit-Ba " match, hailed a cab, and asked to be driven to some place where they could stay. The cabman, thinking that the proper place for strangers (and also not too near the Station, as to fare) would be a High-Class Hotel in the west end, drove thither.

On reaching the hotel the visitors inquired as to the cost of a night's lodgings. When informed that the rooms on the first floor would be two guineas ; on the second floor one guinea ; on the third floor 10s., and on the top floor 5s., they were much taken aback, and on being politely asked if rooms could be booked for them, exclaimed, " Na, na, mister, ye've a fine hoose, but it's nae near heich eneuch."

SOMETHING FOR GOLFERS.

At Pau, the well-known watering place in the South of France, there is a very good Golf Course. Many, and probably the majority of the golfers are British or American. The caddies, are of course all French. On one occasion a player, who was evidently " off his game," foozled frequently, but at last made an extremely neat approach shot, the ball landing nearly " dead." The player's opponent was some little distance away ; but the player, feeling a natural wish for some sign of appreciation, turned to the caddie. The boy at once divined that some admiring expression was expected of him, and exclaimed, with a grin, " Beastly fluke ! "

This incident was mentioned by the Earl of Balfour in his introduction to a golfing Manual.

A FEW SPARKS.

A divinity professor was asked to preside at the baptism of the last arrived infant in the already crowded home of the minister of the parish. The professor gave out for congregational singing one of the paraphrases often used on such occasions in Scotland :

" Let us," he said, " sing from the second verse, ' As sparks in close succession rise.' "

To his consternation he observed that the congregation seemed unable to repress a tendency to giggle.

Afterwards, asking the minister's man what had been wrong, the reply was, " You see, sir, the minister's name is Sparks, and yonder is his tenth bairn."

ABOUT THE AUTHOR

JOHN CAMPBELL HAMILTON-GORDON, 1st Marquess of Aberdeen and Temair KT GCMGGCVO PC (3 August 1847 – 7 March 1934), was a Scottish politician. He served twice as Lord Lieutenant of Ireland (1886; 1905–1915) and served from 1893 to 1898 as the seventh Governor General of Canada. He married Ishbel Marjoribanks in 1877, and they had five children.

DEREK CHARLES EYLES

The delightful images that you find within the covers of this book were created by British illustrator and comics artist Derek Charles Eyles (1902–1974). Eyles was the son of painter and illustrator Charles Eyles, who had worked with the Impressionists in France. Eyles' brother, Geoffrey, was also an illustrator. A thoroughly creative family, overall.

Eyles is renowned for his colour plates and black-and-white illustrations, which began appearing as covers and interior illustrations in boys' annuals in the 1920s and 1930s. Not only did he illustrate magazines like *Wild West Weekly*, he also illustrated novels, including an edition of Jack London's *White Fang*, and children's books such as Charles and Mary Lamb's *Tales from Shakespeare*.

In 1929, Eyles was commissioned to illustrate the jokes you have just enjoyed. Unfortunately, the exact circumstances by which Eyles came to work with Lord

Aberdeen are unknown. However, following publication, Eyles' career went from strength to strength. During the 1930s and 1940s, Eyles painted a series of covers for major publisher Collins' western novels.

Eyles was especially brilliant at drawing horses, which made him perfectly suited to illustrating western narratives, including the adventures of Wild Bill Hickok, Kit Carson and Buffalo Bill. Artists after him were even said to be given samples of his work as examples of how to draw horses properly. However, by the late 1960s the popularity of westerns and other equestrian genres was wavering. Despite finding some commissions in the nursery end of the comics market on titles such as *Treasure, TV Toyland* and *Princess Tina*, Eyles struggled to obtain work.

A diabetes sufferer, Eyles died in December 1974 at the age of 72 following an unsuccessful operation.

THE MARQUESS OF
ABERDEEN AND TEMAIR

The title Marquess of Aberdeen and Temair was created on the 4th January 1916 for John Campbell Hamilton-Gordon, 7th Earl of Aberdeen. In the Counties of Aberdeen, Meath and Argyll, the Scottish title is in the Peerage of the United Kingdom.

The other titles held by the Marquess are: Earl of Aberdeen (created in 1682), Earl of Haddo (1916), Viscount Formatine (1682), Viscount Gordon (1814) and Lord Haddo, Methlic, Tarves and Kellie (1682). These titles are passed down to the Marquess' eldest son and heir. Until this time, the eldest son receives the courtesy title, Earl of Haddo.

The title is still in use today; the present holder of the title is Alexander Gordon, 7th Marquess of Aberdeen and Temair.

DID YOU KNOW ...

- Towards the end of the twentieth century, *Jokes Cracked by Lord Aberdeen* became one of the most sought after out-of-print book in the UK, routinely fetching £100 on Ebay.

- The marriage of Lord Aberdeen to his wife Ishbel was a love match. They were long-time friends and supposedly Lady Aberdeen developed a crush on her future husband at the age of fourteen.

- The Aberdeens referred to themselves as 'We Twa'. Twa is a Scottish variant of the word 'Two'. *We Twa* was also the title of their joint memoir.

- It was widely believed that Lord Loam in JM Barrie's play *The Admirable Crichton* is a satirical depiction of Lord Aberdeen. Like Lord Loam, the Aberdeens organised social clubs for their servants and were rumoured to dine in the servants' hall from time to time. However the Aberdeens' jointly-authored memoir 'We Twa' reprints a letter from Barrie denying this.

- The Aberdeens were famous for their social ideals. They took an active interest in the running of their estate at Haddo, and they shared an intense sense of social responsibility, which ensured a lasting concern for the welfare of their workers; these actions were not considered normal at the time.

- Lord Aberdeen's wife, Ishbel Maria Majoribanks, played an important role in women's rights. She was the first President of the International Council of Women and established the Victorian Order of Nurses in 1897, which continues to play an important role in our healthcare system today.

- Lord and Lady Aberdeen travelled extensively throughout Canada, including a journey to the Canadian Maritimes where they met, amongst others, Dr Alexander Graham Bell, the man credited with inventing the first practical telephone.

- The Aberdeens were enthusiastic sports fans and regularly participated in curling, hockey and sleighing at Rideau Hall, their residence in Canada.

- Lord Aberdeen was made an honorary chief of both the Six Nations and Blackfoot people in Canada.

- Two roads in Canada were named after the Aberdeens; Aberdeen Avenue in Hamilton, Ontario and Aberdeen Street in Kingston, Ontario.

FIND OUT MORE

If you, like us, are fascinated by the enigma that is John Hamilton-Gordon, seventh Earl of Aberdeen, and his illustrator, we highly recommend the following resources to learn more about his life.

We'd like to thank all the contributors to the below sites for having such well-researched information and helping us put together the extra material you found in this book.

The Peerage
(www.thepeerage.com)

The Gazetteer for Scotland
(www.scottish-places.info/)

Clan MacFarlane and Associated Clans Genealogy
(clanmacfarlanegenealogy.info/)

Cracroft's Peerage
(www.cracroftspeerage.co.uk)

Governor General of Canada, archives
(www.gg.ca)

UK Comics Wiki
(www.ukcomics.wikia.com)

And of course, Wikipedia, undoubtedly one of the
greatest sites of all time
(www.wikipedia.com)

Three alluring
on the

Nights of Passion

Three irresistible and inviting romances from
one adored Mills & Boon author!

Nights of Passion

ANNE MATHER

All the characters in this book have no existence outside the imagination of the author, and have no relation whatsoever to anyone bearing the same name or names. They are not even distantly inspired by any individual known or unknown to the author, and all the incidents are pure invention.

First published in Great Britain 2011
by Mills & Boon, an imprint of Harlequin (UK) Limited,
Eton House, 18-24 Paradise Road, Richmond, Surrey TW9 1SR

NIGHTS OF PASSION © by Harlequin Enterprises II B.V./S.à.r.l 2011

Mendez's Mistress, Bedded for the Italian's Pleasure and *The Pregnancy Affair* were first published in Great Britain by Harlequin (UK) Limited in separate, single volumes.

Mendez's Mistress © Anne Mather 2008
Bedded for the Italian's Pleasure © Anne Mather 2007
The Pregnancy Affair © Anne Mather 2007

ISBN: 978 0 263 88436 4

05-0511

Printed and bound in Spain
by Blackprint CPI, Barcelona

MENDEZ'S MISTRESS

Anne Mather says "I've always wanted to write—which is not to say I've always wanted to be a professional writer. On the contrary, for years I wrote only for my own pleasure, and it wasn't until my husband suggested that I send one of my stories to a publisher that we put several publishers' names into a hat and pulled one out. The rest, as they say, is history. And now, more than one hundred and fifty books later, I'm literally staggered by what happened.

I had written all through my childhood and on into my teens, the stories changing from children's adventures to torrid gypsy passions. My mother used to gather these up from time to time, when my bedroom became too untidy, and dispose of them! The trouble was, I never used to finish any of the stories, and *Caroline*, my first published book, was the first book actually completed. I was newly married then, and my daughter was just a baby, and it was quite a job juggling my household chores and scribbling away in exercise books every chance I got. Not very professional, as you can imagine, but that's the way it was.

I now have two grown-up children—a son and daughter—and two adorable grandchildren, Abigail and Ben. My e-mail address is mystic-am@msn.com, and I'd be happy to hear from any of my readers."

CHAPTER ONE

'HE WAS everything a woman might ever want in a man: tall, dark, ruthless good looks masking a dangerous will that had made him a millionaire before his twenty-fifth birthday. He sat beside her on the sofa, too close for comfort, and oozing the kind of blatant sexuality that weakened her defences. Power and determination had made him successful in business, but Lavender had no intention...'

'I don't have to go if you don't want me to, Mum.'

Rachel had been lost in the intriguing love life of her latest heroine when Daisy appeared in her office doorway, but her daughter's words brought a crushing end to that imaginary world.

'Oh, Daisy!' Rachel exclaimed, getting up from her desk to give the girl a swift hug. 'When did I say I didn't want you to go?'

'You didn't,' said Daisy, recoiling from her mother's embrace with all the youthful independence of a thirteen-year-old. 'But I know what you think of Lauren. I don't like her much either. And the last time I visited them they were still living in England.'

Rachel sighed. She was always amazed at Daisy's capacity to understand her feelings. She wasn't always amenable. Like any teenager her age, she and her mother didn't always see eye to eye. But where her father was concerned, there was no contest.

Daisy had known that his invitation to spend at least two weeks of her summer holidays with him and his second wife at their home in Florida could prove controversial. For the first three years of his marriage to Lauren, Steve had only seen his daughter a handful of times, even though Rachel had agreed to share custody. But suddenly, since Steve's move to the company's headquarters in Miami last year, he'd been eager to have her spend every holiday with him.

Rachel hadn't voiced any objections. She wanted Daisy to know her father. But there was still a twinge of apprehension at the thought that Daisy might find life in the United States far more exciting than living here in Westlea, a quiet English country town.

'Look, I don't mind,' she assured Daisy now, refusing to consider how she would feel if Daisy did decide to live with her father. Rachel's unexpected success in recent years as a romantic novelist had proved satisfying, but it certainly wouldn't compensate for the loss of her daughter as well as her husband.

'Well…' Daisy still looked doubtful, and Rachel wanted to hug her again. 'If you're sure?'

'You'll have a lovely time,' said Rachel, unable to resist tucking a strand of dark hair behind her daughter's ear. She paused. 'I just wish your father hadn't arranged for you to travel across the Atlantic with some strange man.'

Daisy laughed then. 'He's not a strange man, Mum,' she protested. 'I have met him before. When Daddy lived in London. He's his boss, actually. His family owns Mendez Macrosystems. Lauren really likes him. I know she thinks he's hot.'

Rachel's jaw dropped. 'Hot?'

'Yeah.' Daisy stared at her. 'Duh. As opposed to boring? Honestly, Mum,' she grimaced, 'if you're writing for a modern audience you ought to know these things.'

'I know.' Rachel was defensive. 'But what makes you think Lauren regards this man as *hot*?' She pulled a face. 'For heaven's sake, she and your father have only been married for four years.'

'And your point is?' Daisy was sardonic. 'Oh, Mum, get real, will you? Women like Lauren are always on the lookout for the next good thing.'

Rachel shook her head. 'I don't think we should be having this conversation, Daisy.'

'Why not?'

'Well…because Lauren is your father's wife.'

'You were Daddy's wife when she decided she wanted him,' pointed out Daisy shrewdly. 'Honestly, Mum, I don't know what you're worried about. If she and Dad get a divorce, you and he could get back together.'

Could they?

Rachel didn't answer her, aware that that option was no longer as attractive as it might once have been. Experience had taught her that Steve Carlyle was not and had never been the man she thought she'd married. Lauren Johansen hadn't been the first female to attract Steve's attention during the nine years of their relationship. She'd just been the richest, and the most determined.

'Anyway, you'll get to meet him yourself before we go,' Daisy went on, reverting back to their earlier discussion. 'Mr Mendez, I mean. When he picks me up to take me to the airport.' She dimpled. 'Wait until I get back and tell Joanne. She'll be so hacked off. I can't wait.'

Rachel groaned. '"Hacked off"? Daisy, what kind of language is that?'

'Okay, green with envy, then, is that better?' Daisy pulled a face. 'Like I say, Mum, you really need to update your vocabulary.'

'Not with words like that,' said Rachel a little prudishly,

and then, realising she wasn't going to get any more work done that morning, she switched off her computer and followed her daughter out the door. 'Anyway, it's lunchtime. Do you want an omelette or a salad?'

'Couldn't I have a ham-and-cheese toastie?' asked Daisy wheedlingly. Lately, since she'd got her period, she was inclined to put on weight rather too easily, and Rachel was trying to wean her onto a healthier diet.

'I suppose so.'

Rachel was pragmatic. Daisy was unlikely to stick to eggs and salads while she was on holiday, so what was one sandwich more or less? Which reminded her, they only had five days before Daisy left for Florida. A depressing thought.

Daisy was due to spend the following day with her grandparents. Steve's mother and father had never approved of their son's behaviour, and as Rachel's parents had died in a car accident when she'd only been a teenager herself, she and the elder Carlyles had always been very close. It meant Rachel would have a whole day to try and catch up with her deadline, which had definitely floundered since Daisy had accepted her father's invitation.

Consequently, she was irritated when the doorbell rang just after eleven o'clock that morning. She wasn't expecting any visitors. There were no edited manuscripts on their way back to her for approval, so it was unlikely to be the postman. And her neighbours knew better than to interrupt her before twelve o'clock.

Getting up, she went across to her office window and looked out. She was seriously considering not answering the door, but the sight of a powerful black SUV standing at her gate caused her to revise her opinion. Who on earth did she know who owned a vehicle like that?

No one.

And then a man stepped back from the shadow of the

overhang and looked up directly at her window. A dark man, she saw, with hair cut so short it was barely more than stubble over his scalp. It was difficult to judge how tall he was from this angle, but Rachel got the impression of height and power, broad shoulders encased in an age-scuffed leather jacket.

She stepped behind the curtain automatically, not wanting him to think she was spying on him, but it was too late. He'd seen her. The second peal of the bell proved it, and with a rapidly beating heart she left her office and hurried downstairs.

As she unlocked the door, she wondered if she was being entirely wise. After all, she was alone here. She didn't know this man, and he certainly looked as if he was no stranger to trouble.

But that was her novelist's imagination taking over, she thought impatiently. He was stranger, yes, but he'd probably picked the wrong address. He might be looking for someone. Julie Corbett, for example. Her flirtatious neighbour two doors down definitely attracted a lot of male attention. The kind of male attention this man had in spades.

She opened the door a few inches, making sure to keep most of her body hidden. Her strappy vest and shorts were not for public consumption, not when she was sure her hips spread every time she sat down at her desk. 'Can I help you?'

The man—she'd been right, he was tall: easily six feet, with a lean, muscled build—grinned at her. His face was darkly tanned, almost swarthy, with well-defined cheekbones, dark, hooded eyes, and a nose that looked as if it might have been broken at some time. He wasn't handsome, as the men she wrote about were handsome, but she had to admit that tough, masculine features and a hard thin-lipped mouth were infinitely more sexy. He was also younger than she was, she decided. But that didn't prevent him from embodying the kind of power and authority that made her catch her breath.

God!

'Rachel,' he said, shocking her still further by his casual use of her name. 'It is Rachel, isn't it?'

Rachel swallowed. 'Should I know you?' she asked faintly, sure that they'd never met before, and he pulled a wry face.

'No,' he said, his accent definitely not English. 'But I know your daughter. Daisy?' And when that aroused no immediate recognition, 'I'm Joe Mendez.'

Rachel felt weak. This surely couldn't be the man who owned Mendez Macrosystems—Steve's boss! It didn't seem possible. Weren't company executives supposed to wear three-piece suits, and ties and lace-up Oxfords? Not black leather jackets over tee shirts and jeans, and sockless loafers that had seen better days.

'I—Daisy's not here,' she said lamely, and Joe Mendez propped a hand against the wall beside the door and regarded her with the same look of tolerance her daughter sometimes employed.

'I didn't come to see Daisy,' he said, glancing behind him at the SUV. 'Is it okay leaving the car there?'

Which seemed to denote an expectation of being invited in. Rachel hesitated. 'It's a quiet road,' she said. Indeed, few unfamiliar vehicles entered the cul-de-sac. 'Um—what can I do for you, Mr Mendez?'

'Joe,' he corrected her evenly. He glanced pointedly over her shoulder. 'May I come in?'

'Oh…' Well, why not? she argued frustratedly. It wasn't as if he was a complete stranger, and she owed it to Daisy to be polite. She stepped back, remembering, as her bare feet protested the chill of the hall tiles, that she was hardly dressed for visitors, but it was too late to think of that now. 'Of course.'

'Thanks.'

Joe stepped into the hall, immediately filling it with his presence, and, leaving him to close the door, Rachel led the way into a rather formal sitting room. It was rarely used, and in spite of the mildness of the day it had a cool, impersonal feel. But she could hardly take him into the kitchen-cum-breakfast room where she and Daisy spent most of their time, could she?

He stood in the doorway, surveying the room, and Rachel gestured rather offhandedly towards the sofa. 'Please, sit down.'

He smiled, slightly uneven white teeth adding to his sensual appeal. Rachel knew she'd never encountered a man like him before and, remembering what Daisy had said, she could quite see why Lauren might think he was 'hot'.

She was relieved when he moved into the room and took a seat on the sofa, although he didn't appear to relax. He sat on the edge of the cushions, legs spread, hands hanging loosely between. And, when he looked up at her with a slightly whimsical expression, Rachel knew he was perfectly aware of the effect he was having on her.

Which made it easier, somehow. If she could just convince herself that she wasn't like all those other women who lusted after him—Lauren, for example—she could handle this.

'Coffee?' she asked brightly, overwhelmingly conscious of her exposed midriff and bare legs. 'I usually make myself a cup at this time of the morning.'

'Sounds good.'

He was easy, and Rachel offered him a smile before quickly exiting the room. Had she time to dash upstairs and put on trousers and a shirt? she wondered as she hurried into the kitchen. But no. That would just be pandering to his conceit, and if you turned up unexpectedly you should be prepared to take people as you found them.

She'd filled the container before going up to work, so all she had to do was turn on the coffee maker. Within seconds the comforting suck and slurp of the filter filled the air and, with a careless shrug, she turned to take two mugs from the wall cupboard above the counter.

'Daisy told me you're a writer,' said Joe Mendez from

behind her, and Rachel almost dropped the cups. Without any apparent sound, he'd left the sitting room and was now standing at the bar where she and Daisy usually ate their breakfast. He'd shed his leather jacket to reveal a tight-fitting body shirt and jeans that rode low on his lean hips, and Rachel couldn't help a certain twinge of resentment that he'd felt relaxed enough to make himself at home.

'Oh, only just,' she muttered at last, setting the mugs on the counter and turning to the fridge for milk.

'You write romantic novels, I understand,' he said, pursuing it. He grinned. 'Where do you get your inspiration?'

Well, not from men like you, thought Rachel, unsure how to answer him. 'I—er—I have a good imagination.'

'Not just that, surely?' He grinned again. 'Daisy's very proud of you.'

Rachel's smile was thin. 'Daisy's biased,' she said, wondering why she felt this need to deny her success. For heaven's sake, she was proud of her achievement. Two successful titles and her agent panting for her next manuscript—it was a would-be writer's dream.

He shrugged then, and, turning away from the bar, he walked to the windows that overlooked the garden at the back of the house. 'Nice view,' he commented, taking in the smooth stretch of lawn, the small summer-house that Steve's father had built when Daisy was a baby. 'Have you lived here long?'

Rachel's lips tightened. 'Didn't Steve tell you?'

He swung round then, hands resting low on his hips, dark eyes frankly curious. 'No,' he said flatly. 'Steve didn't tell me a lot about you. Should he have done? Am I treading on someone's toes here?'

Rachel immediately felt dreadful. 'No,' she said unhappily. 'Sorry. Don't take any notice of me. I was just being bitchy.'

Joe arched his dark brows. 'That still doesn't answer my question: what is Steve supposed to have told me?'

'Oh…' Rachel wished she'd never started this. 'It's just, well, this house used to belong to Steve's parents. They gave it to us when we got married, and…and after the divorce…' She shrugged. 'They wanted us—Daisy and me—to stay here.'

'Ah.' He seemed to understand. 'They didn't approve of the divorce?'

'Something like that.' In actual fact, Steve's parents had been outraged when the son they'd always worshipped had proved to be less than godlike.

Joe looked thoughtful. 'And were you wondering if your ex-husband had sent me here?' he asked after a moment.

It had crossed her mind, but Rachel chose not to admit it. 'I'm just wondering why you came here, Mr Mendez,' she said steadily. Then, as the coffee finished filtering, 'Black or with milk?'

'Black,' he said, as she'd guessed he would. 'And call me Joe, please. Mr Mendez sounds like my father.'

Rachel poured the coffee without answering him. But she was thinking that perhaps she had made a mistake, after all. Perhaps this man wasn't Steve's boss. Perhaps his father was.

The coffee smelt delicious and Rachel, who tended to survive on caffeine during the day, pushed a mug towards Joe Mendez and then lifted her own mug to her lips. It was hot, but so refreshing that she took a generous swallow before looking at him again. 'Shall we go back into the sitting room?'

He shrugged as if it was of little importance to him, but taking his cue from her, he followed her across the hall and into the other room. He waited until she'd seated herself in a tapestry-covered armchair before resuming his seat on the sofa, sampling his own coffee with apparent enjoyment.

'This is good,' he said, glancing round the room as he spoke. Then, his eyes finding hers again, 'I hope I'm not wasting too much of your time.'

Rachel gave a wry smile. 'My work's not that important,' she assured him. She grimaced. 'Actually, I could do with the break.'

'Not going well?'

He sounded genuinely interested and she decided to take his words at face value. 'You could say that,' she admitted. 'Since—well, since Daisy's been invited to Florida, there's been a lot to do.'

Joe regarded her intently. 'You don't want her to go?' he asked shrewdly, and Rachel couldn't prevent the faint trace of colour that entered her cheeks at his words.

'Oh, no. I mean, yes, I want her to go. She hasn't seen her father for almost a year, and it's important for them to keep in touch. It's just…'

'A big step for her to take on her own?' he suggested gently, and she was amazed at his perspicacity.

It suddenly seemed as if she'd misjudged him, and with a rueful shrug she said, 'Yes, I suppose so.' She pulled a wry face. 'I've never even crossed the Atlantic myself.'

Joe grimaced. 'It's not that big a deal. We Americans speak the same language, at least. Even if we don't always understand one another.'

Rachel smiled. 'Are you an American? I thought I detected—I don't know—a faint accent, but I could be—'

'My parents were born in Venezuela,' he interrupted her easily. 'But I've lived in the States all my life. My parents moved to Miami before I was born, and I guess I consider myself an American first and a Venezuelan second.'

Rachel nodded. Almost involuntarily, she was relaxing, and it was only when the phone rang that she realised she still didn't really know why he'd come here.

'Excuse me,' she said, getting up and going out into the hall to use the extension there. 'I won't be a minute.'

He nodded, but she was aware of him getting to his feet

and she made a point of closing the door behind her. Then, hurrying to the phone, she lifted the receiver. 'Yes?'

'Rachel?' It was her mother-in-law, and immediately she thought of Daisy.

'Yes. Is something wrong? Daisy's with you, isn't she?'

'Yes, she's here.' Evelyn Carlyle spoke affectionately. 'We've just been discussing her trip to Florida. Are you sure you're all right with this, Rachel? I mean, Steve has no right—'

'I'm fine with it,' said Rachel quickly, aware of other ears that might be listening behind the sitting room door. 'Is that why you rang, Lynnie?'

'No, no,' Evelyn was swift to reassure her. 'As a matter of fact, I was a little worried about you, dear. Madge Freeman tells me you've had a visitor this morning. She was on her way into town and she saw a strange man at your door, and I just wondered if you were all right.'

Trust Madge Freeman, thought Rachel drily, aware that the elderly lady who lived opposite missed little that went on in the Close. 'I'm okay,' she said now, playing for time. 'How have you had a conversation with Mrs Freeman? Surely she didn't ring you just to tell you I'd had a visitor?'

'Well, no…' Evelyn sounded a little put out. 'Daisy and I bumped into her at the supermarket.' She paused and then continued determinedly, 'So who was it, dear? I told Madge it was probably just one of those double-glazing salesmen.'

Rachel didn't think Joe Mendez would have appreciated being thought of as a double-glazing salesman, but she was curiously loath to discuss her visitor with her mother-in-law.

Which was silly, she told herself, but aware that her conversation might be audible to her visitor, she said, 'It's Mr Mendez. Ask Daisy. She'll tell you all about him.'

'Mendez?' Evelyn evidently recognised the name. 'Isn't that the company Steve works for?'

Rachel sighed. 'It is.'

Evelyn made a sound of impatience. 'So why is he visiting you? Nothing's happened to Steve, has it?'

'Not as far as I'm aware,' said Rachel drily, wondering why her mother-in-law would imagine that she might be informed in such circumstances. 'No, I think he's just come to reassure me that he'll look after Daisy on the flight to Florida.' She hesitated. 'I'm sure Daisy's told you all about it.'

'Well, she's said something,' replied her mother-in-law grudgingly. 'And that's the only reason he came?'

Rachel blew out a breath. 'I think so.' She knew a moment's irritation. 'That is, I'm sure so. But I've got to go, Lynnie. He'll be wondering why I'm taking so long.'

'He's still there?' Evelyn sounded shocked now, and Rachel felt almost guilty for having to admit that he was. 'But it must be over an hour since Madge saw him ringing your bell.'

And your point is? mouthed Rachel silently, copying one of Daisy's favourite expressions. But all she said was, 'I made coffee.' She managed a light laugh. 'And mine's probably cold by now.'

'Hmm.' Evelyn sniffed. 'Well, you'd better get back to your visitor, then, hadn't you? Ring me when he's gone, just so I know you're okay, right?'

Rachel shook her head. Yeah, right, she thought, but with a casual, 'Speak to you later,' she put down the receiver.

CHAPTER TWO

WHEN she re-entered the sitting room, Rachel found it was deserted. The empty mug sitting on the glass-topped coffee table in front of the hearth was the only proof she hadn't imagined her disturbing visitor. Except for Madge Freeman, of course. And that surprisingly testy call from her mother-in-law.

She caught her lower lip between her teeth as a draught of cool air alerted her to the fact that the French doors were partly open. Moving across the room, she saw Joe Mendez on the patio outside, leaning indolently against the basketball post Daisy had had her grandfather erect for her at the beginning of the summer.

As if she'd clumped across the room in hiking boots instead of her bare feet, he turned as she approached the windows. 'I hope you don't mind,' he said as he came towards her. He nodded over his shoulder. 'Who looks after the yard?'

'The yard?' Rachel's brows drew together for a moment as she backed out of his way. 'Oh, you mean the garden.' She grimaced. 'I do. When I can find the time.'

'You do a good job,' he commented, sliding the door closed behind him. 'It's nice. Colourful.'

Rachel smiled. 'That's probably all the weeds,' she said modestly. Then, 'Sorry to be so long. That was my—um—Steve's mother.'

'Ah.' He nodded. 'Mrs Carlyle.' He paused, pulling a wry face. 'Steve asked me to check on them while I was here.'

Rachel stared at him. 'But you said—'

'He didn't ask me to check on you,' Joe assured her flatly. 'That was my idea.'

'To check on me?'

'No.' Joe ran a frustrated hand around the back of his neck, his nails scraping over the stubble at his nape. 'I just wanted to meet you.' He paused, his dark brows descending. 'Not a good idea?'

'No…' Now it was Rachel's turn to look uneasy. She was intensely aware of the way his stomach had flexed when he'd raised his arm, biceps clenching, the dark outline of a tattoo just visible below his sleeve. 'It's just—'

'I guess I wanted to reassure you that your daughter will be safe with me,' he continued, his hand falling to his side again. 'My pilot's the best. Totally trustworthy, totally reliable.'

'Your pilot?' Rachel blinked, and gave a bewildered shake of her head. 'Does that mean you're not using commercial transport?'

'Didn't Steve tell you?'

As a matter of fact, Steve hadn't told her anything, Rachel reflected flatly. The invitation had come in one of his occasional emails to his daughter, and she'd just naturally assumed…

She attempted to regroup. 'Does Daisy know this?' she asked, wondering if Daisy had received another message she knew nothing about.

It wasn't a pleasant thought. She and Daisy had a pretty good relationship, all things considered, and, apart from the usual gripes about homework and curfews, she'd have said her daughter never kept anything from her.

Joe shrugged. 'I guess so,' he said, evidently aware of her disapproval. 'Hey, it's not a big deal. You can come check out the plane for yourself, if you like.'

Rachel gazed at him incredulously. 'And that would achieve what, exactly?' she asked, aware that her voice had risen several notches. 'I think you'd better go, Mr Mendez. I need to speak to Daisy. If—if you have a number where I can reach you afterwards...'

Joe regarded her closely, those intense dark eyes bringing a surge of colour to her cheeks. 'Don't you trust me?' he asked, and Rachel sucked in a disbelieving breath.

'I don't know you, Mr Mendez. I don't know whether I can trust you or not. I just need to think about what you've told me.'

Joe shook his head. 'Okay.' There was a faint trace of hostility in his tone now, and Rachel prayed she wasn't treading on anyone's toes here. Even Steve's, she added reluctantly, though why the hell he hadn't told her what was going on she didn't know.

'So, if I can get back to you...' she ventured unhappily, and then jerked back in alarm when he reached for his jacket lying on the arm of the sofa beside her. For a crazy moment, she'd thought he was reaching for her, and a trace of the panic she'd momentarily felt showed in her face.

But she should have had more sense, she chided herself as he picked up the jacket and searched his inside pocket for a card and a pen. A man like Joe Mendez would have no trouble in finding a woman if he wanted one. He'd scarcely waste his time and energies on a thirty-something divorcée with very ordinary features and dirty-blonde hair.

Linking her fingers tightly together at her waist, she prayed he hadn't noticed her mistake. For heaven's sake, what was the matter with her? It wasn't as if she hadn't dated anyone since Steve had walked out on her. Okay, she'd only slept with one man, but she should still have remembered the difference between civility and sex.

Meanwhile, Joe was scribbling something on the back of a business card, and after a moment he handed it over. 'This proves who I am, and I've given you my present address,' he said somewhat drily. 'I've written my cell number, too. Call me when you've decided what you want to do.'

'Thanks.'

Rachel took the card with nervous fingers, unable to deny the jolt of electricity she felt when his hand touched hers. Her eyes darted to his, but she had no idea if he'd been aware of it. There was a guarded quality about his gaze now, and thick black lashes any woman would have envied swept down to obscure his expression.

'No problem,' he said, hooking his jacket over one shoulder and heading towards the open door. He swung open the outer door and then paused on the threshold. 'Tell Daisy I said hi,' he added tightly before starting down the path to the gate.

Ridiculously, Rachel felt guilty the minute she'd closed the door. She felt as if she'd totally screwed up, and she could imagine how Daisy would react when she told her what had happened. But for goodness' sake, Mendez was a stranger. To her, at least, she amended with an impatient click of her tongue. Just because Daisy had met him before didn't mean *she* had to trust him.

But it was neither his trustworthiness nor Daisy's probable frustration that accompanied her into the kitchen when she went to rinse out their coffee mugs. It was the effect he had had—was still having, if she was honest—on her. Damn it, the hairs on her neck still prickled when she thought about him. And she could remember every detail about him with a meticulousness that bordered on the extreme.

The sound of the phone ringing was a welcome relief, though she suspected she knew who her caller was. And she was right. 'Rachel? I thought you were going to ring me when your visitor had gone.'

'How do you know he has gone?' muttered Rachel to herself, feeling grumpy, but she managed to adopt a reasonable tone. 'He's just left,' she said brightly. 'Um—can I speak to Daisy?'

'No.' Her mother-in-law didn't sound very pleased. 'That was why I was ringing, actually. She's on her way home. As soon as she heard Mr Mendez was there she insisted on taking off. She's going to be very disappointed when she gets home and finds he's not there.'

I'll bet, thought Rachel drily, and not just because of that. 'Okay,' she responded. 'I expect she'll give you a ring later.'

'Hmph.' Evelyn Carlyle snorted. 'Well, remind her to do it, will you? We always like to know she's safely home.'

'I will.'

Rachel couldn't believe she was getting off so lightly, but just as she was about to put down the receiver, Evelyn spoke again. 'So—what did you think of him? Had he only come to reassure you about Daisy's trip? He lives in Florida, doesn't he? It's good of him to offer to escort her, don't you think?'

Rachel pressed her lips together. But only briefly. 'Very good,' she managed, not prepared to get into the details with Evelyn right now. To her relief, she heard a key being inserted in the front door. 'Oh, this sounds like Daisy now. Speak to you later.'

This time she put the receiver down before Evelyn could say anything else and stood, feeling ridiculously apprehensive as Daisy let herself into the house. The girl looked round expectantly, and then, when her mother didn't say anything, she exclaimed, 'Don't tell me he's gone!'

'Afraid so.' Rachel forced a smile and walked back into the kitchen. The two coffee mugs on the drainer seemed to reproach her, and Daisy, following her, gave an indignant cry.

'You gave him coffee?'

Rachel busied herself with tidying the counter. 'Shouldn't I have done?' she asked lightly. 'I always offer visitors coffee, you know that.'

'So why isn't he still here? Grandma only rang about twenty minutes ago.'

'I know.'

'So what? Didn't he like the coffee?'

Rachel sighed and said carefully, 'We'd already had a conversation before your grandmother phoned. You must know that, too. You were at the supermarket when you met Mrs Freeman, weren't you?'

'Yes.' Daisy sounded sulky now.

'Well, then.'

'What I don't understand is why you didn't ring me and tell me he was here.' Daisy scowled. 'You knew I'd like to meet him again.' She shrugged. 'Oh, well, I suppose we'll have plenty of time to talk on the flight.'

She turned away, but now Rachel felt a twinge of impatience. 'Oh, yes,' she said tightly. 'On the flight to Florida. In his *private* plane.'

If she'd had any doubts that Daisy knew what she was talking about they'd have been extinguished at that moment. Her daughter's face suffused with colour, and she couldn't have looked any more guilty if she'd tried.

'He told you,' she said lamely, and Rachel felt a disappointed hollowing in her stomach.

'Unlike you,' she said, regarding Daisy with cool eyes. 'I assume your father informed you of the arrangement?'

'Well, yes.' Daisy hunched her shoulders, looking suddenly much younger than her years. 'I'm sorry, Mum.'

Rachel shook her head. 'And…what? You decided to keep it to yourself?'

'Dad said you probably wouldn't understand.' She hesitated. 'He said there was no need for you to know.'

'Oh, Daisy!'

'I know.' Daisy bit into her lower lip. 'But, well, I didn't think it was that important.'

'So why didn't you tell me anyway?'

Daisy shrugged.

'Because you knew how I'd react,' Rachel answered for her. 'Really, Daisy, I thought we were always honest with one another.'

'We are.'

'Except when your father asks you not to be, apparently,' declared Rachel tersely, aware she was breaking her own rules about not slagging off Steve to his daughter. 'Oh, well, it's done now. But I have to tell you, it's something I need to think about and I've told Mr Mendez the same.'

Daisy gasped now. 'You mean you've implied you might not agree to my going with him?'

Rachel refused to feel cowed. 'I've said I'll ring him after I've spoken with you.' She paused, and then added defensively, 'What did you expect me to say, Daisy? That I've got no objections to you flying for—what?—twelve hours in a plane with a man I hardly know?'

'Daddy says it's about nine hours, actually.'

'Well *nine* hours, then.' Rachel felt angry again. 'Oh, yes, your father knew what he was doing when he asked you not to tell me what was going on.'

Daisy's lips pursed. 'It's not like Mr Mendez is a—a pervert or something.'

'All right. I'll admit he seems respectable enough…'

'Respectable!' Daisy scoffed.

'But I should have been given the full story, not just your father's edited version.'

'I know.' Daisy sighed. 'I tried to tell him that. Like, in my emails. But you know what he's like.'

Not any more, mused Rachel, aware of a surprising wave of relief at the thought. Suddenly the memory of her ex-husband seemed distant and indistinct, usurped by the image of a man whose raw sexuality had assaulted her senses in a way Steve never had.

Not wanting Daisy to detect what she was thinking and attribute any of it to her father, Rachel drew a deep breath and opened the door of the fridge. 'Anyway,' she said, 'I've said I'll think about it, and I will. Now, what would you like for lunch? I have to warn you, I expected you to have lunch at Grandma's, so I don't have anything special to offer you.'

Daisy seemed anxious now. But not about her lunch. 'You're not thinking of changing your mind, are you, Mum?' she asked, and Rachel wondered how sincere her daughter's offer not to go to Florida had really been. 'I mean, you liked him, didn't you?'

'Who?'

'Mr Mendez.'

Rachel shrugged. 'He seemed very nice.' And how insincere was that? 'But that has nothing to do with it.'

Daisy was looking really worried, and despite her resentment towards Steve for putting her in this situation, Rachel felt a reluctant surge of sympathy for her. She was only thirteen, after all, and she didn't deserve to suffer because of their marital politics.

'Just leave it for now,' she said, taking a carton of eggs out of the fridge to avoid looking at her daughter. 'How about pancakes? Or would you prefer take-out?'

The subject was dropped but not forgotten. It was only four days until Daisy was due to leave for Florida, and Rachel knew she couldn't delay indefinitely.

After lunch, Daisy disappeared up to her room and Rachel wondered if she was emailing her father with the latest developments. She spent the afternoon expecting an irate email from her ex-husband, but when she checked her mail before closing the computer there were only two messages: one from a friend in London and the other from her agent.

Supper was not a comfortable meal. Rachel opened a bottle of red wine that she'd been saving for a special occasion—but with Daisy only pushing her pasta round her plate, giving her mother soulful looks every time their eyes met, the effort was wasted.

Eventually, after blocking every opening her mother tried to make, Daisy said, 'How's your book going?' and Rachel was so taken aback she could hardly think of a response. Daisy had never shown any interest in her writing before, regarding it in much the same light as any child regarded a parent's occupation.

'Um—it's going okay,' she said at last, getting up to pour herself another glass of Merlot. 'I expect I'll get it finished while you're away.'

'So I am going, then?' Daisy pounced on the admission.

'I expect so.' Rachel wished she hadn't brought the subject up again.

'Oh, good.' Daisy leant forward and attacked her plate with renewed enthusiasm. 'I knew you wouldn't really stop me from going.'

Rachel shook her head, but she didn't deny it. How could she? But she did intend to speak to her ex-husband about the arrangements as soon as Daisy was asleep.

She managed to catch Steve before he went out for the evening. He was predictably miffed at receiving a call from his ex-wife at home. Any communication between them—infrequent though it was—was usually conducted during office hours, and he was even more annoyed when he heard why Rachel wanted to speak to him.

'Oh, for pity's sake, Rache!' he exclaimed, using the abbreviation of her name that she'd never liked. 'What's your problem? I'd have thought you'd be pleased she wasn't having to travel in an economy seat. Besides, Mendez is a great guy. I don't know what kind of creeps you've been dating since you and I split, but take my word for it, you've got nothing to worry about from him.'

Rachel took a deep breath, pressing her lips together for a moment to prevent the angry retort she wanted to make. Then she said stiffly, 'Very well. But I wish you'd contacted me before making different arrangements.'

'Yeah, right.' Steve was sardonic. 'Why do you think I—?' He broke off and another feminine voice could be heard in the background. 'I know, I know. I'm coming, baby,' he said in an aside, and then, his tone sharpening, 'So, when Mendez gets in touch with you, you won't put up any objections, right?'

'When he…?' Rachel licked her lips. 'Well, as a matter of fact, he's already been in touch.'

'He has?' Steve was wary.

'Yes.' Rachel hesitated. 'He came to the house today.'

Steve swore to himself, and once again Rachel heard that other voice, which must have been Lauren's, making some kind of protest. 'Yeah, yeah, I'm coming,' he said again, his tone much less indulgent now. There was another brief exchange and then he addressed himself to Rachel again. 'Don't tell me you let Mendez know how you felt? Damn it, Rache, the man owns the company!'

Rachel stifled a groan. Until that moment, she'd been assuring herself that it had to be Joe Mendez's father who was the real power behind Mendez Macrosystems, but now she was forced to revise her opinion.

'I—I may have done,' she allowed in a low voice, and Steve swore again.

'Are you completely crazy?' he demanded angrily. 'For God's sake, Rachel, do you want me to lose my job? Is that what this is all about?'

Rachel had been feeling rather guilty for creating a difficult situation, but Steve's attitude really ticked her off. 'You have to be joking,' she retorted coldly. 'Why would I want to run the risk of forcing you to return to England? Believe me, Steve, I have no desire to see your lying face again.'

She'd slammed down the receiver and was standing, staring at the phone, when she heard a stair creak behind her. She turned in time to see Daisy, dressed only in the vest and shorts she used to sleep in, creeping cautiously back up the stairs. She'd obviously heard at least the end of what her mother had said, and her cheeks turned pink with embarrassment when Rachel spoke her name.

'I'm sorry,' she muttered, looking shamefaced. 'I didn't realise it was Dad you were talking to. I—I thought something might have happened to Granddad or Grandma.'

Rachel doubted that, but she wasn't in the mood to start another argument. Not tonight. 'It's okay,' she said. 'I just wanted to speak to your father about the arrangements. Go on back to bed. There's nothing for you to worry about. I'll be up myself in a few minutes.'

Daisy hesitated. 'You and Dad are never likely to get back together, are you?' she murmured regretfully, and Rachel thought how depressing it was when a child was involved.

'No,' she said gently. 'I'm sorry, sweetheart. It's just not going to happen.'

'Oh, well.' Daisy shrugged. 'I guess I can live with it. I mean, you're bound to meet someone else someday. Someone really nice. Not like Lauren at all.'

It was after midnight when Rachel tumbled into bed, but for once she didn't immediately fall asleep. Usually her eyes were so tired she lost consciousness the minute her head touched the pillow, but tonight her mind was too active to relax.

It was ringing Steve so late, she decided. With the time lag, she'd had to wait until after eleven to catch him at home. But it hadn't been something she'd wanted to discuss while he was at the office, even on his mobile phone, with possibly a receptionist or a secretary listening in.

However, it wasn't Steve's image that kept her awake until the early hours. It wasn't his blond good looks and slim athleticism that haunted her sleep. The image she found behind her eyes was that of Joe Mendez, whose tough, somewhat ruthless features and muscled profile ticked every one of the boxes Daisy might have desired…

CHAPTER THREE

THERE was someone at the door. Rachel could hear the bell ringing quite clearly and she struggled up in bed, wondering who on earth would call at this hour of the morning.

But it wasn't the doorbell. As soon as she sat up and got her bearings, she realised it was the phone beside the bed that had awakened her. It was silent now. Daisy must have answered it downstairs, she thought resignedly. It wasn't like her daughter to be up so early, but it was holiday time, not a school morning; go figure.

What time was it? she wondered, groping for the small travelling clock she kept beside the bed. She was horrified when she saw it was after ten o'clock. She rarely slept in, but after the restless night she'd had it was hardly surprising. She must have fallen asleep eventually, but right now she felt decidedly rough.

Pushing her legs out of bed, she swayed a little as she got to her feet. Too much red wine, she thought, hauling on her towelling bathrobe and opening the bedroom door. Wasn't it just typical that, the one morning someone chose to call her this early, she was still in bed?

She almost jumped out of her skin when the phone began to ring again. She'd stepped out onto the landing, wondering where Daisy had got to, when its insistent peal assaulted her ears. Daisy could answer it, she thought, starting down the stairs. It was most likely someone for her.

But Daisy didn't answer it and Rachel looked back up the stairs, wondering if her daughter had slept in too. Daisy's bedroom door was closed, but that didn't prove anything. She tended to regard her bedroom as her private space, and Rachel rarely intruded without an invitation.

Continuing down the stairs, Rachel picked up the receiver in the hall. 'Yes?' she said, the headache that was beginning to throb behind her temples making her sound snappy.

'Rachel?' Her throat dried. Oh God, it was him again. Joe Mendez. He must be ringing to find out what she'd decided. Had he spoken to Steve? 'I just wanted—'

'To know about Daisy,' she interrupted him quickly. 'I did intend to ring you later today.'

'No.' Joe spoke crisply. 'I didn't ring you to find out about Daisy. I know you've agreed to let her go. She told me so herself.'

Rachel blinked. 'She *told* you?' She was confused.

'Wait a second.' There was a momentary shifting of the phone, a muffled protest, and then a reluctant voice said, 'Hello, Mum.'

It was Daisy. Rachel groped for the oak chest that served as both a place to drop the mail and somewhere to sit to change one's shoes and sank down onto it. 'Daisy!' Her voice cracked. 'What's going on?'

'Don't be mad, Mum.' Daisy, at least, knew how she was feeling. 'I had to come and see Mr Mendez. I had to tell him you were okay with me travelling with him.'

Rachel felt dazed. 'Why?'

'Well, because I heard what you said to Dad, and I didn't—'

'Anything I said to your father was between us two, do you understand that?' Rachel's headache felt so much worse now. 'Honestly, Daisy, I thought I could trust you. Now—now I don't know what to think.'

'Oh, Mum.'

'Where are you, anyway?'

'At—at Mr Mendez's house.'

'His house?' Rachel was stunned. 'How did you know where he was staying?'

'It was on his card,' muttered Daisy unhappily. 'You just left it in the hall, and I—I picked it up.'

'Oh, Daisy!' Rachel could hardly take it in. 'You had no right to read that card, let alone go out without my permission to visit someone you hardly know!'

'Don't be like that, Mum, please.'

'How do you expect me to be?' Rachel felt her temper rising. 'I can't believe you'd do something so deceitful. Particularly as I've been awake half the night worrying about this trip.' Well, that was only partly true, but Daisy didn't need to know that. 'And now I discover you've taken matters into your own hands.'

There was another muffled exchange and then Joe said, 'Sorry if this has been a bit of a shock. I guess you've been wondering where Daisy was. I'm going to bring her home, but I felt I ought to let you know she's okay.'

Rachel's shoulders hunched. She was too ashamed to say she hadn't even known her daughter had gone out, but she managed a polite, 'That was kind of you.'

'Yeah, well.' She suspected he might have detected the irony in her voice and his next words seemed to prove it. 'Don't be too hard on her, right? I think she meant well.'

Rachel tried not to feel resentful that this man—this stranger—felt he had the right to advise her about how to treat her daughter. But all she said was, 'Thanks. I appreciate your comments,' and rang off before indignation got the better of politeness.

However, as soon as she'd replaced the receiver she realised she had no idea where Joe's—house? Hotel?—was. She'd hardly glanced at his card. And now she could only guess how much time she might have before they got here.

She was desperate for a cup of coffee, but she didn't dare wait while it brewed. Instead, she spooned grains into the filter and left it to percolate while she took a swift shower.

Her hair was still damp when she stood in front of the mirror in her bedroom, surveying her appearance. Tucking the artificially darkened strands back behind her ears, she decided it didn't look too bad. It was foolish, she knew, but instead of her usual working gear of shorts and a cotton top she'd chosen to wear a dress. It was a simple camisole, in shades of cream and brown, which she thought complemented her lightly tanned skin. The dress ended at her knees, and she left her legs bare.

The shower had eased her headache somewhat, but she took two paracetamol with her coffee. Then, realising she hadn't put on any make-up, she dashed back upstairs, and was in the process of brushing a bronze shadow onto her lids when she heard a car in the road outside.

Her hand shook for a moment, and she was forced to repair the damage before realising she hadn't time to put on any lipstick now. She could hear Daisy opening the door downstairs and, praying she didn't look as nervous as she felt, Rachel smoothed damp palms over her hips and left the room.

Descending the stairs, she felt as if she'd timed her entrance. Which simply wasn't true. She would have much preferred to be drinking her coffee in the kitchen when they arrived, and she hoped Joe didn't think it was deliberate.

Still, she couldn't prevent her eyes from sliding over him before they fastened on her daughter. He was more formally dressed this morning, his charcoal-grey suit and lighter grey shirt fairly screaming their designer label. His only concession to the occasion was the fact that he wasn't wearing a tie. The top two buttons of his shirt weren't fastened and, as she came down the stairs, she was offered a disturbing glimpse of night-dark hair in the opening.

Predictably, it was Daisy who spoke first. 'You look nice, Mum,' she said, and Rachel felt an embarrassing wave of colour surge into her face. Not that she didn't know what Daisy was trying to do. Her daughter wasn't exactly subtle.

But Joe was watching and, although her eyes promised retribution later on, she said, 'Thank you.' Then, more pointedly, 'You should have let me know you were going out.'

'I didn't want to wake you,' said Daisy blithely, and Rachel hoped that Joe didn't think she often overslept.

'How thoughtful,' she managed, before turning to their visitor. 'I'm sorry about this, Mr Mendez. I had no idea Daisy would come to your house.'

'No problem.' His dark eyes were disturbingly intent as they rested on her hot face, and Rachel felt as if her insides had turned to liquid. 'She's quite a character, your daughter.' His mouth twisted. 'And very entertaining.'

'Is she?' Rachel wondered what Daisy had been saying to inspire that kind of response.

But before she could say anything else he spoke again. 'Well, I guess I better get going. I've got a lunch meeting with some business colleagues at twelve o'clock.'

Rachel licked her lips. 'You wouldn't like some coffee before you leave?' she ventured, and then chided herself anew when he shook his head.

'Not right now, thanks,' he said, pulling a face at Daisy when she showed her disappointment. His gaze switched back to Rachel. 'How would it be if I called you later about the arrangements for Monday? I've got your number, if you'll forgive the pun.'

Rachel nodded. 'This afternoon, you mean?'

'Or this evening?' He gave her a quizzical look. 'Will you be in?'

Most definitely, thought Rachel ruefully, but she managed to sound as if she'd had to think about it. 'I'll be here,' she agreed.

'Great.' A trace of a smile appeared. 'Speak to you later then.'

As she watched him walk down the path to the gate, Rachel wondered what had ever possessed her to think that he'd want to spend any more time with her than he had to. He'd done the gentlemanly thing and brought Daisy home, but that was that. Job done.

She closed the door without waiting for him to get into his car. After Monday, she'd probably never see him again. And that was just as well for all concerned. Now all she had to do was deal with Daisy who, she noticed wryly, had already made herself scarce....

Joe drove back to his house in Eaton Court Mews with an odd sense of frustration. He felt as if he'd handled the whole business with Rachel Carlyle badly. But, damn it, he was doing her a favour here, wasn't he? So why the hell did he feel as if he was in the wrong?

He scowled. He wished he'd never offered to give the kid a ride across the Atlantic now. It was creating all sorts of problems he hadn't even thought of when Steve had told him his daughter was coming to Florida for a visit.

In truth, he'd felt sorry for the guy. It couldn't be easy, living the better part of four-thousand miles from your only offspring, and according to Steve his ex-wife had blocked his last few attempts to see Daisy. Naturally she could only come to stay during her school vacations, but at both Christmas and Easter Rachel had had other plans.

That was why he'd suggested that the kid could travel with him. Surely her mother could have no objections to that? He and Steve had known one another for over five years, ever since Carlyle had come to work for Mendez Macrosystems in London, and since his move to Miami last year they'd become friends.

But evidently Steve hadn't chosen to tell his ex-wife of the arrangements. Despite what he'd been told about her, Joe didn't think Rachel's shock at learning that Daisy wouldn't be flying on a commercial airline was simulated. She hadn't known. He'd bet his life on it.

He shook his head. Which begged the question: why hadn't Steve told her? Okay, he was prepared to accept that their relationship must have suffered when they'd got a divorce, but she could hardly blame Steve for that. According to the account he'd heard, there'd been faults on both sides, not least the fact that Rachel had done everything she could to sabotage her husband's career. Ted Johansen had told him that Lauren would never have got involved with Steve if he and Rachel hadn't been having problems. According to him, his daughter wasn't that kind of girl.

Something Joe had reserved judgment about.

Nevertheless, Steve should have explained what was happening. Just because he found Rachel difficult to reason with didn't excuse him entirely, and Joe had every intention of giving him a piece of his mind when he got back to the States.

Now he pulled the Lexus into Eaton Court Mews and drew up outside the house he'd bought on one of his frequent trips to London. He'd liked it because of its character and antiquity, its wisteria-clad walls a far cry from the busy thoroughfare that passed just a few feet beyond the arched entrance to the mews.

He entered via an oak-studded door to one side of the ground-floor garage and took the stairs to the next floor, where the first level of living rooms was situated. It had taken him some time to get used to not calling this the 'second floor', as they did back home, but Charles Barry, his English housekeeper, was gradually educating him.

Charles himself appeared as Joe walked into a comfortably furnished sitting room. Furniture, which Charles had helped him choose, gave the room an attractive authenticity, with lots of polished wood and distressed-leather sofas beneath the narrow-paned dormer windows.

'Mission accomplished?' he asked, referring to his employer's undertaking to deliver Daisy back to her mother, and Joe pulled an amused face.

'I guess so,' he said, without conviction. He shook his head. 'I just wish I didn't have the feeling that I'm the bad guy here.'

Charles, a slim, prematurely grey-haired man in his fifties, arched an enquiring brow. 'Mrs Carlyle doesn't appreciate your consideration, I gather?'

'You could say that.'

'Something of a harridan, is she?'

'Hell, no.' The words were out before Joe could stop them. But they were true. No way could Rachel Carlyle be described as a harridan. And that was possibly one of the reasons why he was feeling so frustrated now.

Charles frowned. 'I detect a note of ambiguity here,' he said. 'Do I take it you're having second thoughts about delivering the girl to her father?'

Joe's jaw compressed. 'Steve didn't bother to tell his ex-wife that Daisy would be travelling with me,' he explained flatly. 'On the Jetstream, I mean. She assumed we'd be using public transport.'

'I see.' Charles considered this. 'And that's created a problem?'

Joe gave a curt nod. 'You got it.'

'Ah.' Charles was thoughtful. 'But surely, now that she's met you for herself, Mrs Carlyle must be reassured?'

'You think?'

'She's not?' Charles looked taken aback. 'So what kind of woman is she? Didn't Mr Carlyle say that she's a writer?' He cupped his chin in one hand. 'I'm imagining a rather…overweight lady, all flowing scarves and Birkenstocks. Am I right?'

Joe couldn't prevent the laugh that erupted from him then.

'You couldn't be more wrong!' he exclaimed, picturing Rachel as he'd first seen her in her cotton vest and shorts. 'No, she's not overweight, Charles. She's not skinny, you understand? She's got some shape. But she's not fat.'

Charles regarded him intently. 'But not young? Not like the second Mrs Carlyle?'

'No.' Joe conceded the point. Steve had definitely gone for looks over intelligence the second time around. It had also helped that Lauren's old man was one of the directors of the company, he reflected, before adding, 'But Rachel's okay. Quite attractive, actually.'

Charles' brows ascended again. 'Well...' He didn't appear to know how to answer that so, changing the subject, he asked if his employer would like something to drink before he left for his meeting. 'You did say you had a luncheon appointment,' he reminded him politely, and Joe glanced somewhat impatiently at his watch.

'Oh, yeah,' He blew out a breath. Then, 'No, that's okay.' He nodded towards the built-in bar hidden behind a wall of bookshelves. 'I'll get myself a soda, if I want one.'

'Yes, sir.'

Charles withdrew and Joe moved across to the windows, staring out unseeingly onto the mews below. He found himself wondering what exactly had gone wrong with the Carlyles' marriage. Sure, he'd heard Steve's—and Johansen's—interpretation of events. But having met Rachel personally, he found it harder to believe that she would neglect her home and family in favour of her career. A woman like that would hardly put up any opposition to exactly how her daughter was to travel to Florida. Indeed, she'd probably be glad of the break from teenage angst, however it was going to be achieved.

Still, he had to factor in the probable resistance she had to Daisy spending any time with her father and stepmother. If Steve was to be believed—and until the last couple of days he'd had no reason to doubt that he was—she'd done her best to turn Daisy against him and Lauren.

His scowl returned. He could so do without this, he thought irritably. Do without this damned lunch with the company's British executives, too. If he hadn't promised his father to follow in his footsteps, and keep all branches of Macrosystems in the frame, he'd have scrubbed any and all business meetings and spent the rest of the day at the nearest race track.

Still, this evening he had his date with Shelley Adair to look forward to. She'd been most put out when he'd cried off the party she'd been giving the evening before. But after his altercation with Rachel Carlyle, he hadn't been in the mood for the kind of noisy reception Shelley favoured. Besides, if he was perfectly honest, he'd expected Rachel to have second thoughts and ring him to apologise and, when she hadn't, he'd gone to bed feeling decidedly aggrieved.

So why was he wasting more time thinking about her? He'd been downright astounded when Daisy had turned up at his door this morning. It had been the last thing he'd expected, and at first he'd thought she'd come because her mother had asked her to. Finding out Rachel hadn't even known she'd left the house had soon disabused him of that notion, and he'd been half inclined to blame Daisy's behaviour on her mother. But bringing up a teenager like Daisy on her own couldn't be easy. That was why he'd reined in his own irritation when Rachel had reacted as she had.

He sighed. Were Steve's complaints about her justified? The way Rachel was acting made him inclined to think again. He just wished he wasn't involved in the situation, wished he didn't have these suspicions that she was the victim here.

CHAPTER FOUR

ON SATURDAY morning Rachel was sitting at the kitchen table, drinking her third cup of coffee of the day and trying to make sense of the pages she'd written the night before, when Daisy came clattering down the stairs.

It was barely seven, and on any normal weekend morning it would have been virtually impossible to get her daughter out of bed before nine o'clock. But clearly Daisy's mind was fixated on the same issue that had kept Rachel awake half the night.

'Did he ring?'

Daisy didn't waste time on polite preamble, and Rachel put down her coffee cup and shuffled her pages into a single pile. 'No.'

'He didn't?' Daisy stared at her aghast. 'I thought that must be why you were up so early.'

'Well, I'm sorry to disappoint you, but no one's rung. Either last night, or this morning.'

Daisy looked dismayed. 'But he said he would ring,' she protested, and Rachel thought that, despite all her efforts to appear grown up, her daughter was still very much a child with a child's simplistic view of the world.

Getting to her feet, she gave Daisy a hug and said, 'I shouldn't worry about it, sweetheart. I expect his meeting went on longer than he'd anticipated, and perhaps he had other plans for the evening.'

Plans that had no doubt included the company of some ravishing female, Rachel reflected drily. A man like Mendez was hardly likely to spend his nights alone. He was far too attractive; far too sexy. He didn't wear a wedding ring—not that that meant a lot, if Steve was anything to go by—but there was bound to be some glamorous socialite who found his slightly cruel good looks and sensual appeal absolutely fascinating. As she did, Rachel admitted reluctantly. Though in her case, she assured herself, it was a purely professional assessment.

'How long does a phone call take?' Daisy pulled away from her mother and went to take a carton of milk out of the fridge. Pouring herself a glass, she added sulkily, 'I wish Dad had arranged for me to fly with British Airways. Then we wouldn't have to rely on anyone else.'

Rachel was tempted to second that, but she was sensible enough to know that, however tardy he might be, they hadn't heard the last of Joe Mendez. 'Give it until lunchtime,' she said. 'Then, if we still haven't heard anything, I'll ring him.' She felt a hollowing in her stomach at the thought but she ignored it. 'Okay?'

'Oh, cool!' Daisy's upper lip was still coated with milk as she came and gave her mother a wet kiss on her cheek. Her delight was unmistakeable. 'Thanks, Mum.'

'You're welcome.' Refusing to consider what she was going to say if she had to contact Mendez, Rachel scrubbed the place Daisy's lips had touched with a rueful hand. Then, wrapping her cotton dressing-gown closer about her, she picked up the manuscript and started for the door. 'I'm going to have a shower,' she said. 'I won't be long. Then I'll get breakfast.'

'I can do that.' Daisy finished her milk and popped the glass into the dishwasher. 'What would you like? I can make French toast.'

'Just toast will do,' said Rachel, guessing the girl was only trying to be helpful. But as she started up the stairs she hoped that, by offering to ring Mendez, she hadn't given Daisy the idea that she wouldn't object if her daughter rang him herself.

Knowing she had to go out sometime today to do some food shopping, Rachel dressed in jeans and a black V-necked tee shirt. She dried her hair and then caught it up in a loose knot on top of her head. She didn't bother with any make-up, and a pair of strappy leather sandals completed her outfit. She looked what she was, she thought, surveying her appearance without conceit: a single mother approaching middle age, with no particular claim to either youth or beauty.

Daisy had the toast ready when she re-entered the kitchen, and there was fresh coffee simmering on the hob. Daisy had taken the time to dress too, though her baggy cut-offs and cropped tank top looked as if they'd spent the night on her bedroom floor.

'There you go,' she said, setting the toast on the table where a jar of marmalade and the butter dish already resided; if her cheeks looked a little pink, Rachel put it down to the heat of the grill.

'This looks good.' Although she wasn't feeling particularly hungry, Rachel buttered a slice of toast and spooned on a little of the marmalade. Then, taking a bite, she looked expectantly up at her daughter. 'Aren't you having any?'

'I had some cornflakes,' said Daisy quickly. 'I thought you wouldn't mind.'

'No.' But Rachel's brows drew together as she spoke. Then, dismissing the suspicion that Daisy wasn't being altogether truthful, she added, 'I'll have to go out later. We've got nothing in the fridge, and I need some fresh bread.'

'But you can't.'

Daisy spoke impulsively and Rachel looked at her with narrowed eyes. 'Why not?'

'Well—because Mr Mendez is going to phone, isn't he?'

'So?' Rachel's gaze turned to one of enquiry. 'We have an answerphone. If we're not here, I'm sure he'll leave a message, and I can ring him back.'

Daisy pressed her lips together. 'But what if he comes round?'

'Comes round?' Rachel was wary. 'Why on earth would he come round?' Not to see her, she was sure. 'He's said he'll phone. And, if he doesn't, I've already said I'll phone him.'

'He's not in,' said Daisy quickly, and Rachel's eyes widened in disbelief.

'He's not in?' she echoed. Then, shaking her head to clear it, she went on, 'How do you know he's not in?'

But she didn't need the girl to answer. She already knew. Daisy had done what she'd been half-afraid she might and had phoned Mendez while she was in the shower.

'I—I spoke to that man who works for him,' Daisy confessed unhappily. 'Mr Mendez calls him Charles.' She bit her lip, perhaps hoping that Rachel would take pity on her. But when it became apparent that her mother wasn't about to speak, she hurried on, 'He—he was really offhand.'

Rachel regarded her disapprovingly. 'And that surprises you?' She shook her head. 'It's barely eight o'clock, Daisy. It's Saturday, and people don't appreciate being woken up so early.'

Daisy's expression lightened. 'So maybe Mr Mendez was really there?' she suggested. 'But this man—Charles—didn't want to disturb him.' She looked encouragingly at her mother. 'Do you think that's what happened?'

'It's possible.' But Rachel suspected it wasn't that simple. It was far more likely that Mendez had slept elsewhere, and her stomach tightened at the thought. Then, dismissing the images that evoked from her mind, she said, 'It would serve you right if Mr Mendez decided that taking you to Florida was more trouble than it was worth. Then your father would be stuck with your air fare. I wonder how he'd feel about that?'

It was a low blow, and Rachel regretted letting her own disappointment rule her tongue. She wanted Daisy to spend time with Steve; of course she did. It was just hard to accept that her daughter wasn't so different from her father after all.

Daisy looked positively mortified now, and, knowing she couldn't let her shoulder all the blame for the way she was feeling, she sighed. 'Look, I'm sure that's not going to happen. But you have to be patient. I imagine Mr Mendez has more important matters than arranging your trip to attend to. If you take my advice, you'll let him get back to you in his own good time.'

'But what if he forgets?'

Rachel's laugh was bitter. 'Oh, I don't think that's likely,' she said drily. 'Now, I suggest you let me finish my coffee, and then you can come with me to the supermarket.'

It was after eleven by the time they got back to the house. Despite Daisy's agitation, Rachel had been determined not to let Joe Mendez think that she, at least, was desperate for his assistance. Daisy was thirteen, after all, and there was no reason why she shouldn't make the journey on her own on a commercial flight. Rachel knew that the air crew could be relied upon to keep an eye on her, and Steve would be meeting her in Miami.

Consequently, it was something of a blow to find the powerful SUV parked at their gate when she turned into Castle Close. Although she'd only seen the vehicle once before, the identity of its owner was unquestionable, and she didn't need Daisy's cry of excitement to reinforce her opinion.

'It's Mr Mendez!' Daisy exclaimed, hopping out of Rachel's modest Audi as soon as she applied the brake. 'I wonder how long he's been waiting? I told you we shouldn't have gone out.'

Rachel reserved judgment on that, but in any case she had

no time to reply. Daisy was already running to the front of the Lexus, full of excitement as she waited for Joe Mendez to open the door.

He did so at once. Long, powerful legs encased in tight-fitting black jeans again this morning appeared; tan-coloured deck shoes, once more without socks, lowered to the pavement. As she stood, Rachel glimpsed a white tee shirt in the open V of a black knitted polo, which exposed his arms and the dark shadow of his tattoo. There was a dark shadow on his jawline too, she noticed, so evidently he hadn't bothered to shave. But the slightly dishevelled look suited him. He was that kind of man.

It was an effort for her to get out of the car, but eventually she did so, aware that Daisy was chattering away happily. Probably blaming her mother for them not having been at home, thought Rachel ruefully. Well, it had been her fault, but she wasn't ashamed of it. If Daisy hadn't taken it into her head to ring the man, he'd have contacted her sooner or later. Or not—as he chose.

Meanwhile Joe was wishing Daisy would stop talking long enough to allow him to speak to her mother. Judging by the reluctance with which Rachel had got out of the vehicle, she wasn't exactly thrilled to see him. But when she opened the boot and started unloading bags of groceries onto the path, he had the perfect excuse to go and assist her.

'Hi,' he said as he reached the pile of plastic carriers. 'Let me help you.'

'I can manage.' Rachel knew she sounded ungrateful, but she couldn't help it.

However, Joe ignored her. Hefting two bags in each hand, he nodded towards the house. 'You go ahead and open the door. I'll follow you.'

Rachel's lips tightened, but short of forcibly wresting the carriers from him, she had no choice but to do as he said.

Rescuing the remaining bag and her handbag, she locked the car and brushed past him. But she was intensely conscious of him behind her as she hurried up the path to the house.

If Rachel was conscious of Joe's eyes upon her, Joe was no less aware of it himself. Contrary to the description Charles had invented, Rachel had a decidedly provocative rear. True, she was no fashion model, but that was to her advantage. The cheeks of her bottom were nicely rounded above legs that were longer than he'd thought. For a woman of—what, thirty-two, thirty-three?—she had an extremely attractive figure.

He blew out a breath as he unloaded the bags onto the kitchen table. Why the hell was he thinking about how she looked? It wasn't as if they even knew one another—not, properly at least—and there was no doubt that she resented him. Ever since she'd learned that Daisy would be flying with him and not on some public airline, he'd hardly had a cordial word out of her. Damn it, it wasn't his fault if she and her ex-husband didn't communicate.

'Mr Mendez hasn't been waiting long.' Daisy came into the kitchen behind them, a beaming smile on her face. 'That's good, isn't it, Mum?'

'I'm sure Mr Mendez would agree with you.'

Rachel's response was full of irony, and Joe's resentment stirred anew. 'I did ring first,' he said, directing his words to her. 'I thought you might be working and not want to be disturbed.'

'So you decided to come and disturb me anyway.' Rachel didn't know why she felt so angry, but she did. And finding Mendez on her doorstep seemed to be the last straw after the way Daisy had behaved. 'I'm sorry. I had some shopping to attend to.'

'I could have spoken to Daisy.'

'You could.'

'Mum—'

Daisy had obviously realised that things were not going as

well as she'd anticipated. But Joe didn't need her involvement, any more than Rachel had wanted his earlier. 'Just leave this to your mother and me,' he said, trying for a pleasant tone. 'Why don't you go and do some packing or something?'

Daisy sniffed. 'Mum,' she said again, the word full of entreaty, and Rachel took a deep breath.

'Mr Mendez is right,' she said. 'Perhaps it would be as well if he and I had a private word. Just go up to your room, okay?'

'But, Mum—'

'Do as your mother says,' said Joe sharply, and Daisy's jaw dropped in surprise.

'You can't tell me what to do,' she protested, any admiration she'd felt towards him momentarily extinguished by his tone.

Joe stared at her. 'Can't I?' he countered, his mood deteriorating rapidly, and her lower lip jutted.

'Mum—'

'Oh, just go upstairs, Daisy.' Rachel didn't appreciate Joe's interference either, but it was easier not to get into it with the girl present. 'Please.' She softened the word with a slight smile. 'I'll call you when you can come down again.'

Daisy pursed her lips but, after a few moments, she slouched moodily out of the room. A few seconds later, they heard her climbing the stairs.

Rachel waited until she'd heard the door to Daisy's bedroom bang closed before giving Joe a frigid look. 'I hope you don't expect me to apologise,' she said. 'Thanks to her father, Daisy is in the middle of all this. Naturally, she feels confused.'

'You think?' Joe propped his hips against the counter opposite and folded his arms. 'I thought that was me.'

'You?' Rachel was taken aback now. 'You're not confused.'

Joe shrugged, as if that might be open for discussion, but all he said was, 'I am also in the middle of this feud you've got going with Steve.'

Rachel tried to calm herself. 'It's not a feud.'

'Then what is it?' Joe's dark brows ascended. 'I gather the divorce wasn't an amicable one.'

'Did Steve tell you that?'

He had, but Joe wasn't about to admit it. 'It seems fairly obvious,' he said, avoiding the question. 'Why don't you want Daisy to spend time with her father? Just because you don't get on—'

'I've never stopped Daisy from seeing her father,' Rachel broke in hotly. 'And, if he's told you I have, he's lying.'

Joe sucked in a breath. 'So how come Steve hasn't had any physical contact with Daisy since he left England?'

Rachel gasped. 'I don't have to explain myself to you!'

'Humour me.' Joe didn't really know why he was pursuing this except that she seemed so frustrated. 'You have to admit, it's twelve months since he and Lauren moved to Florida.'

'I know.' Rachel hesitated, but the need to defend herself drove her on. 'But—well, at Christmas, Daisy didn't want to visit her father. Her grandparents would have been so disappointed if we hadn't had Christmas Day with them, and school started again at the beginning of January.'

'Okay.' Joe shrugged. 'I'll accept that you wouldn't want to send Daisy away at Christmas. But according to Steve she could have visited earlier this year.'

'You mean at Easter?' Rachel's nostrils flared. 'Didn't he tell you? Daisy was ill at Easter. She had glandular fever and, if you know anything about the disease at all, you'll know that it can take months to recover fully. As a matter of fact, I phoned Steve and asked if there was any way he could come and see her.' Rachel's nails curled into her palms when she remembered her ex-husband's response. 'He—he said he already had plans for the holiday. Which obviously didn't include crossing the Atlantic.'

Joe frowned 'He didn't tell me that.'

Rachel snorted. 'I wonder why.'

'You don't like him much, do you?'

'I don't like what he's trying to do to me and Daisy,' said Rachel flatly.

'What is he doing?' Joe was curious.

'It doesn't matter.'

'I'd still like to know.'

'Why?' She turned to the bags on the table and started unloading their contents. 'So you can tell Steve what a mean, resentful cow I am when you go home?'

Joe caught his breath. 'Hey, you've got some attitude there!' he exclaimed. 'I don't think you're mean or resentful. I just think you and Steve have got your wires crossed and you both need to sort yourselves out. For Daisy's sake.'

'Yeah, right.'

Rachel had started putting perishable items into the fridge, but now Joe couldn't prevent himself from moving round the table and grabbing her arm. 'Hey,' he said, immediately aware of her soft flesh beneath his fingers. 'I'm not your enemy.' He released her again, unconsciously rubbing his palm down the seam of his jeans, as if that would remove the tantalising memory of her skin. 'I'm just trying to understand what's going on here. Fill me in. Tell me about when Steve still lived in London.'

Rachel shivered. It was the first time he'd touched her, and she was overwhelmingly aware that her response had been far from indifferent. For a moment, her senses had been assaulted by the clean, male scent of his body, his heat briefly robbing her of the will to move away. She was aware of her nipples pebbling beneath her cotton tee shirt, a melting feeling that centred somewhere low in her abdomen, turning her limbs to water.

Realising she had to get a hold of herself, she shoved the pack of cheese she was holding into the fridge and backed up against the closed door. That was better, she thought, feeling the chill cooling her spine and causing goose bumps to take the place of the beads of sweat that had feathered the back of her neck.

Then, without exactly looking at him, she said, 'Why should it matter to you?'

Joe shook his head. Damned if he knew. He didn't know what the hell he was getting into here, but he knew he couldn't just walk away without at least attempting to understand what was going on.

In an effort to distract himself from the urge to capture her chin in his hand and force her to look at him, Joe propped his hips against the table behind him and folded his arms. 'How often did Daisy see her father before he moved to the States?' he asked, and her green eyes flickered briefly in his direction.

'How often?' He sensed she didn't want to answer him and he wondered why. 'Um—she saw him,' she said with a lift of one shoulder, prevaricating. 'Anyway, that's not why you're here, is it? I expect you'd like to confirm the arrangements for Monday. If you'll tell me where and at what time you'd like us to meet you…'

'My chauffeur will pick her up.' Joe was aware that she was nervous, that she'd like to get this over with and for him to go. He frowned, and then asked curiously, 'What's wrong? Why are you so defensive? Is it because Steve wanted to take Daisy to Florida with him when he left England and you wouldn't let him?'

'What?' Rachel was forced to look at him now, stunned at the accusation. And despite her reluctance to discuss her ex-husband with a virtual stranger, she added tensely, 'Steve never even suggested taking her with him. Did he tell you that he did?'

Joe raked long fingers over his scalp. He should never have started this. 'That was the impression I got,' he said at last, watching the colour drain out of her face. His free hand curled into a fist. 'Obviously I was wrong.'

'Yes.' Rachel drew a choking breath and turned away, unable to look at him any longer. 'Yes, you were,' she continued, pressing her palms against the door of the fridge now, aware that it wasn't helping. 'If—if you must know, I don't think Daisy even noticed when Steve left the country.'

There, she'd said it. Something she'd never said to anyone, not even Steve's mother. But it was true nevertheless. Her ex-husband had spent little time with Daisy when they'd been together, and after the divorce he'd always been too busy with his new wife and her friends—and, of course, his golf—to care that Daisy was growing up without a father.

Joe stifled an inward groan. He knew he'd upset her, knew he'd torn the skin off an old wound that was apparently still raw enough to bleed. And that wasn't his nature. He didn't hurt women; even the women he'd ended relationships with were still speaking to him. Yet, although he'd guessed he was getting into deep water when she'd avoided his question, he'd persisted in probing, in exposing her vulnerability.

His muscles tightened. He should get the hell out of here now, before he did something they would both regret. He didn't even know why he felt such a sense of responsibility towards her, but the fact remained, he did.

Pushing away from the table, he laid an impulsive hand on her shoulder. She jumped, and he realised she was trembling. God, this was a woman who'd been married and divorced, who'd borne a child, for heaven's sake; yet he still felt responsible for her. He couldn't resist; his fingers tightened on the fine bones beneath her tee shirt and the urge to pull her into his arms became almost irresistible.

The air between them was fairly crackling with emotion, and for once he wished Daisy would interrupt them. Hell, this wasn't his problem, he told himself, but that didn't stop him from moving closer until her bottom brushed temptingly against his thigh.

Rachel moved then, jerking away from him, not understanding why her eyes were suddenly filled with tears. She'd shed all the tears she was going to shed for Steve Carlyle, she told herself fiercely. And she didn't need Joe Mendez's pity either. She could just imagine how this would play when he got back to Florida, and the idea that Steve and Lauren might find her stupid feelings amusing was totally humiliating.

'Rachel,' Joe said helplessly, 'I'm sorry.'

'Don't be. I'm not.' She pulled a tissue out of the box on the window sill and quickly blew her nose. 'I'll get Daisy. I expect she's dying to know what's going on.'

Joe groaned. 'What is going on, Rachel?' he demanded, and she was obliged to turn and face him.

'I don't know what you mean,' she said, striving for a lighter tone. But when she attempted to move past him, Joe saw the betraying sparkle of tears on her lashes.

'Hell, Rachel,' he protested, and ignoring all the good advice he'd been giving himself, he caught her about the waist and hauled her into his arms.

CHAPTER FIVE

IT WAS meant to be a way of comforting her, of showing his support, of proving he wasn't a selfish bastard like her ex-husband appeared to be, or so he told himself. But it didn't turn out that way. From the moment their bodies came together, from the moment her tee shirt parted from her jeans and he felt the softness of bare flesh beneath his hands, a knot of pure sensual need twisted in his belly.

She was breathing rapidly, her breasts flattened against his chest so he could feel every agitated gulp she took. Her lips were parted and the warmth of her breath was moistening the skin of his throat, spreading heat to every sensitised extremity.

'Rachel,' he said again, his voice thicker now, and the urge to slide his hand beneath her shirt and find the swollen peaks that were rubbing oh-so-sensuously against his shirt proved irresistible. He could see the pulse palpitating just beneath her ear, and he wondered how it would feel against his tongue.

He thought she said something then, but the faint whisper of her voice was drowned by the pounding of his own heart. With the womanly scent of her body to distract him, it was hard to think of anything but how incredible it would feel to have her naked beneath him.

He was becoming aroused. His trousers were becoming uncomfortably tight, and he guessed if he could feel it she could feel it, too. Not that that stopped him from wanting her, but it was time to grasp what little control he had left and put an end to this madness.

It took an effort, but he pulled his hands from beneath her tee shirt and raised them to her shoulders. Then gently, but firmly, he attempted to put some space between them. It would be easier to think without the innocent sexuality of her body seducing his, he told himself grimly. But when he saw her face, his good intentions crumbled. She looked so bewildered suddenly that something inside him seemed to snap. With a groan of resignation, he abandoned any hope of getting out of this unscathed. Pulling her against him again, he captured her face between his palms and lowered his head to hers.

Her lips were barely parted, but when he skimmed his tongue over the full lower one she caught her breath. Joe pushed his tongue inside, searching, possessing, doing what he admitted he'd wanted to do since he'd first glimpsed those tears on her face.

'Dear God,' he muttered, as desire rose hotly to the surface. His hands slid down her spine, moulding her to him, finding the provocative curve of her bottom before gripping the back of her thighs.

The kiss deepened and Rachel's world seemed to narrow to this man's mouth, this man's hands. Her head was swimming, emotions she'd never experienced before causing her whole body to feel hot and alive. She was drowning in a dark sea of intimacy, of passion, where the satisfaction of her senses was the only thing that mattered.

Joe's senses rocketed, the blood pounding in his ears, his mind spinning dizzily out of control. With his fingers spreading against the back of her head, he crushed his mouth to hers with increasing urgency. He wasn't doing anything wrong, he told himself. Not when she was kissing him back with a hunger that matched his own.

And then, from a distance, Rachel heard a familiar voice calling her. 'Mum! Mum!' There was a pause, which allowed her to identify the sound. 'Mum, can't I come down now?'

Daisy!

Oh God!

Rachel's strangled cry startled Joe. He, too, had heard the other voice, his brain scrambling to remember where he was. Then, like a douche of cold water, it came to him: he was trying to seduce Steve Carlyle's ex-wife.

He pulled away automatically at the same moment Rachel was wrenching herself free. For God's sake, what had he been thinking? What crazy impulse had made him behave like a savage?

Rachel was heading for the door into the hall. He could see she was panicking, unaware that her tee shirt was loose and crumpled and that his stubble had scraped her cheeks. Her hair was loose from its knot. It tumbled down around her shoulders, and Joe wondered how it would feel if he threaded his fingers through the silky strands. However, the look she cast at him over her shoulder brought the whole situation into damning focus.

He'd goofed, and badly. Her expression said it all. And while he wasn't totally to blame for what had happened, if he hadn't touched her the situation would never have developed as it had.

'Hey,' he said, causing her to glance back at him again. However, when she lifted a warning hand to silence him, he muttered, 'You might want to check yourself out before you leave. Or do you want your daughter to know what you've been doing?'

Rachel halted abruptly, her hand going to her tumbled hair, discovering the pins that had held it in place had disappeared. They were scattered all over the floor, she saw with an inward groan, but she didn't have time to find them all now. Pulling open a drawer where she kept pens and notepads, she found an elastic band and, gathering her hair in one hand, she secured it in an untidy pony-tail.

She saw Joe arch a mocking brow as she started for the door again, but her attention was concentrated on her daughter now. 'Just—just give us a couple more minutes, Daisy,' she called when she reached the doorway. 'We're almost through.'

Ain't that the truth? thought Joe as Daisy answered with a long drawn-out, 'O-kay.' Once again, he was asking himself how on earth he'd allowed himself to be distracted. Rachel was attractive, sure, but she wasn't his type. And from the way she was looking at him, he certainly wasn't hers.

She turned back to him with evident reluctance. He sensed she wanted to say something to defend herself, but she must know as well as he did that what had happened couldn't be explained away. 'I think you'd better go,' she said at last, and he could tell she was struggling to appear more composed than she was. She licked her lips, lips that were still swollen from his lovemaking, Joe saw with some satisfaction. 'I don't know what I'm going to do about Daisy. I'll let you know when I've had time to think.'

'To think about what?' Joe sagged back against the table. 'Oh, please, don't tell me you're going to make this an excuse for refusing to let Daisy go and visit with her dad?'

'No.' Rachel squared her shoulders. 'No, she can go. I'm just not sure she should go with you.'

Joe stared at her disbelievingly. 'Why?' he demanded, his patience shredding. Frustration was making him antsy, and he wasn't in the mood for any more of her attitude. 'I hope you're not implying that because I kissed you I'm not to be trusted with your daughter. Grow up, Rachel. You're acting like a spoiled brat.'

'And we both know that's not true, don't we?' she retorted. She shook her head. 'I have to think about this. I'm older

than you. I can't just dismiss what just happened as you apparently can.'

Joe blinked. 'Why do you think you're older than me?' he exclaimed blankly. 'I'm thirty-four, and I know for a fact that Steve's only thirty-five.'

'Steve's not thirty-five!' The words were out before she could prevent them. 'He's two years older than me. He'll be forty on his next birthday.'

Joe looked surprised. 'You're sure about that?' he asked, and she wondered if she'd put her foot in it again.

'I'm sure,' she admitted in a low voice, and Joe realised he hadn't taken Daisy's age into consideration. He remembered Steve telling him in one of his more confidential moments that he'd been married for five years before Daisy had been born.

Rachel had opened the fridge again and was stowing some tomatoes into the salad drawer. Her face was red, and he wondered what she was thinking. For his part, he was trying to come to terms with the fact that she was thirty-seven. She certainly didn't look it. Or act it, he conceded, reliving those moments when he'd been inclined to believe she was as inexperienced as Daisy.

'Look,' he said gently. 'I'm sorry, okay? What happened, happened. I'm not ashamed of it. You're a beautiful woman. I only did what any man in my position would have done.'

Rachel wondered if that was entirely true. She couldn't imagine Steve touching her in that way. But then, she and Steve should never have got married, never have had a baby. It was one of those sad anomalies that Daisy definitely hadn't kept them together.

'Is everything all right?' Daisy was suddenly standing in the doorway, eyeing them both with a mixture of anticipation and apprehension. She frowned at her mother. 'Why is your face red? Is something wrong?'

Rachel couldn't prevent her hand from going to her cheek,

and she glanced guiltily at Joe before saying, 'Nothing's wrong, Daisy. Mr Mendez was just leaving.'

Daisy wasn't stupid. 'Leaving?' she echoed. 'So—are the arrangements for Monday already made?'

'You'd better ask your mother,' said Joe, without sympathy. 'I think she might be having second thoughts.'

He knew a moment's remorse when Rachel turned agonised eyes in his direction, but he refused to pretend that all was well when it so obviously wasn't.

'Why?' Daisy gazed at her mother now. 'I thought you'd agreed to let me go.'

'I did.' Rachel was defensive. 'It's just—'

'Your mother doesn't trust me,' said Joe flatly, pushing away from the table. His eyes bruised Rachel's. 'I suggest you let me know when you've decided what you want to do.'

'Oh, but—'

Daisy's eyes had filled with tears and, before she could beg him to reconsider, Rachel intervened. 'There's no need for that,' she said stiffly. 'Just tell me where and at what time you'd like us to meet you on Monday and we'll be there.'

Joe blew out a breath. 'My chauffeur will pick her up about nine o'clock Monday morning,' he responded. 'If you change your mind again, let me know.'

Shelley was waiting at Eaton Court Mews when he got back.

She'd evidently been there for some time, because a tray of coffee was cold on the table and her face mirrored her impatience with his behaviour earlier.

'Where the hell have you been?' she demanded as soon as he strolled into the sitting room. 'What do you mean by walking out like that? I go to sleep with you beside me and I wake up to find you've gone.'

'Sorry.' But Joe wasn't in the mood to make more apologies and when Charles followed him into the room he turned with some relief. 'Black coffee, please,' he said. 'And perhaps Ms Adair might like to join me. Oh, and do you have any of those English muffins? I could do with something hot and sweet.'

'I hope you're not looking at me,' said Shelley, her tone softening as if she realised this was not the time to start a slanging match. But Joe only shook his head and lounged into a comfortable leather armchair.

'Just food,' he said, and Charles withdrew before another argument ensued.

However, realising he was allowing his frustration towards Rachel to influence his mood, Joe looked up at Shelley standing by the window. 'Have you been here long?'

She shrugged. Although he'd only thrown his clothes on before leaving her apartment, she had evidently taken some trouble with her appearance. A pale blue gauze dress dipped provocatively at her breast before flaring gently to her knees. Four-inch heels added height to her five-feet-ten-inch frame, and her blonde bob had been spiked to perfection. Evidently she'd dressed to please, and he felt guilty that right at this moment her pale good looks left him cold.

'Long enough,' she said now, moving over to his chair and perching on the arm. 'You need a shave, darling. I'm not one of those women who like getting the equivalent of razor burns every time I kiss you.'

Unwanted, the image of Rachel as he'd last seen her flashed into his mind. How was it possible that he'd found her so appealing? So appealing, in fact, that if her daughter hadn't interrupted them...

'Joe, you're not listening to me!' Shelley's voice rose again, and now there were hectic splashes of colour in her cheeks. 'Where have you been? Charles is so tight-lipped. He wouldn't breathe a word.'

'That's what I pay him for,' said Joe laconically, making no response when she slipped her arm around his neck. 'There was something I had to do. An arrangement I had to make for Monday. One of the guys back home asked me to fly his daughter over and I needed to check it out.'

Shelley's shoulders stiffened. 'His daughter?'

'Yeah, his daughter.' Joe glanced up at her. 'You got an objection?'

'Several.' Shelley's eyes flashed. 'To start with, how old is she?'

'Gee, let me see.' Joe pretended to think about it, hoping the distraction would lighten his mood as well as hers. 'In her teens, I guess.'

'Her teens?' Shelley's voice rose even higher.

'Yeah. Thirteen, I think. I can't remember.'

'Oh!' Her relief was evident, but when she bent to rub her lips against his Joe didn't take the bait.

'It's gonna be a busy weekend,' he said, forcing her to draw back just as Charles came back into the room. 'Ah, food! You ought to try one of these muffins, Shell. Charles makes them himself, and they're magic.'

'I'm glad you find something magical,' retorted Shelley huffily, getting to her feet again and surveying him with angry blue eyes. 'I hope this doesn't mean I won't see you again before you leave.'

'Shell—'

'I've brought two cups in case Ms Adair decides to join you,' Charles interposed swiftly as he set down the tray. He walked back to the door. 'Let me know if you need anything else.'

'Thanks.' As Charles disappeared again, Joe shifted forward and broke a piece off one of the warm muffins. In actual fact, he wasn't particularly hungry, but it was a way to avoid Shelley's accusing gaze. 'Come on,' he invited. 'Try a piece.'

'You know I don't eat fatty things,' replied Shelley stiffly. 'And you shouldn't either. They're bad for your cholesterol.'

Joe pulled a wry face. 'Oh, I think it can stand one English muffin,' he murmured drily. 'I promise to use the gym as soon as I get home.'

Shelley's lips pursed. 'You love making fun of me, don't you?'

'No.' Joe reached for the pot of coffee. 'But you sound as if you've had a sense of humour bypass.'

Shelley sucked in a breath. 'I don't understand you, Joe. When you first got here, you couldn't wait to see me. Then, last night, you lost consciousness as soon as your head hit the pillow.'

'I was tired.' There was a distinct edge to Joe's voice now, but Shelley didn't seem to notice.

'You can't have been that tired,' she retorted. 'You were up early enough this morning. You left the apartment without even waking me. I don't think you even took a shower. You certainly didn't leave a message. What was I supposed to think?'

Joe's jaw clamped. She was right, but he didn't like hearing about it. He didn't like the idea that anything that had happened since his arrival in England a week ago should have had any effect on his behaviour. He couldn't tell her he'd left her bed because he'd been having a hot, sweaty dream about another woman. And this morning he'd suffered a serious lapse of judgment, that was all. It certainly wasn't terminal.

'I've said I'm sorry,' he muttered tersely, reaching for his coffee and swallowing it black. He needed a jolt of caffeine to kick-start his brain. He also needed to get his head around the fact that a feisty female with tear-filled green eyes hadn't permanently rocked his reason.

'So…' Shelley's tongue circled her glossy lips. 'Will I see you tonight?'

Joe blew out a breath. 'Not tonight, no.'

'Why not?'

'Because I've promised this guy whose daughter I was telling you about that I'd go and check on his family.'

'His family?'

'His ma and pa.'

Shelley snorted. 'I don't believe you.'

'Your call. But it's true.' He paused. 'You can come with me, if you like.' That way if, by some unlucky chance Rachel should be there...

But he hadn't finished the thought before Shelley broke in. 'You've got to be joking! You want me to spend Saturday night visiting some old couple who're probably senile?' She snorted. 'Give me a break.'

'Okay.' Joe didn't argue. 'Then I guess I'll see you Sunday night before I leave.'

Shelley groaned. 'You know I've got to attend that awards dinner on Sunday evening. I told you at the start of the week.'

'Then I guess we won't see one another until you come to the Caribbean for your photo shoot in November.'

Shelley sulked. 'Couldn't you get out of this visit? For me? Please!'

'Couldn't you miss the awards dinner?' he countered.

'You know I can't.'

Joe shrugged, ashamed to find he was half relieved. 'Impasse,' he said. 'Come on. Drink your coffee. I'm sure you'll have no difficulty finding another man to spend your evening with.'

Shelley stalked across the floor. 'You're a bastard, do you know that?'

'So I've been told,' murmured Joe mildly, but the only response he got was the slamming of the door.

CHAPTER SIX

RACHEL was typing a page of her novel for the umpteenth time when the phone rang.

'Oh, great,' she muttered broodingly, aware that the story wasn't going as it should, and that her agent was probably ringing to check on its possible completion.

'Yes?' she said, the frustration evident in her voice.

And then she pulled a wry face when Evelyn Carlyle said tartly, 'I'm sorry if I'm being a nuisance.'

'Oh, of course you're not.' Rachel was contrite. Since Daisy had left for Florida over a week ago, her in-laws had been a constant source of support. 'I thought it was Marcia. She's been grumbling because I haven't got the manuscript finished.'

'Oh, I see.' Evelyn sounded mollified. 'I should have guessed. You looked tired yesterday. Aren't you sleeping well?'

'Well enough,' said Rachel tersely, aware that it was the man who'd escorted her daughter to Florida, not her manuscript, that was disrupting her sleep. It didn't help to know that, when he'd called on Howard and Evelyn as he'd promised Steve, they'd found him a very personable young man. Evelyn had even expressed the opinion that it was a pity Daisy wasn't older, which had really set Rachel's nerves on edge. 'I just wish Daisy would keep in touch,' she added now, but her mother-in-law was dismissive.

'You know what girls are like. She'll be enjoying herself and calling home will come very low on her list. Besides, Steve would have been on the phone if there was anything wrong.'

Was that supposed to reassure her? For once, Rachel wasn't in the mood to see Daisy's point of view. 'All the same,' she said tensely, 'I think she could have made an effort to send me a postcard, at least. She sent me an email when she arrived, but that's all.'

'And you're missing her. I know.' Evelyn was more sympathetic. 'And Howard and I are no substitute for your little girl. But she's growing up, Rachel. She'll be off to college before you know it. Visiting her father is probably a good thing. It will get you used to her being away.'

'She's only thirteen, Lynnie.'

Rachel couldn't help defending herself, and the older woman sighed. 'Yes. Yes, I know. But the years go by so quickly.' She paused. 'Anyway, didn't you tell me you'd had a call from Paul Davis?'

Rachel sighed. Paul Davis was the man she used to work for before her writing career had taken off. After the divorce she'd had to get a full-time job to help support herself and Daisy, and Paul had been a good employer. The trouble was, he wanted to be more than that, and he'd taken to calling every few weeks to ask her how she was and, occasionally, ask her out.

And she had been tempted to accept his invitation recently, mostly to get Evelyn off her back. Not that her mother-in-law wanted her to get married again. She still nurtured hopes that she and Steve would get back together.

'Yes, he rang,' she said now, resignation setting in at the thought of what was coming next.

'So why don't you go out with him?' Evelyn asked encouragingly. 'He's a nice young man, isn't he? And you deserve some entertainment while Daisy's away.'

'He's hardly *young*,' said Rachel drily. 'He's fifty or there-abouts. And he's never been married, Lynnie. He still lives with his widowed mother.'

'Which shows how dependable he is,' declared Evelyn firmly. 'Come on, Rachel. When did you last have a date?'

Too long ago to remember, thought Rachel ruefully as the memory of that scene with Joe Mendez flashed back into her mind. Sometimes she wondered if that had all been a figment of her imagination too. There was no doubt that it had been an unlikely event.

But then she remembered the nights during the past week when she'd awakened to find her breasts taut and sensitive, and an ache twisting low in her stomach that wouldn't go away. Sometimes she was soaked with sweat, too, her night-shirt clinging wetly to her aroused body. That wasn't her imagination, she knew, and she'd found it very hard to get back to sleep.

'Rachel!'

She'd been silent too long and Evelyn was getting impatient. 'I'm here,' she said. 'I was just thinking, perhaps I should go out with Paul.' *Liar!* 'It may be just what I need.' *To get Joe Mendez out of her head.*

'Oh, good.' Evelyn was pleased, evidently thinking her persuasion had worked. 'Let me know what happens, won't you, dear? Howard and I only have your best interests in mind.'

Rachel hung up the phone, wondering if agreeing to go out with Paul had been rather foolish. But she could hardly admit that the last time she'd slept with a man had been after the divorce papers had been delivered. Accepting an invitation to one of Julie Corbett's parties as a way of getting out of the house had been stupid. Finding herself in Julie's bedroom after one too many vodka martinis with a man she'd thank-fully not seen either before or since had been downright stupid. Fortunately she hadn't been too drunk to ensure he'd used protection, but for weeks afterwards she'd worried in case it hadn't been enough. Still, nothing untoward had happened, but it had been a sobering experience. One she'd vowed would never happen again.

Rachel bought a new outfit for her dinner date with Paul Davis. The low-cut crocheted top and skirt were a delicate shade of turquoise, and complemented the sun-streaked colour of her hair. The top also revealed a tantalising glimpse of cleavage, while the short skirt didn't exaggerate the provocative curve of her hips. The slightly cropped top also skimmed her midriff, as she appreciated every time she moved and a draught of cooler air brushed against her skin.

But the date itself was a disaster. As Rachel realised halfway through the evening when Paul had talked of nothing but his vintage Jaguar, and the extensive model-railway he had laid out in his mother's attic. She wished she'd asked Evelyn to ring her, to give her an escape if any was necessary. As it was, she could see the remainder of the evening stretching ahead of her without any relief from Paul's hobbies.

She had just begun to say she didn't want a dessert, in the hope of cutting the evening short, when her mobile phone started ringing. Knowing Evelyn's penchant for gossip, she guessed her mother-in-law was impatient to hear how she was enjoying herself. Or perhaps she'd heard from Daisy, she thought, glad of any distraction. But when she heard Evelyn's voice, she knew immediately that something was wrong.

'Hello, Lynnie,' she said, hoping she was mistaken. 'This is a surprise.'

'Oh, darling.' Evelyn sounded unlike herself. 'I'm sorry to interrupt your evening. Are you having a good time?'

Not really, thought Rachel. But she said, 'It's fine.' She cast an unwilling glance in Paul's direction. 'What is it, Lynnie? Is something wrong?'

But she knew. Before Evelyn spoke, she felt an uneasy shiver slide down her spine. 'I just thought you'd want to know, that's all,' said her mother-in-law as Rachel's brain raced ahead to a dozen probable scenarios, all of them bad. 'We've had a call from Steve.'

'Steve?' The fingers of apprehension tightened their hold around Rachel's stomach. This must be something to do with Daisy, she thought. Was this why she hadn't heard from her daughter recently? Oh God, she begged, please don't let anything bad have happened to her.

'Rachel!' Paul was speaking to her now, and she looked at him with uncomprehending eyes. 'The waiter wants to know what you'd like for dessert,' he said impatiently. 'He hasn't got all night.'

Rachel blinked. 'Not now,' she told him unsteadily. Then, to Evelyn, 'What is it? What's happened? Is Daisy hurt?'

'Not seriously, I'm sure.' Evelyn sounded as if she half wished she hadn't made the call now. 'There's been an accident…'

'Rachel!'

It was Paul speaking to her again, but Rachel ignored him. 'What kind of accident?' she demanded raggedly. 'When did it happen?'

'Oh, I'm not sure. Yesterday, the day before—Steve didn't say.' Evelyn tried to calm her. 'They were all out on Lauren's father's yacht, apparently. I don't think it's anything to worry about, but—'

Rachel sucked in a breath. She'd known. She'd positively known that Daisy would have been in touch if she could. 'I'm coming home,' she said. 'Right now. I want to speak to Steve myself. I want to know exactly how it happened and why I wasn't told at once.'

'Um…' There was something more, but Evelyn evidently thought better of telling her then. 'Yes, perhaps you should come home,' she agreed. 'Then we can discuss all the details.'

Rachel wanted to say 'What details?' but it would be easier to wait until she could speak to her mother-in-law face to face. 'I'll be about twenty minutes.'

She closed her phone to find Paul staring at her disbelievingly. 'What's going on?' he asked as she pushed back her chair. 'You're not leaving?'

'I'm afraid I am.' Rachel took a breath. 'That was Steve's mother. Daisy's had an accident. I've got to go home so I can call her.'

Paul didn't look pleased. 'I'll drive you,' he said, but she could tell it was the last thing he wanted to do. He'd been enjoying his meal and, judging by his slight paunch, food played a large part in his enjoyment of life. Along with his car and model railway, of course.

'There's no need,' she said now, gathering up her wrap from the back of her chair. 'You finish your meal. I can get a taxi. Thanks for—for everything. I'll probably see you later.'

CHAPTER SEVEN

THE British Airways flight to Miami had been due to land at three o'clock local time, but the airport was busy, and they'd had to circle the immediate area at least twice before being given permission to make an approach. Then, after landing, there were all the usual formalities to attend to, more thorough than ever now since the increase in terrorism, so that it was almost five o'clock when Rachel emerged into the arrivals hall.

She was tired. She'd hardly slept the night before and, although lots of her fellow passengers had slept during the long flight, she'd remained upright in her seat, replaying all she'd learned since Evelyn had rung her at the restaurant.

She'd arrived at the in-laws' house prepared for the worst, and she hadn't been disappointed. What Evelyn hadn't told her on the phone was that Daisy was in a hospital in Palm Cove, which was about twelve miles from downtown Miami. She'd apparently fallen from the Johansens' yacht and hit her head on the bathing platform as she'd gone into the water. Fortunately, one of the crew had realised something was wrong when she hadn't surfaced and he'd dived in after her. He'd managed to bring Daisy back to the surface, but she'd swallowed a lot of water. She'd been unconscious when they'd pulled her back on board.

Rachel had been horrified. Her first thought had been, why

hadn't Steve noticed what had happened? But that hadn't been a question Evelyn could answer. And Steve, when she'd finally tracked him down at the Johansens' house, had been similarly obtuse. 'She's thirteen, for God's sake,' he'd snapped angrily. 'She doesn't need a nursemaid twenty-four-seven.'

Rachel had made no comment about this. She could have said that Daisy should have been wearing a life jacket, which she obviously hadn't been; that, as she'd never been out on a yacht before, he might have taken the trouble to keep an eye on her. But she'd never had much success in arguments with Steve, and she hadn't intended to try now. Instead she'd said, 'I'd like to see her. Would you have any objections if I flew out and visited her myself?'

Steve had been surprisingly agreeable. 'Why not?' he'd said carelessly. 'That's why I rang the old lady. I knew you'd start clucking like a mother hen. If you want to come, I won't stop you.'

As if he could, Rachel had thought grimly, but at least he couldn't accuse her of acting without his knowledge. And when she'd come off the phone, Evelyn had confided that Steve had admitted that Daisy had been asking for her. That was why she'd taken the liberty of interrupting her date.

Now, dragging her suitcase behind her, Rachel made for the exit. The concourse was crowded and she was anticipating a lengthy wait for a taxi when someone caught her arm.

'Rachel,' a familiar voice said. 'I thought I must have missed you.'

It was Joe Mendez, and Rachel stared at him with disbelieving eyes. 'Joe!' she exclaimed without thinking. And then, 'I mean—Mr Mendez. What are you doing here?'

'Didn't I make myself clear?' Joe gave her a rueful smile. 'I came to meet you.' He glanced down at her suitcase. 'Is this all your luggage?'

'I—yes, but—'

'Good. Let's go.' He took the handle from her unresisting fingers. 'We can talk in the car. It's just outside.'

Rachel blinked. 'Um—did Steve ask you to meet me?'

'It was my decision,' said Joe, steering her round a portly woman whose tight jeans emphasised her size. 'Did you have a good journey?'

Rachel made some reply, but her mind wasn't really on her words. He was the last person she'd expected to see at the airport—or anywhere else, for that matter. She'd found a modest hotel in Palm Cove and booked herself a room via the Internet. The hotel wasn't far from the hospital, and it would be easy for her to visit Daisy without making any demands on anyone.

She certainly didn't expect to spend any time with her ex-husband. She'd accepted that they might run into one another at the hospital, but that was all. She was here for one reason and one reason only, and that was to see her daughter. At present, that was the only thing on her mind.

The humidity hit her as soon as they stepped out of the terminal. Until then, the air-conditioning had cushioned her from the oppressive heat outside. Heavy clouds hung over the airport buildings, dark and threatening, and a damp warmth moistened the skin at the back of her neck and sapped what little strength she had left.

A sleek black limousine idled in a no-waiting zone, and Joe headed straight for it, evidently expecting her to follow him. A uniformed chauffeur sprang out at their approach and swung open the rear doors of the car. Then, taking the suitcase Joe had been carrying, he flipped the boot lid and dropped the case inside.

Joe turned and for the first time she was able to take a proper look at him. In a tight-fitting black tee shirt and khaki cargo-shorts, he looked nothing like the CEO of a successful computer company that she knew him to be. Amazingly, his hair had grown a little in the week or so since she'd seen him, but there was the same shadow of stubble on his jawline.

'D'you want to get in?' he suggested, taking charge of the door nearest to him, and Rachel decided not to argue at this time. Although he probably had dispensation to park his vehicle in the area primarily given over to hire cars and taxis, she didn't want to be responsible for him earning a fine.

It was deliciously cool in the limousine, the soft leather giving luxuriously beneath her weight. There was enough room in front of her to stretch out full-length if she wanted to, and for the first time since leaving home she felt herself relax.

It didn't last long. When Joe circled the car and swung in beside her, she stiffened automatically. She could smell his heat, and his maleness, and the front of his shirt was just the slightest bit damp, as if he'd been sweating.

His knee brushed her thigh as he lounged on the seat beside her, bare legs brown and muscular and liberally spread with dark hair. The hairs on his arms were dark too, and once again she could see the shadow of the tattoo that was almost hidden by the short sleeve of his shirt. He looked lean and powerful, and totally at ease.

And just like that her pulse quickened, and she felt a melting heat between her legs. Despite her worries about Daisy, her body had a will of its own. Her breathing grew shallow and she prayed he wouldn't notice. Or if he did that he'd put it down to the suffocating heat outside.

'Okay,' he said as the chauffeur got behind the wheel and they started away from the kerb. 'Did Steve fix you up with a hotel?'

Rachel moistened her lips and smoothed her damp palms over the knees of her cotton trousers. 'I fixed myself up, actually,' she said. 'It's just a small hotel. The *Park Plaza*; I believe it's near the hospital.'

'The *Park Plaza?*' Joe's brows drew together. 'I don't believe I know it.' He leaned forward and addressed the chauffeur. 'Have you heard of the *Park Plaza* hotel in Palm Cove, Luther?' he asked, and the other man nodded.

'Yes, sir,' he said. 'It's on Spanish Avenue. Near the shopping mall.'

'Oh, yeah.' Joe seemed to recognise the location even if the hotel was unfamiliar to him. 'Okay, head in that direction.'

'Yes, sir.'

Luther acknowledged his instructions, and then Joe pressed a button in the arm of the door beside him and the privacy screen slid up between them and the chauffeur. 'Now,' he said, 'I guess you'd like to know how Daisy is this afternoon?' He paused, and when she widened her eyes he added, 'I saw her myself earlier today, and she seems to be making steady progress.'

'Thank God!'

Rachel's response was heartfelt and Joe regarded her with sympathetic eyes. It couldn't have been easy, he thought, learning that her daughter—who'd happened to be four thousand miles away at the time—had suffered a blow to the head that had needed specialist treatment. Joe himself, who'd been prepared, had been shocked when he'd seen the kid. Her face was covered in bruises and one of her eyes was almost completely closed.

'So.' Rachel knew she had to say something. 'How did you come to meet me? I could have taken a cab, you know.'

'Yeah.' Joe shrugged. 'And you could have been waiting a couple hours. I thought you might be glad to see a friendly face.'

'Are you a friendly face?' Rachel looked doubtful.

'I thought so.'

Rachel caught the inner side of her lower lip between her teeth. 'I suppose you're hoping I'll apologise. For—for what happened.'

'Oh, yeah.' Joe's eyes widened. 'And I'm expecting hell to freeze over any minute.' He shook his head. 'I could tell you

I'm sorry, but that wouldn't be true. I wanted to kiss you and I did.' For a moment, his fingers skimmed sensually against her cheek. 'I guess what you really want me to say is that it won't happen again.'

Did she?

Rachel drew back automatically, but he'd already withdrawn his hand. Lounging on the seat beside her, he was like a predator at bay. Yet he didn't scare her. She scared herself. Her skin was still prickling with the memory of his touch.

Knowing she had to say something, she chose a casual tone. 'That would be good,' she said. 'I wouldn't like you to think I'd taken it too seriously.' Although she had! 'I've not exactly been celibate since my divorce.'

Joe regarded her through his lashes. Now why didn't he believe her? he wondered. Her mouth had been hot, hotter than he'd ever imagined it would be, and her response had been all he'd wanted and more. God, if Daisy hadn't been lurking upstairs, he didn't know how far he might have taken it. He'd certainly been aching with the need to bury himself between her legs.

Yet, for all that, there'd been an innocence about the way she'd reacted that didn't gel with the image she was trying to convey now. He had the feeling it was a long time since she'd felt the need to portray herself as an experienced woman. She was trying to be brash, trying to show he hadn't scraped a nerve, but her eyes told an entirely different story. And he felt an almost overwhelming need to show her how wrong she was.

Big mistake.

'Okay,' he said, deciding to let it go for now, even if he was aware that he had a hard-on there was no way he was going to relieve. Thank heavens for baggy shorts, he thought wryly, adjusting his underwear. 'So I guess you'd rather I hadn't come to meet you, yeah?'

'Oh...no.' Rachel knew if she was going to carry this off

she had to act naturally. 'It was—it was very kind of you to put yourself out.'

'I don't look at it as putting myself out,' said Joe firmly, though he had to ask himself why he'd been so eager to come. Steve had put him in the picture and he had been concerned for Daisy, naturally, but wanting to see Rachel again was something else. And he knew it.

Rachel turned her head and tried to concentrate on the view beyond the limousine's windows. They were travelling along a wide road with tall trees growing on either side. On her right, beyond the belt of palms, the Atlantic reflected the overcast sky. Yet could it really be the Atlantic? It looked too placid to be the ocean.

The silence between them was pregnant with tension, and, forcing herself to relax, she said, 'Do you live in Miami, Mr Mendez?'

'It's Joe,' he amended mildly. Then, 'It's not my permanent address, no. But I have a condo out on Miami Beach that I use when I'm visiting the city.'

Rachel wanted to ask where his permanent address was, but it wasn't anything to do with her. Nevertheless, remembering how impressed Daisy had been by the house she'd visited in London, she couldn't prevent herself from saying, with unknowing wistfulness, 'I expect you have a lot of homes.'

'One or two,' he conceded, not wanting to talk about himself. 'Tell me, when did you hear about the accident?'

Rachel's eyes widened. 'Last night. Why?'

Joe managed to hide his astonishment. The kid's accident had occurred three days ago. In Steve's place, he'd have let Rachel know at once. Particularly in the circumstances. 'I guess you must have booked your seat on the next flight?'

'Yes, I did.'

Rachel felt troubled now. Joe's expression wasn't always

readable, but there was something in his face that made her add urgently, 'Why do you ask?'

'No reason.'

Joe's eyes darkened, lingering on her face with a warmth and intensity that brought an embarrassing wave of colour into her cheeks. Looking at him now, she could hardly believe how intimate they'd once been. And while he was probably used to doing whatever the hell he liked, she most definitely wasn't.

Only he mustn't know that.

Dragging her eyes away from his lean, disturbing face, she forced herself to remember why she was here: Daisy. Her daughter should be her prime concern, and she doubted she'd be too impressed to learn that her mother was dwelling on the possible actions of a man she'd convinced herself she didn't even like. Although with his hip only inches from hers, and the remembered awareness of how he'd made her feel when he'd thrust his tongue into her mouth, those sentiments seemed decidedly suspect.

She felt so hot suddenly, a bead of sweat trickling down between her breasts. Which was ridiculous, considering the coolness of the car. To distract herself, she tried to find some interest in the buildings that lined the other side of the wide boulevard: neo-classical styles fighting for space between modern high-rises, the occasional square of parkland a welcome splash of greenery.

'Um, Palm Cove,' she murmured, aware that Joe was still watching her. 'Is it much farther?'

'Not far.' Joe shifted forward in his seat and her heart leapt into her throat. But although his thigh briefly brushed hers, all he did was open a small chilled cabinet set beneath the polished console opposite. Inside was a selection of sodas and mixers, and gesturing, he said, 'Are you thirsty?'

Rachel's mouth was dry, but she doubted a drink would

cure it. Still, the sight of the frosted bottles was appealing, and she said a little breathlessly, 'Do you have mineral water?'

'Water?' Joe studied the contents of the cabinet. 'Yeah, sure. There you go.' He handed her a bottle. 'You need a glass?'

'Oh—no.' Rachel unscrewed the cap with some difficulty. Her fingers were hot and slippery, but thankfully he didn't offer to do it for her. 'This is fine.'

'Good.' Joe closed the cabinet again and lounged back in his seat. Then, his eyes on the slender column of her throat visible above the open neck of her cotton shirt, he added, 'You do know that's where Steve and Lauren live? Palm Cove, I mean.'

Rachel almost choked on the water. 'No,' she gasped, when she was able. 'No, I didn't.' The last address she'd been given was the apartment—or condo—they'd occupied in Miami itself.

'Oh, yeah.' Joe wondered what else Steve hadn't told her. 'They share the Johansen mansion with Lauren's old man. His wife died a couple of years ago, and I guess he got tired of rattling round that old place on his own.'

Rachel's tongue circled her lips. 'So Daisy's been staying there, too?'

Joe frowned. 'That bothers you?'

'Not exactly.' Rachel made a helpless gesture. 'I just wish I'd known, that's all.'

Joe hesitated. 'But you know about the accident, right?'

'Well, I know she fell off the Johansens' yacht and hit her head,' replied Rachel at once. 'And that she apparently wasn't wearing a life jacket. I'll certainly take that up with her father, if I get the chance.' She paused. 'I don't suppose you have any idea when she'll be allowed to leave the hospital? I mean, if she's been there three days already…'

Joe stifled an oath. This was what he'd been afraid of. Evidently, his address wasn't the only thing Steve had kept from his ex-wife, and now Joe was faced with the unpleasant task of having to tell her himself or allowing her to walk into her daughter's room, totally blind to the circumstances of her condition.

He'd been silent too long and Rachel wasn't a fool. She'd noticed his expression and now she demanded, 'Why are you looking so grim?' She swallowed. 'What do you know that I don't?'

Joe blew out a breath. Steve was going to hear about this, he thought savagely. Right now, he felt like pushing the other man's teeth down his throat. It would have given him an immense amount of satisfaction, not to mention relieving a little of his own frustration.

Obviously Rachel had come here unaware of what had happened after Daisy had been helicoptered to the hospital in Palm Cove. She had no idea that Daisy's injuries had been considered too serious to be dealt with by the Emergency Room doctors and that Daisy had been transferred to a specialist neurological unit attached to the far more expensive facility patronised by the Johansens.

'Look,' he said carefully, 'First off, Daisy's going to be fine.'

'Why doesn't that reassure me?'

'But she won't be leaving hospital for a few days yet.'

'Why not?' Rachel felt the water she'd just swallowed churning around in her stomach. My God, what had really happened? What had they kept from her? She should have guessed it had been something more serious than a simple blow to the head. 'Please,' she said, unthinkingly putting a hand on his knee. 'You've got to tell me.'

Despising the inappropriate response his body was having to those soft, damp fingers clinging to his leg, Joe gently but firmly removed them. But he kept her hand between both of his as he said, 'She had to have an operation—'

'An operation!'

Rachel looked horrified and he couldn't blame her. He knew a momentary urge to comfort her, to pull her into his arms and hold her close, but he determinedly suppressed it. He knew where that could lead.

'It was just a small operation,' he said, smoothing her knuckles with his thumb. 'There was some pressure and it had to be relieved. But as I say, she's making great progress.'

Rachel was trembling. He could feel it. The hand he was holding was shaking uncontrollably and, abandoning any hope of remaining objective, Joe slipped his hand around her neck and pulled her towards him.

She didn't resist, probably because she was too shocked to notice what was happening. She pressed her hot face into the hollow of his throat and, seconds later, he felt her tears soaking the front of his shirt.

'God, Rachel,' he muttered, his hands tightening automatically, and then Luther turned and saw them.

The chauffeur knew better than to show any emotion, but Joe realised that during the upheaval of the last few minutes they had reached their destination. The rather tawdry blue-painted facade of the *Park Plaza* hotel was visible just across the intersection and Luther was waiting for further instructions.

With some reluctance, Joe withdrew his arms and, allowing her to rest against the supple upholstery, he lowered the screen an inch or two to speak to the other man. 'Let's go straight to the hospital, Luther,' he said briskly, and the chauffeur didn't demur.

Rachel had found a tissue in her handbag and was engrossed in repairing the damage caused by her tears. She didn't meet Joe's eyes, but he knew she was as aware of what had almost happened as he was. If Luther hadn't turned at that moment, Joe knew he wouldn't have been able to stop himself from kissing her. And that would have been a totally unforgiveable thing to do. Damn it, she needed support, not seduction.

He scowled. He didn't know what the hell was wrong with him. She was *so* not his type. He'd always gone for sophisticated women before; women who, like him, knew the score. Not inexperienced females with one failed relationship behind them and more baggage than he cared to consider.

Yet, when he looked at Rachel, he didn't see a woman who was older than he was and who already had a child. He saw a warm, vulnerable female who, he had to admit, got to him in a way none of his other girlfriends ever had. Sitting there in her travel-stained trousers and creased shirt, her heat-dampened blonde hair spilling untidily about her shoulders, she aroused emotions he would have sworn he didn't possess.

He stifled a groan. Now was so not the time to be having these kind of thoughts. Raking a hand over his own hair, he gripped the back of his neck with a tormented hand. He could feel the tension in his muscles, the tautness in his spine. And knew if he could get his hands on Steve at that moment…

But he couldn't. And he had to deal with it. Even if the kind of temptation Rachel presented drove him crazy in the process.

CHAPTER EIGHT

WHEN the car started moving again, Rachel realised that they weren't turning into the forecourt of the *Park Plaza* hotel.

She'd glimpsed the facade of the building across the intersection as she'd dried her eyes, and had assumed Luther was just waiting for the traffic signals to change in their favour before he made his move. But when the vehicle started away it ignored the entrance to the hotel, continuing down the thoroughfare they'd been travelling on before.

'But, wasn't that—?' she began, only to have Joe interrupt her.

'I thought you might prefer to go straight to the hospital,' he said, settling back beside her. 'I know Daisy's eager to see you.'

'Is she?' Tears pricked Rachel's eyes again, but she determinedly blinked them away. She'd already made a fool of herself by breaking down in front of him. She just hoped he didn't think she was putting on an act for his benefit. 'So—so how serious was this operation?'

Joe blew out a sigh. 'Fairly serious,' he said, after a moment. 'As I said before, there was some pressure on her brain and it had to be relieved.'

Rachel couldn't prevent her gasp of horror. 'My God! No wonder Steve was so reluctant to let me know what had happened.'

'Yeah, well.' Joe tried to be pragmatic. 'It's possible he

wanted to wait until she'd had the operation before he called you. Until the crisis was over, so to speak.'

'You think?'

Rachel looked at him with rain-washed green eyes and Joe knew he couldn't lie to her. 'Okay, maybe not,' he conceded. 'I guess he didn't want to admit he'd screwed up. All I can say in his defence is that as soon as it was realised that she needed specialist treatment he had her transferred to a neurological unit that's used to dealing with head injuries.'

Rachel's eyes widened. 'So she's not at the hospital near the *Park Plaza*?'

'She's at another facility in the town,' he explained evenly. 'She's had the best treatment money can buy, I can vouch for that.'

Rachel caught her lower lip between her teeth. 'I booked into the *Park Plaza* hotel because it was near the hospital,' she murmured, half to herself. And then, realising he was listening to her, she said quickly, 'How much further do we have to go?'

'Not far.' Joe had to suppress the urge to take her in his arms again. He couldn't forget that, if he hadn't gone to meet her at the airport, she'd still be totally in the dark. He saw the white walls of the Steinberg Clinic ahead of them and moved forward again to speak to the chauffeur. 'Pull under the portico, will you, Luther? Then, after you've dropped us off, find somewhere to park, okay?'

'Yes, sir.'

Despite the fact that Rachel had the car door open before either Luther or his employer could forestall her, the two men both came to offer their assistance. 'I can manage, thanks,' she insisted tensely, but this time Joe didn't hesitate before gripping her wrist.

'I'm coming with you,' he said, and they walked through the automatic glass doors into the clinic together. 'Humour me. I'm familiar with the form here. You're not.'

Although Rachel wanted to object, it turned out she was grateful for his presence after all. There was an armed security guard just inside the doors who might well have questioned her identity, and a glamorous receptionist manning the desk who was unlike any hospital receptionist she had ever seen before.

Happily they both recognised Joe, and after some embarrassing affectation on behalf of the receptionist, they were instantly allowed to enter the lift, which was controlled by yet another security guard.

Rachel looked up at Joe as the lift ascended, aware she'd been something less than appreciative of his help. 'Thanks,' she said, touching his arm with a tentative finger. 'I guess I owe you one.'

A knot twisted in Joe's belly, but he managed to keep his tone light as he said, 'I'll let you know when I want to collect, shall I?' And for the first time since he'd told her about Daisy's operation a small smile tilted the corners of her far too delectable mouth.

The lift stopped at the second floor and they stepped out onto a beige-carpeted landing. A nurse's station was situated opposite, and there were swing doors giving access to the private rooms at either side of the hallway.

There were two nurses on duty when they approached, and, recognising Joe, one of them—a curvaceous redhead whose uniform bodice was open to reveal a very impressive cleavage—came to greet them. 'Have you come to see Daisy again, Mr Mendez? I hope she realises what a very lucky girl she is.'

Her eyes had flickered over his companion as she spoke, and Rachel guessed she was wondering what he was doing with someone like her. Ironically, the nurse herself was much more his type, and she'd probably decided that they'd merely shared a lift together.

'Actually, I've brought her a very special visitor,' remarked Joe drily. 'This is Daisy's mother. From England. Is it okay if we go straight in?'

'Oh!' To say the nurse was startled would have been a vast understatement. 'Oh, yes. Yes, go ahead. Dr Gonzales is on his way to see her, but I don't suppose he'll object to her mother visiting her.'

'Good.'

Joe took hold of Rachel's arm just above her elbow and guided her towards the swing doors to the right of the nurses' station. Pushing open one of the doors with his free hand, he allowed her to precede him into a discreetly lit corridor with maybe half a dozen rooms situated along its wide expanse.

Rachel noticed that all the patients' rooms seemed to be on one side of the corridor, with double doors to emergency facilities and operating theatres located opposite. It was very luxurious, very quiet, and Rachel couldn't help a twinge of anxiety that Daisy had had to be treated at such a place.

'This is Daisy's room,' murmured Joe, indicating the third door down. 'I won't come in with you. You'll appreciate a few minutes on your own.' He paused and then, with an unexpected thickening of his tone, he added, 'Don't take any notice of the way she looks. She's going to be fine, I promise.'

Rachel opened her mouth to ask what he meant. But he was already striding back towards the swing doors, and the atmosphere of the place didn't encourage raised voices. Instead, with a deep breath, she put her hand on the handle of the door and pressed down.

Daisy looked lost in the huge hospital bed, her face, what Rachel could see of it, almost as white as the pillows behind her. Rachel had been expecting bruising; what she hadn't expected was the bandage that circled Daisy's forehead, or the swelling around her eye that gave her face a lopsided appearance.

Her heart leapt into her throat and she felt the treacherous sting of tears threatening to betray her again. But she remembered what Joe had said, and the advice implicit in his words, and controlled herself. She mustn't let Daisy see how upset her appearance had made her, and stepping into the room, she said, 'Now what have you been doing with yourself?' in a soft but teasing tone.

Daisy had been lying on her side, staring out of the windows, which Rachel now saw overlooked the gardens at the back of the clinic. Lawns, flowerbeds and pleasant tree-shaded walkways provided a recreational area for patients who were well enough to go outside, and there were still one or two people enjoying the somewhat watery sunshine that had broken through the clouds.

Daisy turned her head at the sound of her mother's voice, and if Rachel had had any doubts about coming, they dissolved at that moment. Daisy's face crumpled, and she held out a trembling hand towards her mother. Rachel didn't hesitate before hurrying across the room to take it, then cupped her daughter's face with fingers that were predictably unsteady.

'Oh, Daisy,' she said, pressing her lips together briefly before bending to kiss the girl's bruised cheek. 'Baby, I'm so glad to see you.'

'Me too,' sniffed Daisy, clinging to Rachel's fingers. 'Oh, Mum, it's been so awful! They had to drill a hole in my head and they had to shave off half my hair.'

'I know, I know, darling.' Rachel struggled to hide her anxiety. 'But it sounds as if you've had the best treatment possible, and that's the important thing.'

'I don't like hospitals,' said Daisy at once, her eyes brimming with tears. 'I don't like being here. I want to go home.'

'And you will,' Rachel assured her comfortingly. 'As soon as you're feeling better.'

'I feel better now!'

'Oh, Daisy.' Rachel took a steadying breath. 'As soon as the doctor says you're fit to leave, you can. I'm sure your father and—and Lauren have been worried sick about you.'

Daisy's chin trembled. 'I haven't seen Lauren,' she said tear-fully. 'Dad says she doesn't like hospitals. Or—or sick people.'

Rachel bit her tongue against the retort that sprang to her lips and, as if realising how inflammatory her words had been, Daisy added hastily, 'Dad said it's because her mother died in hospital. She had some kind of disease that attacks your liver. Cirius, or something.'

Cirrhosis, thought Rachel flatly, resisting the urge to specu-late about whether Mrs Johansen had been rather more than a social drinker, and said, 'That's a shame. She can't have been very old when she died.'

'She wasn't.' Daisy was distracted from her own problems by relating the story. 'Mr Johansen misses her a lot.'

'I bet.' Rachel hesitated. 'You've been staying with him, haven't you?'

'Mmm.' Daisy attempted a nod, but it evidently pained her and she winced. 'Daddy and Lauren live with him,' she went on when she'd recovered. 'He's nice. You'll like him.'

'I doubt if I'll even meet him,' declared Rachel ruefully. 'Once you're out of hospital, you'll continue with your holiday and I'll go home.'

'No!' As Rachel would have moved to the chair beside the bed, Daisy grasped her arm. 'You can't leave,' she protested. 'I don't want you to.'

'Oh, Daisy.' Rachel could see the girl was getting dis-tressed and she tried to reassure her. 'I can't stay here. I have to get back, you know that. Besides, what would your father say?'

'I don't care what he says,' muttered Daisy in a choked voice. 'He doesn't care about me. He only cares about Lauren.'

'Now, Daisy—'

'It's true!' she cried. 'He only wants me here because the company expects their executives to be family men, and he and Lauren can't have any children.'

'Daisy!' Rachel stared at her. 'You don't know that.'

'I do too.' Daisy groped for a tissue from the box on the bedside cabinet and Rachel put one into her hand. 'I heard them talking one night after I was supposed to be in bed.'

'Daisy!' Rachel was torn between her desire to know what her daughter had heard and the equally strong conviction that she shouldn't be listening to gossip. 'I don't think this is anything to do with me.'

'But it is!' Daisy was determined to make her point. 'You know you've always wondered why Dad suddenly started showing an interest in me.'

Rachel's jaw dropped. 'I didn't say that.'

'You didn't have to. I'm not stupid, Mum. I'm, like, thirteen, not three.'

Rachel sighed. 'All the same—'

'Ah, it's Mrs Carlyle, I believe.'

The voice came from behind her and Rachel sprang up from the bed as an elderly man in a white coat and wearing half spectacles came briskly into the room. She hoped he hadn't been listening to their conversation. If so, he must have a very poor opinion of her.

'Um—yes,' she said awkwardly, and the man smiled.

'I thought so.' He came across the room to shake her hand. 'I'm Dr Gonzales. Daisy is my patient. And I have to say she looks much brighter now than she did when I saw her this morning.'

'That's 'cos my mum's here,' said Daisy at once, and Dr Gonzales inclined his head.

'Most probably,' he agreed, consulting the chart hooked to the foot of the bed. 'But we'll see, shall we?' He looked up. 'How is your head feeling now? Do you still have some pain?'

'No.'

Daisy's response was just a little too pat and Dr Gonzales didn't look as if he was deceived. 'Maybe just a little?' suggested Rachel, remembering the way Daisy had winced earlier, and her daughter gave her a resentful look.

'You'd have some pain if someone had drilled your skull,' she countered sulkily as a nurse followed the doctor into the room. 'I'll feel better when I get out of here.' Then, as Rachel widened her eyes in warning, 'Well, I will.'

'I suggest we allow your mother to go and get a cup of coffee,' declared Dr Gonzales smoothly as the nurse began to roll back the sleeve of Daisy's gown. 'She looks a little tired, don't you think?' Then, to Rachel, 'Perhaps we could have a few words later this evening? I'd like to explain what has happened and how long I think Daisy needs to stay here.'

'Of course.' Rachel glanced at her watch. It read almost midnight, but it was still on British time. 'I—er—I need to speak to someone. To arrange about my luggage. If you could give me half an hour?'

'Take an hour,' advised Dr Gonzales kindly. 'I'll be here all evening. You might like to have a rest. Are you staying somewhere close by?'

'The *Park Plaza* hotel,' said Rachel, and she thought he seemed a little surprised by her answer. But he didn't demur.

'Shall we say eight-thirty?' he suggested. 'In my office. The receptionist will tell you where it is.'

Daisy gazed at her despairingly. 'You're not leaving?' She choked back a sob. 'I don't want you to go.'

'I'll be back.' Rachel glanced at the doctor, and he nodded his head almost imperceptibly. She squeezed Daisy's hand. 'You be good, baby. I'll be back before you've even noticed I've gone.'

There was no sign of Joe when Rachel let herself out of Daisy's room and she guessed he must be waiting downstairs. He couldn't have left, she assured herself as she took the lift down to the lobby. Her suitcase was still in the boot of the limousine.

But when the lift doors opened it was Luther who was standing there, waiting for her. 'Mr Mendez had to leave,' he explained politely. 'He sends his apologies and has instructed me to escort you to your hotel.'

'Oh.' Rachel's stomach hollowed with disappointment. Until that moment, she hadn't realised how much she'd wanted to see Joe again. 'Well, thank you.' She glanced uncomfortably at the receptionist, who was watching their exchange with obvious interest. She forced a smile. 'Shall we go?'

The limousine was visible as soon as they stepped out of the doors; its sleek black lines dominated every other vehicle on the parking lot. Luther helped her into the back, then closed the door and got behind the wheel. He moved easily for such a big man, and the smile he gave her through the rear-view mirror was reassuring.

'The *Park Plaza*, right?' he said, and Rachel nodded.

Then, before the screen between them could be raised, she shifted forward in her seat and said nervously, 'Exactly how far away is it? Could I walk from the hotel to the hospital?'

'Not a good idea,' declared Luther without hesitation. 'I guess it's over a mile, and most people hire a car to get around.' He paused. 'That's not your problem. Mr Mendez is letting you have the use of one of his cars while you're here.'

Rachel's lips parted. 'But—he can't do that.'

'Hey, you don't tell Mr Mendez he can't do nothing.' Luther grinned. 'Leastways, not when he's just thinking of your safety. You're a stranger, Ms Carlyle. You don't know the area. It can be a dangerous place, especially at night.'

Rachel shook her head. 'I don't know what to say.'

'Don't say nothing.' Luther was dismissive. 'You just tell Mr Mendez how you feel when you see him again.'

When you see him again.

Considering how Rachel had been feeling about Joe Mendez when she'd landed in Miami, it was amazing how reassuring those words sounded. Did Joe intend to see her again or did Luther mean he might run into her at the hospital? Either way, the prospect was massively—and dangerously—appealing.

CHAPTER NINE

JOE stood at the windows of his condo, looking out at the angry waves crashing against the shore. Although the rain had gone, the wind had picked up in its absence, bending the palms that lined Ocean Drive, and causing the few pedestrians to stay out of reach of the blowing sand.

It was almost dark, and he hadn't even started to get ready for the reception he was due to attend in South Beach. The painter son of one of Macrosystems' directors was having his first showing in one of the art deco galleries on Lenox Avenue, and Joe had accepted an invitation more out of respect for the father than the son.

Of course, when he'd first heard about the showing, he hadn't had any inkling that other matters might be occupying his mind—or that the woman he'd tried his damnedest to forget would have come back into his life. How could he have known that Daisy would have an accident so serious that her father would have to contact her mother? And why, when he'd learned that Steve was making no arrangements to meet his ex-wife, had he decided to get involved? Rachel wasn't his concern, damn it. So why did he feel as if she was?

It was time he put the Carlyles and their problems behind him. For this evening, at least. Tomorrow, he intended to speak to Steve and find out why the hell he hadn't been honest with Daisy's mother. He'd have allowed his ex-wife to arrive in Miami without even knowing where her daughter was being treated.

But it still wasn't his problem, he reminded himself irritably, turning away from the windows and surveying the lamplit room behind him. Pale wood and terracotta-coloured furnishings gave the huge room a stark simplicity, the space maximised by carefully chosen articles of furniture that offered comfort without dwarfing their surroundings.

The penthouse living space had windows on two sides, and leather-seated chairs surrounding an Italian marble-topped table occupied the other embrasure. It provided an intimate dining area, useful when his guests were small in number, but this evening he found no pleasure in his possessions. He was impatient and on edge, unsure why he hadn't waited at the hospital. He'd wanted to, God knew, but things were getting far too heavy. He'd always been in command of his relationships before, but where Rachel was concerned it was a whole new ball game.

And he didn't like it.

The sound of the intercom penetrated his grim introspection, and seconds later his housekeeper came to ask if he was at home to a Mr Carlyle.

'You did say *Mr* Carlyle?' he asked sharply, and in spite of what he'd been telling himself just a moment ago the idea that Rachel might have found out where he lived caused his blood to pump hotly through his veins. After all, Marla was Mexican, and her English wasn't always perfect.

'Mr Carlyle, yes,' she repeated, her brown eyes bright with enquiry. 'You will see him, yes?'

Joe glanced at his watch. He had precisely forty minutes before he was due at the gallery. A quick shower—he ran his hands over the stubble on his jawline and decided he could do without a shave—and a clean shirt and trousers and he would be ready. At least people didn't dress up for these occasions. There'd be punks there in tie-dyed tee shirts and shorts.

'Okay,' he said now. He'd welcome the chance to tell Steve how he felt about the way he'd treated Rachel. Though maybe not tonight, he mused, revising his opinion. It might look as if he had a personal interest.

'Yes, sir.'

Marla departed to let Steve in, and Joe walked across to the bar to help himself to a Scotch over ice. He grimaced. Charles always said that he ruined a perfectly good whisky that way, but Charles wasn't here, and that was the way his father always took it.

There were voices in the foyer—women's voices, he realised—and he felt a surge of irritation when Marla showed both Steve and Lauren Carlyle into the room. Had Steve brought his wife deliberately, hoping Joe wouldn't say anything controversial if Lauren was present? Their friendship had been sorely tested recently, what with the lies Steve had told about his age and Joe's suspicion that Rachel was not the manipulative bitch her ex-husband had always claimed.

'Hey, Joe!' Steve came into the room with an air of phony confidence, holding out his hand towards the other man as if certain of his welcome despite Joe's expression. 'How are you?'

Joe shook hands with some reluctance, accepting the kiss Lauren bestowed on either cheek without response. Her hands clutched his arms, and she took the opportunity to press her scantily clad breasts against his chest as she did so. It wasn't the first time she'd come on to him in this way, and he was well aware of what she was trying to do.

He wondered fleetingly if Steve had put her up to it. Was he prepared to turn a blind eye to Lauren's indiscretions if it ensured his advancement at Mendez Macrosystems? It was a cynical thought, and one Joe wouldn't have considered a couple of weeks ago. But meeting Rachel and Daisy had changed his opinion of Steve's character.

'I hope you don't mind us turning up like this,' Steve was saying now as Lauren returned to slide a sinuous hand under her husband's arm. 'I just wanted to thank you for meeting Rachel at the airport.'

Joe swallowed a mouthful of his Scotch before saying, 'How did you know I went to the airport?' He crossed to the bar to refresh his drink and held up his glass enquiringly.

'Oh.' Steve's colour had deepened a little. 'Nothing for me, thanks.' Then, after Lauren had asked for a glass of white wine, he continued, 'Bill Napier told me where you were. I'd heard you were in the office today, and I wanted to tell you how much I appreciate you visiting Daisy.' He pulled a wry face. 'When I heard you'd gone to pick up Rachel, I had to come and thank you. I mean, it's not as if she needed to make the trip.'

'You don't think so?'

Joe handed Lauren her wine and regarded the other man over the rim of his glass. Sensing some tension here, Lauren said quickly, 'What Steve means is that Rachel has never trusted us to look after Daisy properly. You can't imagine how galling that is, particularly as he's been denied a father's rights for years.'

Joe arched a quizzical brow. 'Daisy did have an accident,' he reminded her, and Lauren met his gaze with an appealing look.

'You're surely not blaming Steve for that?' she protested in a little-girl voice, pouting in a way Joe was sure achieved positive results with her husband. Though not, unfortunately, with him. 'The girl is so clumsy. Anyone can see that. If she wasn't so fat, she might have been able to save herself.'

'Lauren!' Even Steve seemed to realise she'd gone too far, and Lauren widened her eyes indignantly.

'You said that too,' she accused sulkily. 'You said she was just like her mother.'

'Lauren!' Steve spoke again, and this time there was no mistaking the anger in his voice. 'I don't think this is the time to be discussing whether Daisy's fat or not. We came to thank Joe for visiting her. You know better than anyone that it's no fun spending time in a hospital.'

'Oh, that's so true.'

Lauren shuddered dramatically, and Joe's brows rose in surprise. 'I didn't know you'd been in hospital, Lauren,' he said politely. 'I hope it was nothing serious.'

'Lauren's not been ill,' said Steve swiftly. 'She's talking about when her mother was dying and she had to visit her every day.' He put an arm about his wife's shoulders. 'She had such a tough time. She and her father both did.'

Not to mention the late Mrs Johansen, thought Joe drily, wondering why he'd never noticed these flaws in Steve's make-up before. It was as if he was seeing a whole new person, one he didn't particularly like.

'Anyway, I guess you told Rachel where Daisy is being treated,' went on Steve conversationally. 'Knowing her, she'll probably spend all her time at the clinic. Still, it'll give me a break. Trying to keep a kid of thirteen entertained is no joke.'

Joe's brows ascended again. 'You've been spending a lot of time at the clinic?' he queried mildly. 'I didn't realise that.'

Steve pulled a sheepish face. 'Some,' he said, looking a little defensive. 'But you know how it is. I'm no good in the sick room. And looking at Daisy's face just makes me feel sick.'

Joe knew an almost uncontrollable urge to hit him. 'I don't suppose it's much fun for Daisy either,' he retorted, unable to hide the irritation in his voice. 'For God's sake, Steve, she's your daughter! And if you're not exactly responsible for what happened to her, you can't deny you were supposed to be looking out for her when the accident occurred.'

Steve looked indignant now, and Lauren squeezed his arm before giving Joe a reproachful look. 'You didn't mean that, did you, Joe?' she said in a baby voice. 'Steve loves his daughter. He can't help it if Daisy's injuries make him squeamish.'

'Of course he can help it!' Joe was angry now. 'Daisy's injuries will heal, please God, no thanks to him. But what irritates me is the way the two of you seem to have absolved yourselves of all responsibility for what happened. If I didn't know better, I'd have thought you'd informed Rachel of the accident just so she'd take up the slack.'

'It wasn't our fault,' protested Steve, sounding resentful. 'It's all right for you, Joe. You swan into the clinic whenever you feel like it and you know that the staff will fall over themselves to lick your boots. Me, I'm just Daisy's father. They tolerate my presence and that's about it.'

'Perhaps if you spent more time with Daisy they'd have more respect for you,' said Joe harshly. 'As I understand it, you've only visited the kid a couple of times since she had the operation.'

'Three times,' said Steve sharply, as if that let him off the hook. 'And as soon as she's out of there, we'll take her to Disney World.'

Joe rolled his eyes. 'She won't want trips to Disney World,' he snapped in exasperation. 'What she'll need is a little rest and relaxation when she's discharged. Personally, I'd suggest you take a couple of weeks off work and spend time with her. Talk to her, find out what she's been doing since you last saw her. Show her you're her father in more than just name.'

'Oh, but Steve and I are going to New York next weekend!' exclaimed Lauren at once. 'Isn't that right, babe?' She looked up at her husband. 'Daisy's only staying for another week and then she's going home.'

'Daisy won't be flying back to England any time soon,' said Joe finally. He slammed his glass back onto the bar. 'Have you given any thought to Rachel's feelings at all?'

'Rachel?'

Lauren looked nonplussed, and even Steve appeared taken aback by the non sequitur.

'Yeah, Rachel,' said Joe shortly, half wishing he hadn't brought her name up. 'When were you planning to tell her how serious Daisy's injuries were? Damn it, she didn't even know she'd been moved to a specialist facility.'

Steve scowled. 'She'd have found out soon enough,' he muttered, staring down at the Chinese rug beneath his feet. But when he lifted his head and met Joe's accusing gaze, his expression shifted. 'What's it to you? What has she been telling you about me? Was it my fault she was out with some guy the night I called?'

Joe's jaw tightened. Was that true? Had Rachel been spending the evening—night?—with another man when Steve had tried to ring her? He felt a tightening in his gut that had nothing to do with Daisy and everything to do with her mother. Was that why she'd got only half the story? Was he jumping in with both feet when he'd only got half the story too?

'I suggest we say no more about it,' he declared flatly. 'As you say, it's really nothing to do with me. My only concern is that Daisy gets the best treatment possible.'

'Hey, that's my concern too!' exclaimed Steve, his tone indicating some relief at Joe's capitulation. 'And we'd better be making a move. I want to visit Daisy before her mother can poison her mind against me again.'

Rachel's room at the *Park Plaza* hotel was hardly a five-star accommodation. But it was clean and the bed was reasonably comfortable. So much so that, when Luther dropped her off, she was grateful just to flop down onto it and close her eyes.

She was so tired. Her body didn't care what time the clock said; she'd flown the Atlantic and she felt utterly exhausted. Finding out that Daisy's injuries were more serious than she'd been told hadn't helped either. Without Joe's support and guidance, she'd have been whistling in the wind.

She refused to consider what meeting Joe again had meant to her. She'd been so sure that if they did meet again she'd be able to handle it. But she was afraid she was beginning to rely on him more and more. And that was stupid. Joe Mendez was not a man a woman like her could depend on, and she was fooling herself if she thought he found her anything more than a minor distraction.

It had been dark outside when she'd closed her eyes, but when she opened them again the room was filled with sunlight. Scrambling up, she managed to bring her watch into focus, her breath catching when she saw the time. Not that she needed the watch to tell her it was morning. She'd slept for twelve hours straight, still dressed in the shirt and trousers she'd worn to travel in.

Her head throbbing now, she glanced round and saw her suitcase standing just inside the door where the porter had left it. Swinging it up onto the crumpled coverlet, she found the key in her bag and hastily unlocked it.

Seeing the clean clothes laid out inside reminded her that she hadn't had a shower for two days. She felt hot and grubby, the air conditioner making only half-hearted inroads into the room's humidity. Stripping off her clothes, she padded barefoot into the adjoining bathroom and turned on the shower.

Fifteen minutes later, she felt infinitely cleaner and brighter, and rummaging in her case, she brought out navy linen shorts and a pink tank top. There was no hairdryer, but it was so hot she knew her hair would dry naturally. Then, content she wouldn't embarrass her daughter, she grabbed her bag and left the room.

Daisy had been on her mind ever since she'd opened her eyes. She hadn't forgotten that she'd promised to go back the previous evening, and aside from Daisy's distress she'd let Dr

Gonzales down, too. She was also desperate for a drink. She'd had nothing since the bottle of water Joe had given her in the car, and she was sure her headache was partly due to dehydration.

Thankfully, there was a coffee shop and a small pharmacy attached to the hotel, and she was able to buy herself a coffee to go and some chocolates for Daisy. Normally she wouldn't encourage her to eat rich confectionery, but these were exceptional circumstances. Then, sipping the coffee, she went outside to look for a taxi.

There was no taxi in sight, but she refused to consider what Luther had said about Joe lending her a car. And luckily, a taxi arrived soon afterwards. The driver offloaded two passengers and their luggage and she was able to grab it. 'The Steinberg Clinic, please,' she said, sinking into the back seat.

It was after nine o'clock when she got to the clinic, and she stowed the half-drunk styrofoam mug of coffee in a waste bin before going in. As luck would have it, a young man was manning the desk this morning, and after she'd identified herself he had no problem in directing her to the second floor.

She was aware of the security guard watching her as she took the lift, but she reached the second floor without incident. She had to identify herself again at the nurses' station and then she was allowed to make her way to Daisy's room. But when she opened the door, she discovered Daisy already had a visitor.

Joe Mendez was lounging on the wide windowsill beside her daughter's bed, and Daisy was giggling at something he'd said. There was such an air of camaraderie between them that Rachel almost felt as if she was intruding. Yet she was glad Daisy wasn't on her own, she told herself. Even if she'd never expected to see Joe again.

Joe got up from the sill as Rachel stepped into the room, and Daisy, sensing another presence, turned her head. 'Mum!' she exclaimed eagerly. And then, as if remembering Rachel had promised to come back the night before and hadn't, her expression changed. 'I thought you'd forgotten I was here.'

'Oh, Daisy!' Rachel rolled her lips inward, pressing the box of chocolates to her chest like a shield. 'I fell asleep,' she admitted honestly, uncomfortably aware that Joe was listening. Then, turning to him, 'Um—thanks for visiting Daisy again, Mr Mendez. It's very kind of you.'

Joe tucked his palms into the back pockets of his trousers and swayed back on his heels before replying. He was formally dressed this morning, his pin-striped grey shirt and charcoal-grey trousers indicating a business meeting. 'I was passing,' he said. Then, his eyes darkening, 'Did you sleep well?'

'Too well,' murmured Rachel, feeling the heat rising up her throat as he continued to look at her. Were her breasts puckering? she wondered. Was the film of perspiration she could feel breaking out all over her visible? She lifted her hand and made a futile attempt to fan herself. 'It's very hot.'

'It's Miami in August,' remarked Joe drily, but Rachel noticed it didn't seem to bother him. He looked so cool—and gorgeous, she thought, looking away before he noticed the effect he was having on her. Dear heaven, she was behaving like a schoolgirl. She had to stop reacting in this way.

'Mr Mendez comes most days,' put in Daisy, apparently deciding she'd been ignored long enough. She fumbled for something half-hidden beneath the coverlet. 'Look what he's brought me.'

She produced something that looked like the iPod Rachel had bought her at Christmas. But it was smaller and slimmer, and when Daisy touched a switch a small screen flickered to life. 'It's a video iPod,' she said proudly. 'Isn't it great? I can download videos as well as music and watch them on the screen.'

'Really?' Rachel was impressed in spite of herself, but there was no way she could allow her daughter to accept such an expensive gift from him. She licked her lips and turned to

Joe again. 'It's very nice,' she said inadequately, 'But Daisy can't keep it.'

'Mum!'

Daisy's cry of protest was predictable, but Rachel couldn't help that. 'It's too much,' she said, avoiding Joe's dark gaze. 'I'm sorry.'

'But Mum…'

Daisy was getting tearful now, and Joe felt a surge of impatience as Rachel held her ground. He'd wanted to do this for Daisy; wanted to give her something to make her time in hospital more fun. And give him an excuse to visit her again, he admitted ruefully. Because, now that Rachel was here, he definitely wanted to see her again, whatever excuse he had to make.

'Mum, you can't stop me from having it,' Daisy was saying sulkily. 'It's mine, not yours. Mr Mendez has already downloaded a load of teen movies, so I'm not bored while I'm lying here.'

'I'm sorry,' Rachel muttered, but now she couldn't prevent her gaze from shifting to Joe's dark face. He should have known better, she thought crossly. He hardly knew the child.

'How about if Daisy only borrows it while she's in the hospital?' he suggested mildly. 'I don't mind. I've got a stack of them lying around the place. It's no big deal.'

Not for you, maybe, Rachel brooded, aware she was fighting a losing battle. Joe was determined to win this argument and she was fairly sure there was humour lurking behind his eyes. He was probably enjoying her confusion. Another anecdote to regale her ex-husband with perhaps?

'Please, Mum.' Now that she saw a glimmer of hope on the horizon, Daisy was prepared to be docile. With an appealing smile, she added, 'Are those chocolates for me?'

'What?' Rachel became aware that she was practically squashing the box of chocolates to her chest. 'Oh, yes.' With

a hurried gesture, she handed the box over. 'Sorry. They may
be a bit soft.'

'Unlike the giver,' murmured Joe, crossing the room and
dropping the mocking remark in her ear. Then, turning back,
'Bye, Daisy. I guess I'll see you *both* later.'

CHAPTER TEN

'THANKS, Mr Mendez.'

Daisy evidently thought the controversy was over, but as Joe closed the door behind him Rachel knew she wasn't prepared to leave it like that. 'I won't be a minute,' she said to her startled daughter, and jerking open the door again, she stepped into the corridor outside.

'Mr Mendez!'

Closing Daisy's door, she called his name, and Joe, who had almost reached the double doors into the reception area, paused at once. Turning, he saw her, and Rachel couldn't deny a ridiculous sense of satisfaction when he strolled back to her.

'Hi,' he said, as if they hadn't just been involved in a dispute in Daisy's room. 'What can I do for you?'

Rachel pressed the palms of her hands together, not knowing how she was going to handle this. 'I wish you hadn't given Daisy such an expensive present,' she said at last, and Joe's mouth took on a cynical twist.

'Well, hey, and I thought you were going to thank me for loaning you that automobile,' he remarked drily, hands on his hips. 'I should have known better.'

Rachel sighed. 'I don't know anything about an automobile,' she said, ignoring what Luther had told her. 'And you're deliberately confusing me...'

'Am I?' He didn't sound concerned. 'So?'

'So…' Rachel glanced up into his disturbing face, wishing she had more experience in these matters. These days all her knowledge of men seemed to come from books she'd written or read, and she couldn't manipulate Joe Mendez like she could one of her characters. 'I—er—I'd like your word that you won't turn Daisy's head with any more extravagant gifts. She's an impressionable teenager, and although we're not poor by any means, I can't afford to spend hundreds of pounds—dollars—every time she sees something she wants.'

A muscle in Joe's jaw jerked spasmodically. 'You don't pull your punches, do you, Ms Carlyle?' he said coldly. 'Believe it or not, I didn't give Daisy the video iPod with any intention of turning her head or encouraging her to believe that she can get anything she wants without working for it.'

'No?'

It was obvious Rachel didn't believe him, and Joe felt compelled to go on. 'No,' he said flatly. 'I don't care what you believe, but I haven't always been in the happy position of being able to afford anything that takes my fancy either. Growing up, my family was like yours, except we were immigrants. I didn't go short, but I always knew I'd have to work if I wanted to make a success of my life.'

Rachel stared at him. 'But your family owns a multi-million-dollar company,' she protested, and Joe gave an angry snort.

'Yeah, they do now,' he conceded. 'My father was fortunate enough to understand computers, and between us we found a way to use macro technology to simplify disciplines in science and economics. We were lucky. Our idea took off. But that was only ten years ago, after I left Harvard.'

'Harvard!' Rachel's eyes widened and Joe pulled a wry face.

'Yeah, Harvard,' he agreed. 'What can I tell you? I was a bright student. A guy can get sponsorship if he's clever enough.'

'And you were? Clever enough, I mean?'

'No.' Joe found he couldn't lie to her, even if his answer caused her to give him a cynical look. 'Actually, my grandparents supported me.' He grimaced. 'That part was easy. Staying there wasn't.'

'Oh, well…' Rachel shrugged. 'It's nothing to do with me, is it?'

'No, it's not.' Joe's voice was terse and she could sense he was impatient. 'But you've made it a bone of contention between us and I'm entitled to defend myself.' He raked a hand through his short hair, causing it to spike on top of his head. 'Damn it, I don't know why we're having this conversation. It's obvious you don't believe a single word I've said.'

Rachel blinked. 'I didn't say I didn't believe you.'

'You didn't have to.' His voice was harsh. 'God, why do I let you get under my skin?'

Rachel swallowed. The corridor seemed very empty suddenly. 'I didn't know I did,' she protested, feeling the flesh on her arms prickle with anticipation, and he scowled.

'Well, you do,' he told her roughly, and she thought he was going to turn and stride back the way he'd come. But instead he reached for her, pulling her in closer so he could cover her mouth with his.

Desire came hot and fast, her bones melting as his hungry tongue thrust into her mouth. His hands gripped her hips, jerking her against him, and the hardness of his body was unmistakeable.

Joe groaned. This wasn't meant to have happened. He'd spent over a week—and all of last night, incidentally—telling himself that he'd imagined the effect she had on him. He'd known women before, plenty of them, and he'd always been able to walk away without looking back. For God's sake, he hadn't even slept with Rachel, yet he hungered for her with a need that defied description.

There was something about her that made the blood run hot in his veins and caused a wholly carnal reaction in his groin.

For heaven's sake, he'd been half-aroused since she'd walked into Daisy's room in those so-conservative shorts that nonetheless displayed the sexy length of her legs.

He'd wanted to touch her then, to run his fingers up the insides of her thighs and discover for himself if she was as aroused as he was. He'd wanted to bury his face between her breasts and lick the beads of sweat from her delectable cleavage.

His hands slid around her, finding the curve of her spine, the provocative separation of her bottom. He moulded her to him, her softness a delicious counterpoint to his hardness, and knew that, whatever happened, he was going to see her again.

With her nipples probing the fine silk of his shirt, it was hard to let her go. But he had to. Dragging his mouth from hers, he ran his thumb over her bottom lip with an urgency that revealed his raw frustration.

'I've got to go,' he said harshly. 'But I want to see you again.'

Rachel swayed a little as he spoke. It was an effort to think coherently when her head was swimming, and the knowledge that once again he had the advantage was causing goose bumps to feather her skin.

But she couldn't let him see how shaken she was, and with a determined effort she said, 'I suppose you're bound to see me again when you come to visit Daisy,' as if that thought didn't fill her with panic. 'I'd better get back—'

'Wait!' Once again, Joe's hand captured her arm. 'I mean I want to see *you* again.' He paused. 'Have dinner with me. Tonight.'

'I can't.'

It was an instinctive denial born of a need to protect herself, but Joe wouldn't accept it. 'Why can't you?' he demanded. 'You're not seeing Steve, are you?'

'Steve?' Rachel looked astounded. 'Heavens, no.'

'So maybe you feel some loyalty to this guy you're seeing back home?' he suggested, feeling his stomach clench at the thought.

But Rachel only shook her head. 'Paul's a friend, that's all,' she said firmly.

As if Joe was something more than that!

'Okay, then...'

'There's Daisy to consider,' she said, realising belatedly that she could have used Paul as an excuse.

'Does that mean, if you didn't have Daisy to consider, you'd have no objections?' he queried, and when she didn't respond, 'They settle Daisy down for the night before nine o'clock. I could pick you up outside.'

Rachel sighed. 'Why?'

'Why?' Joe's hand fell to his side. 'You need to ask?' His eyes were suddenly dark and intense. 'Rachel, you know why.'

She shifted uneasily. 'I can't believe there isn't some other woman waiting for you to ask her out.'

Joe scowled. 'Okay, maybe I would have no difficulty in getting a date for this evening, but I don't want anyone else, I want you.'

Rachel bit her lip. 'If you feel guilty about what happened just now,' she began and Joe uttered a strangled oath.

'I don't feel guilty!' he snarled, wondering if he'd ever had to beg for a date before. 'I just want to spend time with someone who doesn't care about getting their picture in the papers or how much money I have in the bank. But okay, yeah, I want to sleep with you. And despite your reaction, I think you want to sleep with me.'

Rachel took a step backward. 'And you assume I'll go out with you after that?'

'Why not?' Joe's eyes rested sensually on her mouth. 'Come on, Rachel. Live dangerously for once. I've read one of your books, and I know your heroines don't get freaked out when a man tells them he's attracted to them.'

'My heroes don't expect sex on a first date,' she retorted indignantly, and Joe spread his hands in a gesture of defeat.

'Okay,' he said. 'Just dinner, then. How's that? I promise I won't try to jump you in the restaurant.'

Rachel shook her head. The temptation to do as he said and live dangerously was strong, but for the last few years she'd avoided any kind of emotional entanglement. She had no intention of allowing herself to be hurt again, and something told her any pain Joe inflicted would not be easily repaired.

Still…

'Just dinner?' She lifted her head, and Joe made a sign of assent. 'All right,' she said. 'But I have to warn you, I didn't bring any special clothes with me.'

Joe's grin was smug. 'Come as you are,' he said drily. 'Nine o'clock downstairs, right?'

Rachel's tongue circled her lower lip. 'Right.'

'Good.' Joe's voice was husky, and before she could stop him he'd wiped her lip with his finger and brought the moisture he'd collected to his lips.

Daisy wasn't very impressed when Rachel recovered herself sufficiently to enter her daughter's room again. 'What have you been doing?' she grumbled. 'I thought you came to see me, not spend time arguing with Mr Mendez.'

Arguing? Rachel felt a hysterical desire to laugh. 'Oh, it was nothing important,' she said. 'And you needn't worry, you can keep the video iPod as long as you're in here.'

'Yes.' Daisy made a fist, but then she sobered. 'Come and sit down.' She patted the bed beside her. 'I have something to tell you.'

Rachel was wary, but she seated herself on the side of Daisy's bed. 'What?'

Daisy offered her a chocolate from the box before saying, 'Dad and Lauren came to see me last night.'

'They did?' Rachel refused the chocolate before adding, 'It's just as well I didn't come back, then, isn't it?'

'Well, no, actually.' Daisy popped the rejected chocolate into her mouth. 'I think he expected you to be here.' She paused again, examining the contents of the box. 'I think that's why he brought Lauren.'

'Really?' Rachel realised that, apart from caring about Steve's treatment of Daisy, she couldn't care less about him or Lauren. 'I thought you said she didn't like hospitals.'

'She doesn't.' Daisy shrugged. 'Maybe she didn't trust Dad to be alone with you.'

'Oh, please.' Rachel stared at her. 'I don't think that's likely, do you?'

'You never know.' Daisy regarded her critically for a moment. 'You've changed, Mum. You look really pretty these days. If you could just get used to wearing more trendy gear, I think you'd be surprised at how good you look.'

'Gee, thanks.' Rachel didn't know what to say. She couldn't remember the last time someone had paid her such a nice compliment. Except when Joe had said she was beautiful, of course. But he'd had his own reasons for saying that.

'Anyway...' Rachel was eager to leave the subject of her appearance. 'How are you feeling this morning?' She studied the girl's face intently. 'You know, I do believe the swelling round your eye is going down.'

Daisy pulled a face. 'I still look like Frankenstein's sister,' she grumbled. 'Dr Gonzales says I've been very lucky, but I don't know. Do you think my face will ever look normal again?'

'Of course it will.' Rachel was optimistic. 'And you always look good to me, baby.' She sighed. 'Which reminds me, I didn't get to speak to Dr Gonzales last night, either. I hope he'll forgive me for wasting his time.'

'Gonzales is okay, I guess.' Daisy was resigned.

'Well, Joe—Mr Mendez, that is—thinks so. When he told

me you'd had to have an operation, he assured me you'd received the best treatment there is.'

Daisy frowned then. 'But Dad had already told you that, hadn't he?'

Rachel stifled a groan. 'He said you'd had an accident,' she said, prevaricating. 'I dare say he didn't want to worry me.'

Daisy didn't look as if she believed her. 'Anyway,' she said, 'when you do talk to Dr Gonzales, could you ask him when I can get out of here and go home?'

Rachel considered. 'Well, I should think that's up to your father,' she said. 'You've still got a week of your holiday left.'

Daisy pouted. 'But I don't want to finish my holiday,' she protested. 'I want to go home. Back to England. With you.'

'Oh, Daisy…' This was an eventuality Rachel hadn't anticipated. 'I don't know whether you'll be allowed to fly straight after a— Well, after an operation.' She tucked a strand of Daisy's hair behind her ear and drew back. 'Besides, your father will want you to stay.'

'You think?' Daisy spoke surprisingly cynically for a girl of her age. 'Now that he's done his duty, I don't think he can wait to get rid of me. I know Lauren can't.'

'Daisy!'

'Well, it's true. They were talking about going to New York next weekend, and I'm not included in that.'

Rachel bit her lip. 'Well, let me talk to Dr Gonzales.' *And your father*, she thought grimly. 'Then I'll let you know what he says, right?'

'All right.' Daisy managed a small smile. 'I do love you, Mum.'

'And I love you,' said Rachel fiercely as a nurse came into the room. She got to her feet. 'Now, I'll go and see if I can get some answers.'

As it turned out, Dr Gonzales wasn't available to speak to her that day. One of the nurses explained that he also worked at one of the hospitals in Miami itself, and unless there was an emergency he wouldn't be in until the following day.

There was no way Rachel could class Daisy's sudden desire to leave the hospital as an emergency, and she had the unenviable task of explaining to her daughter that Dr Gonzales' world didn't revolve around her.

Daisy complained, naturally, and she got herself into such a state that the nurse who came to check on her suggested Rachel should go and get some lunch and let Daisy have a rest. 'There's a coffee bar downstairs,' she said pleasantly. 'It will do you both good to have a break.'

The coffee bar was almost empty, and Rachel helped herself to a ham sandwich before ordering another coffee. Then, carrying her tray to a window table overlooking the forecourt of the clinic, she made an effort to eat. She should have been hungry, but so much had happened since her arrival she had little appetite.

Still, the sandwich was delicious, and after a few mouthfuls she realised she was hungry after all. She finished it and was enjoying sipping her coffee when someone sat down at her table. It was a man, and she was about to pick up her coffee and find somewhere else to sit when she realised it was Steve.

Looking at him, she thought she could forgive herself for not recognising him straight away. He'd lost weight and his skin was deeply tanned. He should have looked fit and healthy, but he didn't, and she wondered if living with Lauren wasn't quite the sinecure he'd imagined it would be.

'Hi,' he said flatly. 'Daisy said I'd find you here.' His eyes appraised her with surprising interest. 'How are you? You look—good. Different, but good.'

'Compliments from you?' Rachel was sardonic 'Gee, I wonder why?'

Steve's jaw jutted. 'Don't be like that, Rache. I'm just trying to be friendly. There's no point in you and me falling out with one another, is there?'

'Isn't there?' Rachel's look was incredulous. 'You don't think keeping the truth about Daisy's injuries from me was a little thoughtless?' She shook her head. 'Not to say downright deceitful.'

Steve scowled. 'You don't think that the way you're reacting now is why I didn't tell you?' he countered. 'I knew you'd panic. You always do.'

'I don't panic!' exclaimed Rachel defensively. 'But I was worried. And I had a right to know.'

'Why?' Steve looked sulky now, much like Daisy did when things were not going her way. 'So you can get the custody order changed?'

'No.'

'That's what you said,' Steve reminded her. 'You said if anything happened to Daisy…'

'While she was with you,' Rachel finished for him. 'Yes, I remember.'

'There you go, then.'

'Well, I suppose accidents do happen,' said Rachel a little wearily. 'But you do realise she should have been wearing a life jacket, don't you?'

'Yeah, yeah.' Steve put both elbows on the table and ran his fingers through hair that was thinning at his temples. 'But Lauren had said, well, how pale Daisy's skin looked, and you don't get a tan wearing a life jacket all the time.'

Rachel shook her head. 'So, have you spoken to her today?'

'Daisy? Just to ask where you were.'

'You don't think she'd have appreciated you showing some concern?'

'Why?' Steve was offhand. 'She wants to go home, you know? I don't think Miami has lived up to her expectations.'

You mean you haven't, thought Rachel impatiently. 'And you and Lauren have other plans, right?' she suggested drily, and Steve gave her a quick look.

'What do you mean?'

'You're planning a trip to New York, aren't you?'

Steve's arms dropped onto the table. 'Who told you that?' He frowned. 'Was it Mendez?'

'Joe?' The word was out before she could prevent it, and she saw the familiarity hadn't gone unnoticed. But Steve had evidently decided not to push his luck, because all he said was, 'Yeah, Joe Mendez. I know he doesn't approve.'

'Doesn't he?' Knowing Joe as she was beginning to, that didn't surprise her.

'He takes too much upon himself,' muttered Steve petulantly. 'Spending time with Daisy. Meeting you at the airport. What was that all about?'

Rachel looked down at her coffee, hoping he wouldn't notice the sudden colour in her face. 'Well, you weren't planning on meeting me,' she pointed out quietly, and Steve made a sound of disgust.

'It would have been all the same if I was,' he countered aggressively. 'Since he offered Daisy a ride in his plane, he's done nothing but poke his nose into my affairs.'

'I'm sure that's not true.'

'Isn't it?' Steve shrugged. 'You don't know him like I do. I used to think he was my friend. Now I'm not so sure.'

Rachel lifted her head. 'Can I ask you something?'

Steve was wary. 'What?'

'Why did you lie about your age?'

'Oh, yeah.' Steve scowled at her. 'You couldn't wait to rat on me, could you? This is a young man's country, Rache. Why shouldn't I take off a few years? Plenty of women do.'

Rachel finished her coffee and put the cup aside. 'I'd better go,' she said. 'Daisy will be wondering where I am. Why don't you come with me?'

Steve made no attempt to move. 'She wants to go home, you know,' he said again. 'She wants to go back with you.'

Rachel shook her head. 'I don't think Dr Gonzales will allow that.'

'What do you mean?'

'It's too soon after the operation. She'll probably need a few more days' rest when she gets out of the clinic.'

'Well, I won't be here,' said Steve flatly. 'I've promised Lauren I'd take her to New York, and I can't let her down.'

'But you don't mind letting your daughter down?' Rachel suggested mildly. 'I think you need to go and see Daisy, Steve. Get your priorities in order.'

She excused herself to go to the bathroom, and when she came back Steve had gone.

CHAPTER ELEVEN

DAISY was alone when Rachel went back up to her room. Apart from asking if Rachel had seen her father, she seemed indifferent to the fact that he'd apparently left without saying goodbye. Rachel guessed that this was one of the reasons why she wanted to go home. Where Steve was concerned, only Lauren seemed to deserve his undivided attention.

Daisy fell asleep soon afterwards and Rachel took the opportunity to go back to her hotel and get changed. She could hardly go out for dinner in her tank top and shorts, and she was grateful now that she'd pushed the crocheted top and skirt she'd been wearing for her date with Paul Davis into the suitcase.

Then, before taking a shower, she rang Evelyn and Howard and told them what was going on.

Naturally, they were both disturbed to hear how serious Daisy's accident had been, and Evelyn said she'd give Steve a piece of her mind next time she was speaking to him. But Rachel knew that was unlikely. Since the rift between them had been breached, Steve's parents would be unlikely to do anything to create more hostility.

She rang off, promising to keep them informed of what was happening, and then took another shower. She even washed her hair again, aware that the heat and humidity had left a sticky film over her skin. Or was that being with Joe? she wondered, combing her hair back from her face and regarding her reflection with critical eyes. There was no doubt that when he touched her her temperature soared out of sight.

It was later than she'd expected when she got back to the hospital, and Daisy had already had her evening meal. She didn't appear to have missed her mother. When Rachel entered the room, she was engrossed in one of the films Joe had loaded onto the video iPod, but her eyes widened when she saw her mother had changed.

'That's new, isn't it?' she asked, and Rachel realised she'd bought it after Daisy had left for America.

'I had a date with Paul Davis,' she said offhandedly. 'I had to have something to wear.'

'It's nice.'

Daisy offered her approval before returning to the film, and Rachel spent the rest of the evening flicking through the magazines the nurse had brought her from the visitors' lounge. They didn't stop her nerves from jangling every time someone opened Daisy's door, but they helped keep her mind off seeing Joe again.

It was completely dark when she stepped outside later. But the heat hadn't dissipated. It wrapped itself around her like a damp blanket. Yet the scents of night-blooming blossoms seemed accentuated somehow, their fragrance giving the warm air a sensuous appeal.

Rachel had half expected Joe to be waiting for her in the foyer, but when the lift reached the ground floor only a female receptionist and two security guards were gathered about the desk. 'Have a pleasant evening, Ms Carlyle,' the receptionist called cheerfully, and Rachel was heartened by the fact that people were beginning to recognise her.

All the same, she wasn't happy standing out on the forecourt. At night, the clinic had a whole new ambience, and an awareness of how vulnerable she was to possible thieves or muggers couldn't help but cross her mind. After all, it was after nine o'clock. She couldn't remember when she'd last gone out so late at home. If ever.

When a low-slung dark vehicle swung into the grounds of the facility, Rachel drew back in alarm. The car was unfamiliar to her, and when it drove under the portico where she was standing she considered going back inside.

Then a window was lowered, and Joe said, 'Hey, Rachel!'

He was driving himself this evening, and he stopped the car beside her and thrust open his door. 'I'm late, I know,' he added, pulling a sheepish face. 'The traffic on the turnpike was murder.'

Rachel's tongue circled her lips. He had no idea how glad she was to see him. 'I haven't been waiting long,' she said quickly, and managed a slight smile when he looked down at her.

'You should have stayed inside,' he commented, his dark eyes taking an intense interest in her appearance. She was glad now she was wearing the new outfit. For the first time in his presence she didn't feel her age. 'A beautiful woman alone is always vulnerable.'

A beautiful woman! He'd said it again, and Rachel felt a shiver of anticipation slide down her spine. It didn't matter that she knew she wasn't beautiful. It was just so good to pretend she was.

'So…' Joe indicated the car behind him. 'Shall we get going?'

'Why not?' Rachel nodded, noticing how attractive he looked in lightweight cream trousers and a dark brown shirt. His collar was unfastened, and his folded-back sleeves displayed forearms liberally dusted with dark hair. There was a slim gold watch on his wrist, and a heavy gold ring occupied the smallest finger of his left hand. He was nothing like Steve, she thought. And wasn't she grateful for that?

The low sports-saloon had the distinctive smell of leather combined with what she recognised as an expensive men's cologne. And mingling with the rest was the singular scent of a heated male body.

The engine roared to life, and Joe swung the powerful vehicle out into the stream of traffic. Dozens of pairs of head-lights streamed towards them, illuminating palm trees and huge planters filled with flowering shrubs. Waxy anthuriums and scarlet proteas grew in careless profusion, reminding her of the semi-tropical climate, the heat of which had been briefly relieved by the fresh breeze blowing in her face.

'There's a tropical storm off Cuba,' Joe commented as she tucked her tumbled hair behind her ears. 'With a bit of luck, it won't come our way.' Then he smiled. 'How's Daisy tonight?'

Rachel thought how ironic it was that Joe seemed more concerned about her daughter than the girl's father. 'She's fine.' She paused. 'She really loves the video iPod. She's been watching one of the films you downloaded for her.'

'That would be fun for you.'

'Well, we did talk a little. Mostly about the fact that she wants to come home with me.'

'To England?'

'Hmm.' Rachel nodded. 'I've explained that Dr Gonzales might not agree. I've got an appointment to see him tomorrow morning.' She hesitated and then went on, 'I half wish she could. Steve has other plans, I think. He didn't expect this to happen.'

Joe's fingers tightened on the steering wheel. So Lauren had apparently got her way about the proposed trip to New York. He didn't know why he felt so angry about the way they were treating Daisy, but he did. She wasn't his daughter, but that didn't stop him from caring what happened to her.

'Why don't you stay on for a couple more weeks?' he found himself saying, almost without his own volition. 'I have a house on Biscayne Bay you could use. It would give Daisy time to recuperate.'

Rachel caught her breath. 'I couldn't do that.'

'Oh, right.' Joe frowned. 'You've got a deadline for your book. I'd forgotten about that.'

'The book's not a problem.' Rachel lifted her shoulders. 'I wouldn't be able to work if I was worrying about Daisy.'

'So what is the problem?' asked Joe quietly, bringing the powerful sports car to a halt outside what looked like a private dwelling. 'You don't want my help, is that it?' His eyes narrowed. 'What are you afraid of, Rachel? That I'll expect some personal compensation in lieu of rent?'

'No.' Rachel glanced anxiously towards the building they were parked outside, wondering if she'd been entirely wise to trust him after all. 'I—we, that is, Daisy and I—we can't stay in your house.' She shook her head. 'However innocent your offer is, it wouldn't be right.'

She thought Joe swore, but he thrust his door open without saying anything more and seconds later he was at her side of the vehicle, offering her his hand. His fingers were surprisingly cool considering the temperature, or perhaps it was the sweaty slipperiness of her own that made such a contrast.

Rachel's skirt slid along her thighs as she swung her feet to the pavement, and Joe felt another surge of frustration at the effect those slim bare legs had on his libido. For God's sake, what was wrong with him? She wasn't the kind of woman to get involved with. The word 'commitment' simply wasn't in his vocabulary.

Meanwhile Rachel was making an effort to smooth her tangled hair. Threading her fingers through it, she was intensely conscious of how her action exposed a provocative wedge of her midriff. Had Joe noticed? she speculated, her pulse quickening. Of course he had. She caught her breath. Was he wondering how far she was prepared to go?

The appearance of a young man wearing a black waistcoat over a crisp white shirt and pin-striped trousers brought a welcome breath of sanity to the situation. 'Evenin', Mr

Mendez,' he greeted Joe familiarly. 'Evenin', ma'am; welcome to the *Sea House*. And how are y'all this evening? Hopin' that tropical storm gives us a wide berth, I'll bet?'

'You got it.' Joe forced a smile and handed over his car keys. Then Rachel felt his hand in the small of her back. 'Come on.' He ushered her up the steps into a lamplit foyer. 'The food here is excellent. I always come at least once when I'm in Miami.'

The *maître d'* met them in the foyer; a short, dark-skinned man of Latino ancestry, he greeted Joe like a long-lost brother. 'Joe, my man,' he said, shaking Joe's hand warmly. 'I heard you were in the city and I was wondering if you were going to pay us a visit this time around.'

'Would I miss tasting your seared sea bass?' asked Joe goodnaturedly, his hand slipping naturally about Rachel's waist. 'Meet Henri Libre, Rachel. He's another South American exile who's made a name for himself in Miami and New York.'

'How do you do?'

Rachel allowed the little man to take her hand, supremely conscious when Joe's fingers moved against her skin. If his intention was to ensure she was aware of him, he was wasting his time. She'd been aware of no one else since he'd arrived at the clinic.

The restaurant was through opaque glass doors, and it was instantly cooler once the doors closed behind them. Henri offered them a drink at the adjoining bar, and Joe asked her if she'd like a cocktail. 'You must try Antonio's margaritas,' he said, nodding to the barman. 'He makes the best cocktails in the city.'

Rachel was helped onto a stool at the bar, and presently a broad-rimmed glass was set in front of her. 'Try it,' Joe said, watching her. 'I've told Antonio to hold the salt.'

The tequila caught the back of Rachel's throat, and for a moment she felt as if she couldn't get her breath. Then the alcohol found its way to her stomach and she took a steady-ing gulp of air. The last thing she needed was to get tipsy, she thought. Being with Joe was intoxicating enough as it was.

Leaving her glass on the bar, she half turned to survey the room behind her. From what she could see, the restaurant was small and intimate, lamplit booths and carefully arranged trellises of greenery providing both privacy and anonymity for the guests. Which was probably why Joe liked it, she reflected a little cynically. A man of his wealth and power was bound to attract attention wherever he went. Yet, despite his obvious attraction for women, he didn't strike her as the kind of man who would court notoriety.

'Don't you like it?'

Joe, who she noticed had accepted only a soft drink, drew her attention, and she swung round again, bumping her knees against his. 'Oh, sorry,' she said as he parted his legs to ac-commodate her. But instead of allowing her to move back to the bar, he imprisoned her knees between both of his.

'My pleasure,' he said. 'So, tell me, do you like the mar-garita?'

Rachel glanced at the drink. 'It's very nice,' she said breathily. Then, in an effort to distract herself, 'You're only drinking tonic.'

'I need to keep my head around you,' said Joe huskily. His eyes darkened as they rested on her mouth. A tiny drop of liquid rested on her lower lip, and before he could stop himself he'd leant forward and captured it with his tongue. 'Have you any idea how good you taste?'

Rachel swallowed. 'I don't think you should make fun of me,' she protested, and Joe stifled a rueful laugh.

'Oh, baby,' he said. 'I'm not making fun of you.' He hesi-tated, and then continued roughly, 'Myself, maybe. I'm the one who's drowning here.'

Rachel shook her head. 'You don't have to flatter me.'

'For God's sake!' Joe swore then. 'I'm not flattering you, damn it.' His hands dug into her knees for a moment and then he released her. 'Hell, that ex-husband of yours did some number on you, didn't he?'

'I don't know what you mean.' Rachel reached for the margarita again, needing the punch of the alcohol to steady her nerves.

'Sure you do,' said Joe, his expression sardonic. 'But okay, we'll play it your way. For the time being, at least.'

Thankfully, Henri returned to offer them menus, and then later to ask what they'd like for dinner, and for the next few minutes Rachel was able to pretend she wasn't out of her depth. But she had to admit that Joe's analogy had been apt— though she was the one who was drowning, not him.

Eventually, they were shown to a table by the windows. The lamplight was reflected in the glass and Rachel realised why the restaurant was called the *Sea House*. Their booth over-looked a rocky promontory, and discreetly placed lights illu-minated the water below. There was no moon, but the restless waves lapping against the shoreline were distinctly audible.

She ate scallops with tempura vegetables, and an escalope of seared sea bass with a delicate truffle sauce. The food, as Joe had told her, was delicious, and despite her nerves Rachel found herself enjoying it.

Joe chose the wine, and if she'd reserved judgment about the margarita she had no such doubts about the smooth Chablis. It slid effortlessly down her throat, and she hardly noticed that the waiter refilled her glass several times through-out the meal. It was all wonderful, and unbelievably relaxed; and she was sorry when the time came for them to leave.

'I've had such a good time,' she said, regarding Joe with shining eyes. 'I don't know what else to say.'

'You could say you'll accept my offer of the house on Biscayne Bay,' Joe murmured, capturing her hand that was lying beside her plate. His thumb probed the sensitive veins on the inner side of her wrist before sliding down to caress her palm. 'I really wish you would.'

Rachel sucked in a breath. 'And what would you do?'

'Me?' Joe lifted her hand and rubbed his lips against her knuckles. 'You don't think I'm suggesting we should share the place, do you?'

Rachel hesitated, her stomach fluttering nervously. 'You—you're not?'

'No.' Joe regarded her over her quivering fingers. 'I told you, I have a condo on Miami Beach. The house on Biscayne Bay has been in my family for years. My sister used to live there before she moved to Los Angeles. I never have.'

'Oh!' Rachel was nonplussed.

'Does it make a difference?'

It shouldn't have, really, but she couldn't deny it did. If Daisy had to stay in the United States for a while, it would be so much better for her than living at the *Park Plaza* hotel.

'Maybe,' she said at last, withdrawing her hand as Joe got to his feet. 'Can I think about it?'

Joe shrugged, but Henri Libre was at his elbow, and he didn't say anything more until they were outside the building. Then, as the valet went to get his car, he bent his lips to her ear. 'Why don't I show you the place? It might help you make up your mind.'

A particularly strong breeze caused Rachel to sway a little, and she wasn't sure if it was the wind or the amount of wine she'd consumed that made her feel so unsteady suddenly. But when Joe stepped closer, and slipped a protective arm around her waist, she knew she didn't want the evening to end.

'Yes,' she said, barely audibly, and wondered exactly what she was agreeing to.

The valet reappeared with Joe's car, and after brief fare-wells they were on their way. It was quite late; after midnight,

Rachel guessed—but there was still plenty of traffic on the main highway.

She leaned her head back against the soft leather squabs and closed her eyes for a moment. It had been a wonderful evening, she thought, guiltily aware that she'd only thought of her daughter very fleetingly. But it was so long since she'd allowed herself any real indulgence whatsoever.

An awareness that the sound of the traffic was fading caused her to open her eyes again, and they widened in dismay when she realised they were heading in the wrong direction. She was sure they'd driven south from Palm Cove, and they were still driving south, with the lights of the city behind them.

She was about to voice her concerns when Joe took the off-ramp into a residential suburb. Here the streets were quieter, even deserted at times. Houses sheltered behind iron gates and high stone walls that were overhung with vines and bougain-villea. Some of the roads were lined with trees, palms and live oaks, the scents of night-blooming stocks mingling with the tang of the sea. Their exotic fragrance invaded the car, a heady mix of salt and sweetness.

'Where are we?' she exclaimed, not exactly worried, but not exactly relaxed either. She was sure this wasn't the way back to her hotel.

'We're in Coral Gables,' replied Joe casually as they ne-gotiated a cross street where the signs were predominantly Spanish. 'It's an attractive neighbourhood. In actual fact, it considers itself a separate city within the Greater Miami area.'

Rachel licked her suddenly dry lips. 'And we're here because…?' Though she suspected she already knew.

'You said you'd let me show you the house we were dis-cussing earlier,' said Joe, glancing her way. 'Don't worry. It's not much farther.'

Rachel let out a nervous breath as they turned onto a yet narrower road. She glimpsed a sign that read *Viejo Avenida*, which she thought meant Old Avenue. But the headlights were already illuminating wooden gates ahead, bright with scarlet hibiscus.

'This is it,' said Joe, and as if by magic the gates opened to allow them through. 'Don't be put off by all this vegetation. If it bothers you, I'll have Ramon cut it back.'

'Oh, no.'

The involuntary denial was out before she could prevent it. But although she couldn't yet see much of the house, Rachel thought the gardens were a delight. The headlights swept over an old banyan tree guarding what appeared to be a stone fountain; the fountain gleamed with lichen, a stone angel pouring water from a stone urn.

The drive was enclosed by kudzu and oleander, and a covered porch was cloaked with flowering vines. Rachel saw this before Joe doused his headlights, and in the shadows she saw him looking at her now.

'Would you care to see inside?'

CHAPTER TWELVE

How could she refuse?

Besides, sitting here in the darkness, she felt far more aware of him than she would be in the house. 'If you like,' she said, trying to sound casual. She pushed open the door and got out into the almost total blackness. The air seemed marginally cooler here.

How far away was the sea?

She heard the gates close behind them, and guessed Joe had used whatever instrument had opened them on their arrival to complete the task. Evidently her hope that Ramon, whoever he was, had opened them at their approach was wishful thinking. There were no lights that she could see anywhere. Joe even produced a flashlight to guide them to the front door.

He handed the torch to her as he found the key, and the door swung inward. Half expecting a draught of musty air—usual when a house had been unoccupied for a while—Rachel was pleasantly surprised when the air inside seemed relatively fresh. Scented, even, she thought, smelling verbena. Someone looked after the place. As Joe Mendoza was the owner, what else could she have expected?

Nevertheless, it was quite a relief when Joe found the switch and the interior was suddenly illuminated. She turned off the flashlight as Joe closed the door behind them, her breath catching in her throat at the beauty of her surroundings.

The house was old. That was obvious. Probably built in the twenties, she suspected, and extravagantly designed accordingly. An Italian-marble tiled foyer gave access to a handful of rooms, all elegantly furnished from what Rachel could see. Lots of rich wood and fine leather; Tiffany lamps gleaming in the reflected light from the hall.

The walls of the hall were panelled in pale oak, and boasted a gallery of art-nouveau paintings that she guessed were worth a small fortune. A staircase that folded back on itself climbed the far wall, a stained-glass window at the first landing highlighted by a Venetian glass chandelier.

'Welcome to *Bahia Mar*,' said Joe lightly. 'As you've probably guessed, the house backs onto the water.'

Rachel took a breath. 'I thought I could smell the sea.'

'Yeah. Well, one of the waterways that runs into the bay,' agreed Joe, glancing about him. 'Let's go into the living room. I'll switch on the outside lights for you to see the garden.'

Beyond French doors, a paved terrace looked inviting. Chairs and loungers were set around a table, whose canvas awning was securely tied against the wind. Rachel noticed how the bushes surrounding the terrace were bending in the current of air that blew off the water. Joe slid the door back only wide enough for them to step outside.

Despite the wind, the air was still hot and humid, the whirring of the night insects strong in Rachel's ears as she stared out beyond the reassuring circle of light. She could hear the sucking sound of the water, but it was too dark to see much more. Yet all around her the garden seemed alive with an odd kind of excitement, an excitement that couldn't help but quicken her awareness of the man beside her.

'I keep a boat here sometimes,' Joe offered as she went to grip the wooden rail that separated the terrace from a veritable jungle of tropical vegetation. Thick vines bent in the wind, scattering raindrops in all directions. 'Be careful,' he warned as she moved to where a flight of steps disappeared into the darkness. 'It rained earlier, and they're probably slippery as hell.'

Rachel decided to take his advice and stay where she was. Much as she would have liked to go farther, she would prefer to do so in daylight when she could see where she was putting her feet. Not all visitors to the garden would be friendly, she reflected. She could imagine how she'd feel if she stepped on a snake or a huge spider.

'The dock is at the other end of the garden,' said Joe, touching her elbow. 'I'd show you, but we'd both get soaked to the skin.'

Which was as good an excuse as any to take their clothes off, he thought, even if getting naked with Rachel might not be such a good idea. He'd promised her dinner; that had been all. And he was trying to keep his word.

Nevertheless, showing her the house at night when he'd known Ramon and his wife, who looked after the place for him, had retired to their quarters in the grounds wasn't the wisest idea he'd ever had. Not when Rachel was looking so delectable, her silky hair tumbled by the wind.

He closed and locked the French doors after they'd returned to the house, and then followed Rachel back into the entrance hall. He watched as she looked about her, studying her surroundings, touching the delicate petals of an orchid, gliding her fingers over the polished surface of a chest his father had brought back from Venezuela.

'Well,' he said, resisting the urge to touch her again. 'What do you think?'

'About the house?' Rachel shrugged, and when she did so the neckline of her top slipped seductively off one shoulder. 'It's beautiful,' she answered, seemingly unaware of what had happened. 'More beautiful than I could ever have imagined.'

'So?' Joe's enquiry was unnaturally tight.

Rachel hesitated. Then she looked up at him, her green eyes wide and appealing. 'Do you think I could see upstairs?' she asked, and Joe felt an unfamiliar tension in his gut.

'Upstairs?' He sucked in a breath.

'Unless we'd be disturbing anyone,' she said. 'You mentioned—Ramon, was it?'

'Ramon and Maria—his wife—look after the place,' Joe told her swiftly. 'They have their own quarters separate from the house.'

'So it's all right if I look upstairs?'

Joe regarded her tensely. 'If that's what you want.'

'It is.' Rachel was amazed at her own temerity. 'How many bedrooms are there?'

She'd started up the marble staircase as she spoke, slim, bare legs revealing a shapely calf to his helpless eyes. Joe knew he had to follow her. She'd expect it. But damn it, what was going on here? He had the uneasy feeling that he'd lost control of the situation.

Rachel stopped, looking down at him enquiringly, and he realised she was waiting for his reply. 'Um, six,' he said, forcing his brain to think of something other than the memory of how her mouth had felt when he'd kissed her. 'You— you and Daisy could choose any two you liked.'

'Hmm.'

Rachel nodded before continuing on to the top of the second flight. Then, her hand resting on the sculpted balustrade, she waited for him to join her. The landing stretched away in a semi-circle, wrought-iron spindles shadowy in the muted light from below.

Joe located the switch that illuminated a row of alcoves along a carpeted hallway that led away from the landing and, going ahead, he threw open the door into what used to be the master suite. Stepping back, he allowed her to precede him into the room.

A lamp beside the four-poster bed provided enough illumination for her to admire the traditional-style furniture. Oak chests of drawers, a tall armoire, tapestry-covered armchairs with matching footstools. Most of the floor was concealed beneath an enormous hand-woven carpet, the dark-wood boards surrounding it polished to a rich shine. Filmy sheers hung at long windows, pale against the night outside.

Rachel had expected to be impressed, and she was. The house—its appointments—were all she had imagined and more. Somehow, because of Joe's background in computers, she'd been prepared for something slick and modern. But *Bahia Mar* had all the beauty of a bygone age.

She could never stay here, she thought regretfully. As much as she admired the place, she simply couldn't see herself going to bed in a room like this. Her whole wardrobe would probably fit in the armoire, let alone the adjoining dressing room. And she hadn't seen the bathroom yet. It would probably be a homage to sensual indulgence too.

She wondered suddenly if Joe brought all his women here. How many women had shared the luxury of that four-poster bed? He said he didn't live here, but that didn't mean he hadn't stayed here. It was the ideal hideaway for the man who liked his privacy.

Joe was still standing by the door, watching her, and Rachel wondered what he was thinking. Evidently her fear—or was that anticipation?—that he'd brought her here to seduce her had been totally unfounded. She'd really thought, earlier that evening, that he'd wanted more than the breathtaking kiss they'd shared at the bar. And while the sane and sensible part of her brain applauded his restraint—if that was what it was— the excitement she'd felt in the garden was in her blood.

Apart from that ghastly evening at Julie Corbett's, she'd been celibate for the past eight—or was that nine?—years.

She and Steve had separated long before he'd moved out of
the house. Why shouldn't she take a chance for once? Why
shouldn't she have at least one night to remember?

It took some courage, but she crossed to the four-poster and
flopped down on one side of the bed. The bed might be old,
but the mattress was new and bouncy, the cream silk coverlet
cool beneath her bare thighs.

Joe hadn't moved, his dark face unreadable in the
shadowy light. Had he stiffened, or was that just her imagination? He was probably thinking she was crazy, she reflected. She hadn't exactly encouraged him to think that she
wanted more.

She felt so hot, an aching longing stirring deep in her belly.
Her whole body felt tingly and alive with needs she'd almost
forgotten. And she certainly couldn't remember an occasion
when Steve had made her feel that, if he hadn't touched her,
she'd have died of frustration.

Turning, she raised one knee to the coverlet, aware that as
she did so almost the whole length of her other leg was
exposed. Then, sliding her hand over the smooth silk, she
raised her eyes to his taut face. 'Do you mind if I try it?'

Try what? wondered Joe grimly, a pulse throbbing at his
jawline. Did she realise what her childish display was doing
to him? Did she know how amazingly sexy she was? Probably not, he decided. But that didn't change how he felt.

'Do you need my permission?' he asked now, an edge to
his tone. 'You seem to be enjoying yourself.'

'I am.' Rachel's skirt rucked high above her knees as she
clambered onto the pile of pillows Maria had arranged below
the headboard, and Joe caught a glimpse of white lace before
she subsided onto her back. She dug her heels into the coverlet
and raised her arms high above her head. 'Mmm, it's so comfortable.' She turned her head towards him. 'But I'm sure you
know that.'

Joe's face was tense. 'What's that supposed to mean?'

'Oh...' Rachel considered her words before replying. 'I'm sure you've slept in this bed before.'

Joe shook his head. 'No.'

'No?' She rolled onto her side to face him. 'So which room do you usually use?'

'Believe it or not, but I've never stayed here,' he said harshly. 'What do you think it is? Some kind of *love nest*?'

Suddenly Rachel felt very embarrassed—and very cheap. She sat up abruptly. 'I'm sorry,' she said. 'You must think I'm very rude and very ungrateful.' She swung her legs towards the side of the bed. 'Perhaps we ought to go now. It was good of you to show me the house, but I'm afraid I'm going to have to refuse your offer.'

Joe blew out a breath. He'd upset her now and that hadn't been his intention. He had to remember she wasn't like the women he was used to associating with. And while that ought to be enough to cool his ardour, somehow it didn't.

Rachel dropped her feet to the floor and bent, searching for the heels she'd discarded earlier. When a pair of black suede loafers moved into her line of vision, she looked up in astonishment, her gaze moving over powerful legs, a flat stomach and a broad chest to a lean, disturbing face. She also registered the prominent bulge at the junction of his thighs, but her eyes skittered away from its obvious significance.

'What offer would that be?' Joe asked, squatting down in front of her so that their eyes were almost on a level. 'I thought for a moment you had something to offer me.'

Rachel shook her head. 'I was being silly,' she said hurriedly. She dragged her eyes away and glanced down at her feet. 'Where on earth did I leave my shoes?'

Joe was silent for a moment and then he leant towards her, supporting himself with a hand at either side of her. 'Forget your shoes,' he said huskily, bestowing a feather-light kiss on the pulse that beat so erratically below her ear. 'I was thinking of taking your clothes off, not putting them on.'

Rachel's mouth opened and she stared at him disbelievingly. 'You don't have to say that,' she protested quickly. 'I mean, you really don't.'

Joe uttered a low laugh. 'Hey, don't bail on me now, sweetheart. There's only so much provocation a man can take.'

Rachel drew back onto her elbows, her heart racing. 'I—I didn't mean to provoke you,' she said, although she had. But she was no *femme fatale,* and she suspected he was just being kind.

'Well, you did,' Joe countered, his voice thickening. 'But don't worry about it.' He put his hands on her knees, and pushed himself to his feet. Then, straddling her legs, he moved until his own knees nudged the side of the bed. 'As a matter of fact, you've been provoking me all evening.'

'Joe…'

'Rachel,' he said gently, resting one knee on the mattress beside her. His thumb brushed her jawline as he tilted her face towards him. 'You don't think you're the only one who has feelings, do you?'

Oh, God!

When he bent and captured her mouth with his, Rachel's mind spiralled. He pressed her back against the pillows, supporting himself on his hands. The scent of his skin teased her senses, and her body felt both weak and yet incredibly strong.

Her lips parted, and Joe's tongue pushed urgently into her mouth. He kissed her with a hunger that amazed him. It was becoming harder and harder to control the urge to rub his aching erection against her, but he knew if he allowed that to happen she'd know instantly how aroused he was.

She lifted a hand to his cheek, soft fingers stroking the roughness at his jawline, probing the sensitive hollow of his ear. Her hand slipped to the nape of his neck, pulling him closer, and despite all his good intentions Joe couldn't keep that small distance between them.

And touching her meant giving in to the emotions that were driving him on. The lissom feel of her body beneath his was all he'd imagined and more. He had to admit, if only to himself, that he'd never wanted a woman as he wanted Rachel at that moment. Feeling her breasts crushed beneath his chest, the intimacy of his leg wedged between her thighs, was driving him crazy.

His mouth trailed from her lips to her throat, to the scented hollow of her cleavage just visible above the neckline of her crocheted top. He let his hand slide beneath the top, his palm spreading against the firm, warm flesh of her midriff. Her skin was like silk, but he'd known that. It wasn't as if he'd never touched her before.

His mouth found hers again and this time her tongue came to mate with his. The kiss deepened, hardened, and between his legs the erection he'd been trying to ignore for the past hour demanded satisfaction. It didn't help at all when she arched up against him and her hip brushed the almost painful swelling in his trousers. It only added to his frustration, to the needs he could no longer do without.

He groaned and Rachel's eyes flickered open. 'Is something wrong?' she asked, unaware of the sensual invitation in her voice.

'Yeah.' Joe gritted his teeth. 'I want you.' He threaded his fingers through the hair above her ear and managed a rueful smile. 'But I guess this is the point where I offer to take you home.'

Rachel looked up at him with eyes that shredded his good intentions. 'I don't think that's what you really want, do you?'

'What I really want?' Joe closed his eyes for a moment, struggling with his conscience. 'What I really want is to have you naked beneath me. To know you want me as much as I want you.'

Rachel took a deep breath. 'Well, I do,' she confessed honestly. 'But, well, it's been a long time since I allowed a man into my life.'

'Yeah.' Joe bent and allowed his tongue to probe her mouth before adding softly, 'I guessed. Despite the sexy seduction.'

Rachel's cheeks were flushed with pleasure. 'Am I sexy?'

'You better believe it.' Joe spoke a little thickly. 'And I'm flattered that you trust me. It means a lot.'

Rachel hesitated. 'Do you think I'm desperate for affection?' she asked uneasily, and Joe stifled his laugh against her neck.

'Hey, I'm the one who's desperate,' he said, his voice roughening as he unbuttoned her bodice. His eyes darkened when he saw her breasts fairly spilling from the lacy bra she was wearing. 'But we'll talk about that later. Right now, I've got something else in mind.'

CHAPTER THIRTEEN

HER bra followed her top onto the floor, and Joe made a sound of satisfaction as he bent to take a swollen nipple into his mouth. He nibbled at the hardened tip, his teeth giving more pleasure than pain, his tongue caressing the rosy areola until Rachel was shifting restlessly beneath him.

He skimmed his hand over her ribcage, his fingers lingering over her navel. A sexy little moan drove him onwards, and when he baulked at the waistline of her skirt she shifted to allow him to slide the offending garment over her hips.

'Beautiful,' he said, bending to bestow a trail of kisses across her stomach. Her panties were surprisingly flimsy and he tugged gently at the elastic, sending a quiver of anticipation into her thighs.

Rachel's mouth seemed dry of all moisture. Her breathing was shallow, her breasts rising and falling with increasing urgency as he parted her legs. Then, with exquisite delicacy, he drew her panties down her legs and replaced their small amount of protection with his hand.

She was wet, he discovered as the sensual smell of her arousal rose unmistakeably to his nose, and he groaned a little as he lowered his head to taste her essence. 'Sweet,' he muttered huskily as she twisted breathlessly beneath him. 'I knew you'd taste as good as you look.'

'Please…'

Rachel wasn't used to this sensual assault on her senses. Her hands groped for his head, wanting him to go on doing what he was doing, and at the same time wanting so much more. Heavens, she was virtually naked, and he was still wearing his clothes.

'Relax,' he said, lifting his head, his eyes dark with unguarded emotion. Then, ripping open the buttons of his shirt, he sent it to join her clothes on the floor. She caught her breath at the sight of his chest, at the dark tattoo of an exotic orchid twisting over his shoulder. And thought that only a man as comfortable with his masculinity as Joe would allow a flower, however intriguing, to be etched on his skin.

His shoulders were broad, his stomach flat and ribbed with muscle, and an arrowing of dark hair found its way from his chest to disappear below the waistband of his trousers. His zip bulged with the thrust of his erection and, with a daring she hadn't known she possessed, she let her nails stroke provocatively over the taut metal.

Joe groaned again, reaching for his buckle and pulling it free. Seconds later, he'd kicked off his trousers, and his shaft sprang sensuously into her waiting hands.

'Be gentle with me,' he muttered half-humorously as she let her fingers slide over his length, amazed that he was still in control. But he sucked in a breath when her thumb found the sensitive tip, and she wriggled down to take a bead of moisture into her mouth.

Joe moved then, bearing her back against the cushions again, and taking her mouth in another devastating kiss. 'God, Rachel,' he muttered, releasing her mouth at last to bury his face in the scented hollow of her shoulder. 'I want you so much. And I don't think I can wait any longer.'

'Then take me,' she said tremulously, lifting his head to cradle it between her hands. 'I want you too, in case you hadn't noticed.'

He parted her legs then, kneeling between them and nudging the swollen nub of her womanhood with his aching shaft. But the sight of her delectable body—open and ready for him—was too tempting to ignore, and with a feeling of satisfaction he pushed into her waiting sheath.

She was so tight that he could hardly believe she'd had a baby. And despite her vain boast of experience, it was obvious it had been a long time since any man had made love to her. Which pleased him greatly, he acknowledged, aware of his own selfishness at the thought. He wanted her not to be experienced, he realised. He wanted this to be a new intimacy. And judging by the way she was responding to him, he was going to get his wish.

But then the urgency of his own needs took over. Taking her mouth again, he eased into her completely, feeling her muscles contract around him with supreme pleasure. She was tight, but she fitted him perfectly. Their bodies could have been made for one another, and when he pulled back and pushed into her again, the sound they made was like music to his ears.

Quickening the pace, he felt her muscles tighten. She was so hot, so responsive, and he knew she was close to climax when her nails dug painfully into his neck.

'Take it easy, baby,' he said, despite the fact that his own control was slipping. But when she lifted her legs and wound them about his hips there was no holding back.

The developing spasms of her orgasm were gripping him, and he didn't attempt to hold back his own release. The sensation that overtook him proved he was experiencing something he'd never experienced before. He shuddered uncontrollably for what seemed like hours, but was probably only for a few minutes, his hips pumping every drop of moisture from his body.

Belatedly, he acknowledged that he should have drawn back before he climaxed. But with her arms around his neck

and her ankles digging into his buttocks, he doubted he'd
have had the strength. Besides, he'd never had such a feeling
of completeness. He felt drained, shattered, barely able to drag
himself away from her before slumping heavily onto the bed
beside her.

He thought he must have slept for a while. When he opened his
eyes again, it was still dark outside, but he was alone. The space
where Rachel had been lying was empty. And when he smoothed
his hand over the coverlet he found it was already cold.

Pushing himself up onto his elbows, he stared broodingly
around the room. Where the hell was she? There was no sound
from the bathroom, so he was fairly sure she wasn't in there.
Damn, where had she got to? Surely she hadn't done something stupid like leave the house?

Joe didn't feel like getting up. His body was still in that
pleasant state of inertia that follows really good sex, and all
he really wanted to do was make love with Rachel all over
again. The way he felt right now, he'd have been happy to
spend the rest of the night making love with her. But he sensed
that wasn't going to happen. Not when he didn't know where
the hell she was.

He scowled, aware that he'd never been in this situation
before. He'd always been the one to call the shots in a relationship. And it hadn't escaped his attention that he was using
the words 'making love' far too frequently.

His scowl deepened, and kicking the covers aside, he got
up from the bed. His body ached a little as he bent to grab his
trousers from the floor, and that only added to his frustration.
This was not supposed to happen. What had happened to his
no-strings policy, for heaven's sake?

Leaving the button at his waist unfastened—this was so not
over, he told himself—he shouldered into his shirt and caught
a glimpse of himself in the long cheval-mirror across the

room. He looked grim, he thought. And petulant. Not a good look for someone hoping to persuade another person that they were making a big mistake.

Breathing deeply, he took a moment to calm himself. Then, leaving the bedroom, he made his way to the top of the stairs. What the hell time was it anyway? he wondered, trying to focus on the face of his watch. It looked like a quarter to four. He blinked. Was it possible? Of course it was. Rachel could be miles away by now.

There was no sound from downstairs either, and he made no attempt to muffle his footsteps as he descended to the hall below. No lights, he noted. Well, if she was still here, she was certainly keeping a low profile.

His stomach clenched. He didn't want to accept that he was worried about her, but he was. Damn it, did she blame him for what had happened? Or was she feeling guilty because, for the first time in goodness knew how long, she'd taken some time for herself? Time that didn't include Daisy.

Daisy!

He scowled again. He liked the kid; of course he did. But it bugged him that she was appropriating so much of Rachel's time when her father had eschewed all responsibility for his daughter. Still, without Steve he'd never have met Rachel, and whatever beef he had with Carlyle, that was a situation he didn't care to contemplate right now.

With an increasing sense of desperation, he searched all the ground-floor rooms, even going into the kitchen on the off chance that she might have decided to get herself a drink. But then the memory of that cold place beside him intruded, and he realised that she could have made herself a dozen drinks in the time it had taken for the bed to cool.

He went back into the living room, not switching on the lamps this time, and made his way by the light streaming in from the hall to the bar. Pouring himself a generous shot of bourbon, he raised the glass to his lips. But before he could take a drink something moving on the patio outside attracted his attention.

He slammed the glass back down onto the counter, uncaring that he spilled some of the whisky in the process, and moved to the sliding-glass doors. Whatever it was he'd seen seemed to have disappeared, and with the wind tossing leaves and flower petals across the paved area, it was easy to explain what had distracted him.

But then, as he turned away, he saw a flutter of turquoise cotton flapping against one of the loungers. He stared for a moment, hardly daring to believe his eyes, and then realised that it was indeed Rachel, sitting outside, apparently unaware, or uncaring, that she'd practically scared him out of his mind.

He didn't think before opening the door. The slider slammed back against its housing and Rachel's wide, startled gaze turned in his direction. 'Oh,' she said ineffectually. 'You're awake.'

'Yes, I'm awake.' It was an effort to keep the anger out of his voice, and he doubted he had. 'What the hell are you doing, sitting out here? Don't you know I've spent the last half hour looking for you?'

'I—no.' Rachel got to her feet a little unsteadily, but Joe refused to feel any sympathy for her. She'd scared the hell out of him! 'I just needed some air.'

'Air?' Joe was scathing. 'You call this air?'

'Well, the wind is refreshing,' she said defensively. Then, as if recovering a little of her spirit, 'I didn't know I had to report all my movements to you.'

Joe closed his eyes for a moment. Then, raking his nails over his scalp, he said roughly, 'You don't, of course. I'm sorry. I was—worried, that's all.'

He saw her stiffen. 'You don't have to worry about me. I'm used to taking care of myself.'

'Yeah, yeah.' Joe realised he was going about this in entirely the wrong way. 'But I was worried. I thought— Well, never mind what I thought.' He glanced behind him. 'Let's go back inside.'

Rachel hesitated, but after a moment she moved towards the house. She had to pass Joe as she did so, but when he put out a reassuring hand to grip her upper arm she flinched away from his touch. With an air of injured dignity, she went past him, not stopping until she was standing in the middle of the entrance hall.

Joe slammed the glass door closed and then paused in the living-room doorway, raising one hand to support himself on the lintel above his head. He was aware that his action caused his zip to open a little wider, but he didn't try to stop it. If she could see what being with her was doing to him, then so be it. Maybe it would achieve what his attempt at conciliation had not.

However, when she said nothing, he had to try again. 'Look,' he said, 'Why don't we take this upstairs? It'll be morning soon. Then I'll take you back to your hotel.'

Rachel held up her head. 'I'd like to go now, please. I would have called a cab, but I didn't know the number.' She bit her lip as another thought occurred to her. 'I'm assuming they don't lock the doors after midnight or anything like that?'

'Hardly.' Joe knew a cynical desire to laugh. The idea of a hotel like the *Park Plaza* locking its doors before half its patrons were in residence was too ludicrous to call. He sucked in a breath. 'Don't go,' he said huskily. 'I realise I've upset you, but that's just the way I am. This evening has meant a lot to me, damn it. Can't we go back to where we were before you decided to take a walk on the wild side?'

'I didn't—' began Rachel, and then realised he didn't mean that in reality. 'And I'm sorry if I worried you. I didn't consider how you might react when you found I wasn't with you.'

Joe managed a rueful smile. 'I guess not,' he agreed,

dropping his arm and taking a step towards her. 'So, why don't we begin again?' His eyes darkened. 'Do you have any idea how sexy you look without any make-up?' He shook his head. 'Not many women can say that.'

'And you've known quite a few,' murmured Rachel, retreating a step so the distance between them remained the same.

Joe's smile disappeared. 'That has nothing to do with us,' he said. 'For God's sake, Rachel, you're not going to bring my past into this, are you?'

'Why not?' Rachel had had plenty of time to think while she'd sat out on the patio, and although she'd discovered that she didn't regret what had happened, she'd decided it was never going to happen again. It was too dangerous. She wasn't cut out for this kind of relationship, and while she'd been flattered that he'd wanted her, she had the distinct feeling that the only person likely to get hurt in this situation was herself.

And wasn't that a joke?

'Rachel…'

Joe was tired and frustrated, and her attitude baffled him. He should have had that drink while he'd had the chance, he thought. It might have helped him to make sense of what was going on.

'What was it Steve said?' Rachel continued. She frowned. 'Oh, yes: that this is a young man's country. Well, I guess that applies to women as well.'

Joe's brows drew together. 'You've been talking to Steve?'

'Yes.' Rachel nodded. 'He came to the hospital this afternoon.'

Joe felt a twinge of something he refused to recognise as jealousy. 'Was Lauren with him?'

'No.'

'And you didn't think to tell me?'

Rachel's eyes widened. 'Why should I tell you?'

'Oh, I don't know.' Joe scowled. 'Maybe because I thought my opinion mattered to you.'

Rachel sighed. 'It does.' She took a deep breath. 'He didn't stay long.'

Joe hesitated. 'And how did you feel? Seeing him again after—what's it been?—a year?'

'Slightly more than that.' Rachel shrugged. 'It was okay. I felt sorry for him, actually.'

'*Sorry* for him?' Joe couldn't keep the frustration out of his voice now. 'What are you saying? That you still care about the guy? That even after the way he's behaved—'

'No, no.' Rachel interrupted him. 'It's been a long time since I cared about Steve Carlyle.'

'So that's not what all this is about?'

'Steve?' Rachel didn't pretend not to understand. 'No!'

Joe could feel his pulse quickening, anger causing the blood to rush headlong through his veins. 'Then what is happening here?' he demanded. 'I thought you wanted this just as much as I did. You certainly gave me that impression. So what did I do wrong?'

Rachel hardly knew how to answer him. 'I— You didn't do anything wrong,' she murmured unhappily. 'It's just, well, it was good while it lasted, but it's over now—'

'Like hell!'

'It is.' It took an effort, but she raised her eyes to his face. 'I like you, Joe. I like you a lot. And I know I owe you a lot, too. Daisy and I both do.'

'You don't owe me.' Joe was incensed, as much with his own unfamiliar emotions as by what Rachel was saying. 'I just don't understand what's going on.'

Rachel took a step backward. 'I'm sorry,' she said. 'Maybe I'm not explaining myself very well.'

'You're not!'

'I just don't think we should see one another again.'

'Are you crazy?' Joe swore then, and she took another step back.

'I'm sorry,' she said again. 'I know I probably seem very old-fashioned, but that's what comes of living a fairly conservative life. And whatever impression I've given you, I don't do this sort of thing.'

'What sort of thing?'

'Sleep with men I hardly know,' she replied quickly. 'You might not believe this after—well, after Steve—but I still believe in marriage; in commitment. For Daisy's sake, I have to think of the future. Our future. And we both know this was not what being with you was all about.'

Joe stared at her. And then said something he never thought he'd hear coming from his mouth. 'How do you know that?'

'Oh, please.' Rachel heaved a sigh. 'Don't pretend. When you invited me out, you admitted you'd have no trouble finding another date.'

'Maybe I was bragging.' Joe's jaw compressed.

'I don't think so.'

'So I've had girlfriends. What's so unusual about that? You went out with some guy yourself back in England.'

Rachel closed her eyes for a moment. 'Paul Davis is just a friend. I told you that.'

'Okay. Shelley Adair is a friend.'

Shelley Adair! Rachel couldn't help but recognise the name of the internationally known model.

'Who you just happen to sleep with,' she said, wondering why they were even having this conversation. For pity's sake, a man who'd shared Shelley Adair's bed could have no serious interest in her. Beyond a minor curiosity, that was.

'It might interest you to know that I haven't slept with another woman since the morning I kissed you in your kitchen back home,' Joe retorted. 'Damn it, Rachel, what do you think I am?'

Rachel couldn't answer that. Instead she said quietly, 'I think you're a very attractive man. And if it's any consolation at all, being with you was—incredible. I've never...' But she broke off at that point, realising she could hardly confess that being with Steve had never been like being with him. Joe was Steve's friend, after all. 'I've had a wonderful evening.'

Joe groaned. 'So why are you running out on me now?'

'You know why.'

'Because you want commitment?' For the first time the word didn't stick in his throat.

'No!' Rachel backed all the way to the door. 'I don't expect anything like that from you.' She shook her head. 'Joe, it was good, really good, but we live in different worlds, you know that.'

'How different?'

Rachel gazed at him helplessly. 'You know how. I don't have homes all over the world. I don't drive expensive cars or fly around in private planes.' She spread her hands. 'Believe it or not, I wouldn't want to. I'm—I'm quite happy with my life. I have my daughter, I have my work. I don't need anything else.'

'I don't believe that.'

'Well, that's the way it is.'

'No.' Joe's scowl deepened. 'For God's sake, Rachel, at least admit that you wanted me.'

Rachel bent her head, unable to meet his anguished gaze any longer. 'I'm not saying I didn't,' she muttered in a low voice. 'Oh, please, Joe, call me a taxi. Let me go back to the hotel.'

The pulse at Joe's temple beat a crazy tattoo, and before he could stop himself, he said harshly, 'All right. You want commitment, I'll give you commitment! Marry me! Stay in Florida as my wife!'

CHAPTER FOURTEEN

JOE flew into a private airfield north of Miami. Emerging from the airport buildings, he was relieved to find Luther waiting for him with the limousine. He had rung the chauffeur from the Jetstream and supplied him with his expected time of arrival, but it was always good not to encounter any problems at the end of what had been a rather harrowing trip.

'You okay, sir?' asked Luther with some concern as Joe slid into the back of the vehicle, and Joe pulled a wry face before replying.

'I've been better,' he admitted, glad to escape the humidity outside the car. His father suffering a stroke had not been something he'd ever expected, and although the old man was now on the road to recovery, it had been a worrying couple of weeks.

'And Mr Mendez?' the chauffeur added as they slipped into the traffic heading for downtown. 'Mr Napier said he'd heard he was out of the hospital, which must be a relief.'

'It is.' Joe nodded. 'Thankfully, it was only a minor attack. His doctors say there's no reason why he shouldn't be as good as new in time.'

'That's good to hear.' Luther had worked for the family for over twenty years, and both Joe and his father appreciated his loyalty. 'So are we heading for the office?'

'No.' Joe's jaw compressed. 'Take me to the condo, will you, Luther? I've got some personal business to attend to.'

'Yes, sir.'

Luther never questioned his instructions, and not for the first time Joe was grateful for his perspicacity. After all, there was no practical reason for him to be back in Florida only two weeks after he'd left, and Luther must know that. Bill Napier, the managing director of the Miami division of the company, didn't need him to hold his hand.

So why was he here?

Joe had no desire to answer that question. When he'd left here, despite the seriousness of his journey, he'd been heartily glad to be putting as many miles between himself and Rachel as he could. After what had happened at the house on Biscayne Bay, he'd needed the objectivity that distance usually provided. It annoyed the hell out of him that he was back here now with no more impartiality than he'd had when he left.

Telling Luther he wouldn't need him any more that day, Joe took one of the high-speed lifts to the penthouse floor. He liked the condo. It was fairly small—just four bedrooms—and convenient, but it wasn't home. He had two houses he called home: one in Eaton Court Mews in London, and the other an elegant brownstone on the Upper East Side of Manhattan.

Marla met him in the high-ceilinged entry. 'Mr Mendez!' she exclaimed warmly. She, too, had been informed of his return. 'It's good to see you again, Mr Mendez. Ah, but you look so tired! How is your father? Much better, I hope?'

'Much better,' agreed Joe, tugging off the tie he'd worn to his interview with his father's specialist that morning. His parents were living in New York for the summer, and his father had been treated at one of the major facilities in the city.

'But you are still worried about him, no?' fussed Marla, following him into the spacious living room. 'You should have stayed in New York, Mr Mendez. Whatever problems they are having at the Miami office could surely wait until your father is out of danger?'

'He is out of danger,' said Joe tolerantly. 'And there is no problem at the Miami office.' He paused. 'That's not why I've come back.'

'Ah.' Marla looked puzzled. 'So how long are you staying? If you are just here for a few hours—'

'I'll be staying longer than that,' Joe told her flatly, wishing she was more like Luther. Marla always had too much to say for herself. She treated him more like a surrogate son than an employer.

Her dark brows arched now, and Joe knew she was waiting for him to explain. 'There's someone I have to see,' he said, giving in with some impatience. Then, more briskly, 'I've had lunch. I'll let you know if I'll be in to dinner.'

'Yes, sir.' Marla lifted a careless shoulder and moved towards the door. Then she halted. 'Oh, I almost forgot, Mr Carlyle called yesterday afternoon. I told him you were not here, that you were still in New York.' She hesitated. 'I don't think he believed me.'

Joe paused in the middle of unbuttoning his shirt. 'What do you mean, he "called"? Did he phone? Is that what you're saying?'

'No.' Marla looked offended now. 'He *called*. From the lobby downstairs. I told him you were not here, and—'

'Yeah, yeah.' Joe didn't need a rerun of that particular part of the conversation. He frowned. 'Why do you think he didn't believe you?'

'I don't know.' Marla shrugged. 'I get these feelings sometimes.'

'And he didn't say anything else?'

'Oh, yes.' Marla could be very annoying at times. 'He asked if I knew where Mrs Carlyle was.' She huffed a little. 'As if anyone should know that better than him, eh?'

Joe could feel his nerves tightening. 'And that's all he said? Did you know where Mrs Carlyle was?'

'I think so.' Marla considered. 'I told him I hadn't seen Mrs Carlyle since she came here with him that evening over two weeks ago.'

Joe's patience stretched. 'And?' he prompted.

'And nothing.' Marla spread her hands. 'But if you ask me he and Mrs Carlyle are having problems, yes. Why else would he come here and practically accuse you of kidnapping his wife?'

'Oh, come on.' Joe stifled an oath. 'I think that's an exaggeration, don't you?'

All the same, he didn't like the idea that Steve and Lauren might have split. A pulse throbbed in his temple at the thought that Steve might be heading back to England in the not too distant future. If Steve and Lauren were having problems—and, remembering the way she'd behaved with him, it wasn't beyond the realms of possibility—Ted Johansen, as Lauren's father and a major shareholder in the company, might well insist that his contract be terminated.

Marla shrugged when he didn't say anything more, and after she'd left him Joe wandered over to the windows and stared out at the sunlit ocean creaming onto the beach below. Looking at the placid scene, it was hard to think how it must have looked a couple of weeks ago. When a tropical storm had hit the coast some miles north of the city, its backlash had been felt as far south as the Everglades.

But Joe hadn't been here to see it. He'd just had news of his father's collapse and had been heading north at the time. His mind had been full of the anxiety he was feeling for both his father and his mother, the responsibilities he had as their only male offspring weighing heavily on his shoulders.

Of course, as soon as he'd assured himself that his father's condition was stable, as soon as he'd satisfied himself that his mother and his sister—who'd flown over from California—

were coping, he'd found himself reliving everything that had happened at the house on Biscayne Bay.

In hindsight, he knew he'd behaved recklessly; no woman— least of all a woman like Rachel—would have taken his proposal seriously. It had been said in the heat of the moment, and Rachel had treated it with the contempt it deserved.

The trouble was, he hadn't seen it that way at the time. Despite an initial sense of relief when she'd refused his offer of marriage, he'd been angered that she could dismiss it so casually. Damn it, he'd never proposed to a woman before, and he'd felt insulted when she'd practically thrown it back in his face.

But—and it was a big 'but'—that hadn't prevented him from making arrangements to return to Florida as soon as his father was home from the hospital. He'd tried to tell himself that his main reason for coming back was to see Daisy again, to assure himself she was making satisfactory progress. Despite the fact that her mother had refused his offer of accommodation, he had arranged with Dr Gonzales that they should stay on at the clinic until Daisy was well enough to go home. But in his heart of hearts, he knew he couldn't wait to see Rachel again. He had to see her, he thought grimly. If only to convince himself that she'd saved him from making the biggest mistake of his life.

He turned abruptly away from the windows, aware that that assertion had a distinctly hollow ring. That despite the fact that he'd only known the woman for a few weeks, his proposal hadn't been as reckless as he was trying to claim. Okay, she was different from the women he was usually attracted to, but perhaps that was part of her appeal. There was no doubt that the notion of marrying anyone hadn't even been in his thoughts when he'd turned up at her house that morning four weeks ago. Yet for some reason the idea had grown on him, and although he was trying to dismiss it, the fact was it wouldn't go away.

Which was ridiculous, he told himself. And sad. He had to get Rachel out of his life for good and resume his normal existence. She'd disrupted his routine, sure, but he wasn't cut out for marriage. Not yet, anyway. He certainly wasn't cut out to be any kid's stepfather, and to imagine Daisy calling him 'Dad' was simply beyond belief.

All the same, he was looking forward to seeing the girl. She'd been quite a character, and he'd been flattered, admittedly, when she'd apparently accepted him into her life. But how she'd feel if he was going to marry her mother would be something else, he mused shrewdly. But then, he reminded himself again, that wasn't going to happen, so why was he even considering it?

He'd had a shower and was pondering whether or not he needed a shave when he heard voices coming from the living room. One was Marla's. It was unmistakeable. The other, also female, had an English intonation, and ignoring all the sane advice he'd been giving himself, Joe's heart leapt.

'Rachel,' he breathed, aware of a totally ridiculous lift of his spirits. Had she heard he was coming back to Miami? Without bothering to put on any clothes, he emerged from the bedroom wearing only a towel slung about his hips for decency's sake.

But it wasn't Rachel.

The two women had evidently heard his approach, and when he reached the living room door the younger turned from addressing Marla to give him a beaming smile.

'Darling!' Shelley Adair exclaimed, rushing across the room to fling her arms around his neck. Her glossy mouth sought his without hesitation, her thinly clad body pressed seductively to his, anticipating his response.

But Joe couldn't respond. Not in the way she expected, anyway. For the first time in his life, her alluring beauty left him cold. She'd obviously taken some trouble over her ap-

pearance; her filmy silk sheath clung to the slender lines of
her body. But he realised, with a sense of disbelief, that he
preferred a woman with more flesh on her bones, a woman
who didn't regard her appearance as the most important factor
of her life.

Yet, despite his instinctive withdrawal, Shelley didn't seem
to notice. Or purported not to, at least. 'I've missed you so
much,' she said, apparently putting his reticence down to
Marla's presence. 'Have you missed me, darling? I know I
couldn't wait until November to see you again. And when I
had a couple of days free...'

Joe was hardly listening. Looking over Shelley's shoulder,
he met Marla's eyes and knew she wasn't deceived. 'Um—
make up one of the guestrooms for Ms Adair,' he said tightly.
Then, easing himself away from Shelley. 'Give me a minute,
will you? I'll just get dressed.'

'But Marla doesn't need to make up a room for me,'
Shelley protested, her narrow brows drawing together as the
possible reasons for his behaviour seemed to occur to her. 'I
can share your room, can't I?' She gave a slightly nervous
laugh. 'Unless you've got someone else in there?'

'No, I—' Joe found himself stumbling over the words.
'That is— Make up the guestroom, Marla. Ms Adair will tell
you how long she's staying.'

Shelley's mouth had turned sulky now. 'What's going on
here, Joe?' she demanded. 'Why are you being like this?'

'Would Ms Adair like a drink or some coffee?' suggested
Marla, evidently doing her bit to ease the situation.

'Why don't you go and do whatever it was you were doing
before I got here?' snapped Shelley, in no mood to be mollified by a housekeeper.

'And why don't you sit down and calm yourself while I get
some clothes on?' said Joe, refusing to let her rile him.
'Thanks, Marla. You can go. I'll let you know if I need you.'

Marla, who also had a fiery temper, took his advice. But the door had hardly closed behind her before Shelley sprang into the attack again.

'What the hell do you mean, embarrassing me in front of your servant?' she demanded, almost stamping her foot in fury.

'We don't have servants in this country, Shelley,' said Joe mildly. 'Marla is my housekeeper. And you embarrassed yourself.' He paused. 'You should have phoned before you left England, and I'd have explained the situation. But as you're here, you're welcome to stay as long as you like.'

Shelley stared at him. 'So why am I being given the cold shoulder? I read about your father, and I'm sure it's been a difficult time for you. As a matter of fact, I was in two minds whether to fly to New York. But then I remembered you'd told me you were going to spend some time in Florida, and besides, I didn't want to intrude on your family at a time like this.'

'Yeah, well...' Joe was starting to feel chilled, and the beginning of a headache was probing like needles at his temples. 'As I say, the condo's yours if you want to use it. I'm leaving tomorrow anyway. I want to get back to New York.'

Shelley gasped. 'You're not serious!'

'I'm afraid I am.'

'But I've flown all this way just to spend some time with you.'

'I know, and I'm sorry.' But Joe knew there was little sympathy in his voice. 'You should have contacted me before you booked your flight. Naturally, I'll reimburse you for your ticket.'

Shelley sniffed. 'You think money can buy anything, don't you?' she choked.

'No.' But Joe suspected he had, until Rachel had proved him wrong.

'Well, you can keep your money,' said Shelley now. 'And you can shove your offer of the condo. I'm leaving, Joe, and if I walk out that door you'll never see me again.'

* * *

Rachel travelled home from London on the early-evening train.

She'd had a very successful day. The new book had been completed a week ago, and Marcia had rung to say the publishers had loved it. Today's lunch at the Ritz had been her way of thanking Rachel for allowing her to represent her. And although the book had proved harder to complete than either of her other two novels, evidently it hadn't affected her writing.

But now she was heading home again. And although she'd been initially buoyed by the compliments that had been paid her, as the shadows lengthened so too did her sense of isolation.

Which was ridiculous, really. She wanted to go home. Of course she did. If only to tell Daisy all about her day. She also wanted to see her face when she gave her the video iPod she'd bought for her in Oxford Street. It was like the one she'd insisted Daisy leave with the nurses for safe-keeping when she'd left the clinic. Rachel had been sure that they'd be happy to have the excuse to contact Joe again, particularly as he hadn't been around since that devastating night at the house on Biscayne Bay.

Daisy had been quite put out about it. Not knowing all the facts, she'd come to the conclusion that he'd got bored with her company. Were all men like her father? she'd asked Rachel, and Rachel's heart had ached for her daughter. Ached for herself, too, she acknowledged now. He'd obviously found something—or someone—else to keep him amused.

Thankfully, Daisy's condition had continued to improve, and Dr Gonzales had been extremely pleased with her progress. However, as Joe had suspected, it was another ten days before he allowed her to fly home to England.

Having rejected Joe's offer of accommodation, Rachel had been inordinately grateful when Dr Gonzales had offered them both rooms in the convalescent wing of the clinic. It had been so much better for Daisy than living in the stuffy confines of the *Park Plaza* hotel. Although Steve had visited his daughter again before he left, he and Lauren had departed for New York on schedule.

Daisy had gone back to school two days ago and was already a minor celebrity, according to her. Naturally, she'd glossed over her father's part in it. Instead, she'd concentrated on telling her friends how she'd flown in a private jet and spent time in a famous clinic. She'd had to tell them about her operation to excuse the hair that had been shaved from her head. But the Johansens' Miami mansion and their luxurious yacht had probably figured far more prominently than her tumble into the ocean.

It was cool outside the station. It was September, and already the nights were drawing in. Rachel looked about her, surprised to find that Howard and Daisy hadn't come to meet her. They usually did after one of her infrequent trips to London, but tonight there was no sign of Howard's modest car.

Trying not to worry—Daisy's health was always foremost in her thoughts—Rachel found a taxi and gave the driver her in-laws' address. Daisy was supposed to have gone there after school. Lynnie always gave her something to eat— Daisy was usually hungry—and then prepared a meal for when Rachel got home.

There was a strange car parked in the Carlyles' driveway, Rachel saw as she got out of the cab. Immediately her heart skipped a beat. Who could it be? she wondered anxiously. The Carlyles had few visitors. She prayed that nothing had happened to any of them. It looked suspiciously like the doctor's car.

She hurried up the path to the house. She had a key and she let herself into the hall without further ado. She could hear voices from the front room that was only used on special occasions. Her heart almost stopped altogether. Could it be Joe? Then the sitting-room door opened and Evelyn stood on the threshold. Her face was flushed and excited, and Rachel knew at once that it wasn't bad news she had to deliver. 'Come and see who's here!' she exclaimed, not allowing Rachel to take off her coat before pulling her into the room. 'It's Steve. Isn't that wonderful news?'

CHAPTER FIFTEEN

RACHEL slept badly.

It had been an exhausting day and she was tired, but her brain was too active to sleep. The scene in her mother-in-law's sitting room kept going round and round in her head, and no matter what she did she couldn't relax.

Steve had had no right to come crying to his mum and dad just because his marriage to Lauren had hit a bad patch, she brooded resentfully, and then chided herself for the thought. They were his parents, after all, not hers.

All the same, it was hard for her to feel any sympathy for him. This was the man who'd walked out on her and Daisy nine years ago, who'd abandoned his wife and daughter in favour of a much younger woman. He'd had no sympathy for them then. He'd virtually cut them out of his life.

She was up at six, making herself a cup of coffee, when Daisy appeared in the kitchen doorway. Like Rachel, she wasn't dressed, and judging from the puffy circles around her eyes, she hadn't slept too well either.

'Hi,' she said, sliding in and slumping down into a chair at the table. 'May I have some of that?'

Rachel looked surprised. 'Since when have you liked coffee?'

'It's okay.' Daisy was dismissive. 'I had some when I was staying with Dad and Lauren. They don't drink tea, you know?'

'Don't they?' Rachel would have preferred not to think about Daisy's father. 'Oh, well, it's what you're used to, I suppose.'

'Mmm.' Daisy put her elbows on the table and rested her chin on her hands. 'I suppose I could have had tea if I'd wanted, but it was easier just to go with the flow.'

Rachel nodded. 'Well, the kettle's boiled, so you can please yourself. If you'd prefer tea, I'll make you a cup.'

Daisy lifted her shoulders. 'I don't really care.' She paused. 'Perhaps I'll just have orange juice. Is that all right?'

Rachel sighed. 'Daisy, you can have whatever you like.'

'Okay.' Daisy sounded a little miffed now and, getting up from the table, she went to get the carton of orange juice from the fridge. 'Whatever.'

Rachel watched as the girl filled a glass with the juice, and then when Daisy resumed her seat at the table, she poured her coffee and joined her. 'So,' she said brightly, 'You're up early.'

Daisy pulled a face. 'So're you.'

'Yes.' Rachel took a sip of the coffee, savouring the flavour of the beans. Then, deciding to take the bull by the horns, 'Didn't you sleep well?'

Daisy shrugged. 'Did you?'

'No.' Rachel sighed. 'I had a really bad night, actually.' She grimaced and then added with rather less discretion, 'So what's new?'

Daisy frowned. 'Don't you usually sleep well?'

'Oh…' Rachel didn't want to worry her daughter. Daisy didn't need to know that she hadn't slept well since that night at Joe's house. 'I sleep okay. How about you? Have you got a headache? Is that why you're up so early?'

'No.' Daisy shook her head. 'And if you're still worrying about my operation, don't. I hardly ever feel it now.'

'That's good.'

'Yes.' Daisy still looked troubled. 'But I didn't sleep very well either.' She paused, drawing her upper lip between her teeth and gazing at her mother with anxious eyes. 'It's just—' She broke off for a moment and then the words came in a rush. 'If—if Dad comes back to live in England, will I have to live with him?'

The air left Rachel's lungs on a gasp. 'What?'

'I said, if Dad—'

'Yes, yes.' Rachel had to stop her from repeating it. 'Daisy, why would you ask a thing like that? What has your father been saying to you?'

'It wasn't him,' muttered Daisy unhappily. 'It was Grandma. When I went to help her carry the tea things in from the kitchen, she said that if Dad and Lauren didn't get back together he might decide to stay here.'

'I see.' Rachel took another mouthful of her coffee to give herself time to think. She might have known Evelyn had something like this in mind. She'd been so excited when she'd opened the sitting-room door. 'Well…' She tried to be impartial. 'He might stay here.' Although she doubted it, remembering that Steve had moved to Miami to advance his career. 'But why would you think you'd be living with him?'

'Oh…' Daisy blew out a breath. 'Well, Grandma said if Dad was here I could live half the time with him and half with you.' She sniffed. 'But I don't want to live with him.'

Rachel felt shocked, but not really surprised. Evelyn had never given up hope of them getting back together, and this was probably her way of trying to engineer it.

'Look,' she said now, 'No one's going to force you to live anywhere. If you want to stay here, that's okay—but equally, if later on you want to spend time with your father, then that's okay, too.'

Daisy stared at her. 'Do you mean that?'

'Of course I mean it.' Rachel got up from her chair and went round the table to bend and give her daughter a reassuring hug. 'Daisy, all I want is what's best for you. Don't you know that?'

'Oh, Mum!' Daisy turned and buried her face against her mother's neck. 'I love you.'

'And I love you too,' said Rachel, feeling tears prickling behind her eyes. 'Now, drink your orange juice and I'll make us both some breakfast.'

Daisy sighed. Then, after taking a healthy swallow of the juice, she said thoughtfully, 'Mum, do you ever wonder why Mr Mendez didn't come to see me before I left the clinic?'

Rachel was glad she could blame the heat of the pan for her suddenly flushed cheeks. 'Of course not,' she said impatiently. *Just every other day!* 'Scrambled eggs all right?'

'Well, I know why,' declared Daisy smugly. 'Dad told me. Well, he told all of us, actually. What with Mr Mendez coming to see Grandma and Granddad before he went back to Florida and them knowing him too.'

Rachel swallowed. 'Really?'

'Yes, really.' Daisy eyed her slyly. 'Do you want to hear why?'

No! Yes! Rachel forced herself to keep her attention fixed on the eggs. 'If you want to tell me,' she said, trying not to sound as agitated as she felt. 'Pass me a couple of plates, will you?'

Daisy grumbled, but she obediently got up and took two plates out of the cupboard. 'You're not really interested at all, are you?' she muttered. 'And I thought you liked Mr Mendez.'

'I did. I do.' Rachel wondered how Daisy would feel if she told her how much. 'Go on. I am interested, honestly.' *Honestly!*

Daisy handed over the plates and then she said, 'His father was taken ill. Dad said he had to rush back to New York to be with him.'

Now she had Rachel's whole attention. 'His father?' she echoed faintly. 'Are you sure about this?'

'Mmm.' Daisy nodded, apparently pleased that she'd surprised her mother at last. 'And you know what else?'

Rachel hardly dared ask. 'No.'

'Mr Mendez was the one who arranged for us to stay at the clinic until I could come home.'

'*No!*' Rachel was stunned. 'How do you know all this?' she demanded, the pan of eggs forgotten.

'Dad told—'

'Yes, but why would your dad tell you something like that?'

Daisy shrugged. 'We'd been talking about me having the operation, and Grandma said how good it was of Dr Gonzales to let us stay on at the clinic.' She paused. 'Dad laughed, and said Gonzales couldn't afford to do a thing like that. He said Mr Mendez had arranged it before he left for New York.'

'Oh, Daisy!' Rachel didn't know what to say, what to think. After the way she and Joe had parted that night, she'd never have expected him to care what happened to them. But he had. And the knowledge tore aside the fragile veneer of indifference she'd worn since she'd got home.

'Mum?' Daisy sensed that something she'd said had upset her mother. 'What's the matter, Mum? It was kind of him, wasn't it? Well, I thought it was, anyway, after the way you described that hotel.'

'No— I mean, yes, it was kind of him. Very kind.'

'So why are you looking so weepy? Are you going to cry?'

'Don't be silly!' Rachel sucked in a breath. 'Of course I'm not going to cry. It's just that— Oh God!' The smell of burnt eggs had come to her nostrils, and she turned back to find them smoking in the pan. 'Damn!' She sniffed hard, but this time she couldn't prevent the tears from spilling down her cheeks. 'These are ruined!'

'It doesn't matter.' Daisy hurried forward to take the pan off the heat. 'We can have cereal or toast. I'm not very hungry. Are you?'

'Not very.' Rachel tore a kitchen towel from the roll and used it to blot her eyes. 'I'm sorry. I should have been watching what I was doing.'

'I distracted you.' Daisy scraped the remains of the eggs into the waste disposal and plunged the pan into the sink. Then she cast her mother another doubtful look. 'You did like Mr Mendez, didn't you?' she added shrewdly. 'That's why you're upset.'

'I'm not upset,' said Rachel, but Daisy didn't look as if she believed her.

'Do you think we'll ever see him again?' she asked. 'I wish we could. I really liked him, and I think that he liked me.'

'I think he liked you too,' said Rachel, recovering her control. 'Now, what's it to be? Cereal or toast?'

Daisy frowned, but when she spoke it wasn't to state her choice of food. 'He's not like Lauren,' she said, and Rachel didn't know whether to be relieved or sorry. 'I mean, he's got plenty of money, hasn't he? But he doesn't go on about it like she does. She is such a pain. Did I tell you what she said about me being fat? She said I'd have to watch what I eat for the rest of my life.'

Rachel managed a smile. 'Obviously Lauren hasn't heard of puppy fat. In a couple of years, you'll be as slim as she is. And you have to admit, Lauren is a beautiful woman,' she added drily, doubting Lauren would have been as generous about her.

'She's not as pretty as you,' retorted Daisy staunchly. 'And I don't want to be as skinny as her. I suppose Mr Mendez likes skinny women, doesn't he?' Her eyes widened suddenly. 'Do you think he's the reason she walked out on Dad?'

It was a possibility that hadn't occurred to Rachel until Daisy voiced it. But she thought about it a lot in the days and nights to come. According to Daisy, her father had told his parents that Lauren had left the Johansens' mansion just a few days after Joe had left for New York. He hadn't mentioned Joe, of course. But like Daisy, Rachel could see the connection.

During the following week, Rachel avoided all Evelyn's

attempts to bring her son and her ex-daughter-in-law together. Naturally, she expected Daisy to spend time with her father, and Rachel had no problem with that. But she herself had no desire to listen to any more of Steve's self-pity. His parents had sympathy for him. He was their only child, after all. But she didn't have to share their feelings—not when his selfishness had had such a dramatic effect on all their lives.

Then, the following Friday, she arrived home from the supermarket to find a disturbingly familiar vehicle parked at her gate. It was the four-by-four Joe had been driving when he'd come to her house before. A sleek black SUV with tinted windows and alloy wheels.

Rachel's heart skipped a beat. Then skipped another as she parked her car and the driver's door of the SUV was pushed open. It was Joe. She knew that even before he thrust a long, powerful leg out of the car. She felt it in her bones, she thought, trying to control her breathing. It was like a visceral recognition that sapped her strength and left her feeling weak and vulnerable.

She watched from the safety of her car as he got out and gave an involuntary stretch, as if he'd been sitting there for quite some time. The action separated the hem of his black tee shirt from low-slung jeans, exposing a muscled wedge of brown skin. And just the sight of him made her realise how much she'd longed to see him again.

Then he turned and looked at her, and she knew she couldn't sit there any longer. Thrusting open her door, she followed his example, making an event of locking the car before starting along the pavement towards him.

'This is a surprise,' she said, striving for normality. Then, as a thought occurred to her, 'Are you looking for Steve?'

Joe's brows descended. 'Is he here?' he demanded in a harsh voice, and a shiver slid down Rachel's spine.

'No,' she said quickly, wondering if he'd already tried

Steve's parents. 'Have you been to the Carlyles'? He's staying with them.'

Joe's mouth tightened. 'As if I care,' he said, nodding towards the house. 'Shall we go inside?'

Rachel swallowed. 'You're not looking for Steve?'

'No, I'm not looking for Steve,' he agreed grimly. 'Now, in your own time…'

Rachel hesitated, tempted to point out the flaws in his attitude. But then, deciding there was no advantage in provoking a sharper reprimand, she opened the gate and went up the path to the door.

The house was cool. She'd lowered the thermostat before leaving for the supermarket, and she wondered if he felt the chill. As he was only wearing a tee shirt, and he'd recently come from a much warmer climate, surely he had to notice the difference in temperature?

But that wasn't her concern, she reminded herself, and leading the way into the sitting room, she said brightly, 'Have you been waiting long?'

'Long enough.'

Joe was curt. He paused in the doorway, making no attempt to take up her offer to sit down, and she decided he was still nursing a grievance over what had happened the last time they'd been together.

'Um—Steve said your father was ill,' she ventured when the silence between them lengthened to uncomfortable proportions. 'How—how is he now?'

'Much better.' Another monotone response.

'That's good.' Rachel wrapped her arms about her midriff, realising she was feeling the cold even if he wasn't. 'Was it something serious?'

'A stroke.' Joe regarded her with dark, brooding eyes. 'Didn't Steve tell you that?'

'No.' Rachel moistened her lips. 'Actually, I've hardly seen

Steve since he got back. Daisy has, of course, but he and I— Well, we don't have a lot to talk about.'

'Don't you?' Joe arched those dark brows now, and there was a trace of cold mockery in his gaze. 'As I understand it, Steve still has feelings for you.'

'What?' Rachel was astounded. Then a thought occurred to her. 'Did Lauren tell you that?'

Joe didn't immediately reply, and her nerves stretched alarmingly. Of course, she thought. Whatever he said, he was here to ascertain the situation so far as Lauren was concerned. And if that meant getting the facts from her instead of Steve, then so much the better.

'As a matter of fact, Lauren's father told me what happened,' Joe said at last. 'According to him, Lauren found out you and Steve had been spending a lot of time together while Daisy was in the clinic.'

'That's ridiculous!' Rachel gasped. 'He and Lauren were away for most of the time we were there.'

'Oh, yeah.' Joe realised that, in his fury at discovering what he'd thought was her duplicity, he'd forgotten all about that. 'So it's not true?'

'Of course it's not true.' Rachel was staggered that he should think it was. 'In any case, why does it matter to you?' She paused, and then said what she was thinking. 'Unless you want Lauren for yourself.'

'Give me a break!' Joe stared at her disbelievingly and then shook his head. 'I'm not interested in Lauren! I don't even like the woman.'

Rachel felt totally confused. 'Then *why* are you here?'

'For pity's sake!' Joe stifled an oath. 'Why do you think I'm here? I came to see you, Rachel. No one else. For some reason…' He lifted a hand and squeezed the back of his neck. 'For some reason, I can't get you out of my head.'

Rachel felt a quiver begin in the pit of her stomach and

spread down into her legs. A trembly, achy feeling enveloped her and she badly wanted to sit down. *This couldn't be happening*, she thought. Or, if it was, it was for all the wrong reasons.

That night in Miami, she'd known he wanted her. Damn it, she'd wanted him, and for the first time in her life she'd acted without considering the consequences. And because it had been so good, she had to believe he wanted her now. But she had no intention of being another of his conquests—someone he could seduce and discard as soon as the next attractive prospect came along.

Yet, looking at him, it was incredibly hard to think sensibly. What woman wouldn't be flattered that a man like him would fly all the way over the Atlantic to see her again? Okay, she knew he had homes in London and New York, and he probably hadn't made the trip just to see her. But he was here—tall, dark and incredibly sexy—and her limbs turned to water at the memory of what making love with him had been like.

He was staring at her, his eyes dark and intent, and she knew she had to say something. Something that would prove to him she'd meant what she'd said in Miami. Something that would stop him from touching her and discovering what a terrible liar she was.

'Um—well, I'm very flattered,' she said at last, grateful that he'd moved out of the doorway while he was speaking and was no longer blocking her only means of escape. 'But—you know—I told you before, this isn't going to work.'

'Why not?'

He took a step nearer and Rachel moved behind the sofa, anxiously calculating the distance to the door. 'You know why not,' she said, keeping her tone matter-of-fact. 'I thought I explained the situation that night in Miami.'

'The night you rejected my proposal of marriage?' suggested Joe harshly, and Rachel edged a little nearer to the door.

'It wasn't a real proposal of marriage,' she protested. 'You know that as well as I do. You wanted your own way and you weren't getting it. I think you said the first thing that came into your head.'

'No!' Joe was very definite about that. 'Believe me, offering marriage is not the first thing that comes into my head when I'm with a woman.'

'I believe you.' Ridiculously, Rachel felt a little offended now. Abandoning any attempt to be subtle, she quickly walked towards the door. 'That was why I didn't take you seriously,' she added stiffly. She glanced back over her shoulder. 'I think you ought to go.'

She'd only taken a couple of steps across the tiles when he came after her. Catching the sleeve of the knitted woollen jacket she'd worn to go out in, he practically dragged it off her shoulders in his haste. Then he swung her round and pushed her back against the wall of the hall behind her.

He wasn't gentle. There was a roughness to his actions that was reflected in the dark eyes that raked her startled face. 'This isn't over,' he said harshly, cupping her chin in a sur-prisingly callused hand. Then he bent his head towards her and his mouth came hungrily down on hers.

As always, when he touched her, Rachel's limbs turned to water. It was so much easier to think sensibly when her mouth wasn't locked with his. She closed her eyes, lost in a web of sensation that was so pleasurable, so erotic, that her head swam with it. The tactile delight of his tongue in her mouth caused an actual pulse to beat between her legs.

'You drive me crazy,' he muttered at last, drawing back to look down at her with smouldering eyes. His thumb scraped possessively over her lower lip. 'And God knows you don't give me any encouragement.'

Rachel swallowed, the room steadying as the realisation of what she was doing brought a return of sanity. 'I won't be your mistress, Joe,' she said shakily. 'And if that's why you're here, you're wasting your time.'

'Am I?' He trailed one hand down her throat to the demure neckline of her cotton shirt, and she couldn't prevent a shiver of anticipation. Her skin pebbled and his mouth twisted in satisfaction. 'So, you don't like me to do this?' he suggested, dipping his hand inside her shirt and allowing two fingers to probe inside her bra. Her nipple hardened automatically, and a smile replaced the smug expression on his face. 'Really?'

'Yes,' she choked, knowing there was no point in denying it. 'Yes, I don't deny you can make me want you. But—but that's not the point.'

'What is the point, then?' demanded Joe, his tone hardening perceptibly. 'I've proved that we want each other. Isn't that enough?'

'No.' She tried to push him away from her, but he wouldn't let her. 'Joe, be sensible! I'm older than you.'

'Only a little.'

'I've got a child.'

'So what?'

She shook her head. 'You're not being reasonable. I—I can't be as irresponsible as you.'

'I'm not asking you to be irresponsible,' said Joe huskily. His hand found the button at the waist of her jeans and he opened her zip. Then, resisting her attempts to stop him, he slipped his hand between her legs. 'As I say,' he added a little unsteadily, 'I've proved that you want me. You can't deny it when I can feel how much.'

Rachel trembled. 'Please, Joe…'

Joe gazed down at her for a long, disturbing moment, and then he removed his hand and put both arms around her. He pulled her to him, her jeans slipping dangerously low on her hips as he did so. 'Okay,' he said, giving in to the urge to kiss the vulnerable curve of her neck. 'If you insist on waiting until our wedding night, then so be it.' He lifted his head, his lips tilting teasingly. 'I won't force you, even if we both know who would win.'

Rachel could only stare at him. 'You don't mean that,' she protested.

'That I won't force you? Of course, I—'

'No! No, not that.' Rachel was impatient now, her small hands gripping his upper arms, keeping him away from her as if her life depended on it. 'Joe, don't joke about this. It's really not very funny.'

'Who's joking?' His dark brows arched in what she was sure must be mocking indignation. 'Okay.' He took a step backward and went down on one knee. 'If I have to beg, I'll do it. Rachel, will you do me the honour of becoming my wife?'

CHAPTER SIXTEEN

RACHEL felt tears pricking at the backs of her eyes. 'I—I wish you wouldn't do this,' she said, clutching her jeans around her waist. She took a deep breath, admitting defeat. 'All right. You've won. I'll go to bed with you. Now, please, get up. You look silly, kneeling there.'

'Well, thanks for that,' said Joe flatly as he rose to his feet. 'Do I take it you're turning my proposal down again?'

'Don't make fun of me, Joe,' said Rachel tremulously. 'I've said I'll go to bed with you and I will.' She glanced at her watch. 'Though not when Daisy's due home from school. I wouldn't like her to come home and find us together.'

Joe rocked back on his heels. 'Ah, well, there, you see, I can't agree to that.'

'Agree to what?'

'To us not being able to spend time in bed together when Daisy's around.'

'Joe—'

'No, listen to me.' He grasped her upper arms, all humour vanishing from his dark, arresting features. 'I love you, Rachel. Do you hear me? And I really do want to marry you. I want you, me, and Daisy to be a family. Well, for the time being,' he added as she gazed up at him with disbelieving eyes. 'If you're not too old,' his eyes twinkled, 'we might make another baby or two. If that's what you want, of course.'

Rachel took a shaky breath. 'You—love me?'

'Yes, I love you.' Joe took his hands from her arms and rested his palms against the wall at either side of her head. 'God knows why,' he added whimsically. 'You're not exactly good for my ego.'

'You don't need me to pay you compliments,' said Rachel, her mouth a little dry now.

Joe sucked in a gulp of air. 'Not exactly the response I wanted,' he told her tensely. 'Does that mean what I think it means?'

Rachel swallowed. 'And that would be?'

'Oh, you know.' Joe rolled his eyes. 'I'm good to go to bed with, but when it comes to choosing a life partner...'

'Don't!' Her anguished cry cut him off. With trembling fingers she cradled his face and then pressed her fluttering lips to his mouth. 'I love you. Why do you think I refused your first proposal? Because I couldn't bear for you to make fun of something so—so serious.'

'Ah, God!' Joe lowered himself against her, his mouth crushing hers with all the pent-up emotions he'd been denying for so long. 'I wasn't making fun,' he told her at last when he lifted his head. 'Okay, maybe I didn't want to admit it, even to myself, but I think I've loved you since that morning I came here to talk about Daisy's trip. But you're right about one thing: that night in Miami, I would have said anything to persuade you to stay.'

'Then—'

'Let me finish.' Joe allowed his knuckles to brush her anxious lips. 'When you refused to take me seriously, I was seriously ticked off. I thought, what the hell, I don't need this. That was why I let you go.'

Rachel frowned. 'So what made you change your mind?

If you have really changed your mind,' she added doubtfully, and Joe groaned.

'Oh, baby, I changed my mind about an hour after you'd left me.' He shook his head. 'I had every intention of seeing you again. Then I got that call from my mother, telling me my father was very ill, and I realised I was going to have to go away without resolving the situation between us.'

Rachel could hardly believe this was happening. 'So, have you been back to Florida since we came home?'

'Oh, yeah.' Joe was rueful. 'And believe me, I was pretty annoyed when I found you'd left the clinic without letting me know. Then, when I had Lauren's father ringing me, telling me that she was heartbroken because you and Steve had shut her out while Daisy was in the clinic, I felt even more aggrieved, I can tell you.'

'But that's not true!'

'I know, I know.' Joe's tongue touched the pulse palpitating below her ear. 'But you have to give me some credit for being bloody jealous.' He grimaced. 'You have to understand, I'd spoken to Daisy's doctor before I left and ensured you'd have somewhere to stay until I got back—'

'Yes, I know,' she interrupted him a little breathlessly. 'Steve's parents had apparently said how grateful they were to Dr Gonzales for organising it, and he told them it was you who'd arranged it.' She shook her head. 'It was so kind of you.'

'It wasn't kind,' he interrupted now. 'Sweetheart, I needed to know you were somewhere safe, somewhere I didn't have to worry that one night some drunken jerk might try and force his way into your hotel room. The *Park Plaza*'s okay, but it doesn't have the most salubrious reputation, and I wanted to ensure you'd be waiting for me when I got back.'

'Oh, Joe.'

'Yeah, "oh, Joe",' he echoed drily. 'And then, when I heard Steve was back in England, naturally I thought the worst. I'm a man, what can I say? A man who doesn't care for the idea that his woman is seeing another guy.'

Rachel caught her breath. 'Am I your woman, Joe?'

'You are if you accept my proposal,' he said huskily. 'Which reminds me, I don't believe you've given me an answer yet.'

Rachel and Joe were married in New York just before Christmas. Joe would have liked the ceremony to happen sooner, but out of respect for his father, who'd naturally wanted to attend, he'd delayed the date for a couple of months. And as he'd ostensibly taken up residence at his London home—which meant he could spend most of his days and nights with Rachel—he'd had no real cause for complaint.

Rachel had been anxious about how Daisy would react to the news that Joe was to be her stepfather, but she needn't have worried. 'I knew you liked him!' Daisy had exclaimed triumphantly. 'As soon as I realised you and Dad weren't going to get back together, I hoped you'd find someone else. And Joe's really cool, isn't he? Not to mention loaded!'

'Daisy!' Rachel had stared at her daughter. 'I hope you don't think I'm marrying Joe because he's got lots of money?'

'No.' Daisy spoke grudgingly. 'I know you're far too goody-goody to do a thing like that.'

'Daisy!'

'Well.' Daisy had the grace to turn red. 'You are. I just hope Joe loves you as much as you love him.'

'He does.' That was something Rachel had no doubts about.

'I know.' Daisy sighed. 'Grandma's going to be so…' She broke off, and Rachel decided she didn't want to know the word her daughter had been about to use. 'Disappointed,' she added at last. 'I think she's still hoping you and Dad might get back together.'

Rachel hesitated. 'How about you?' she asked gently, and Daisy shrugged.

'I knew it wasn't going to happen. I remembered what you'd said before I went to Miami, and then when you met Joe again…'

'So you approve?'

'Mmm.' Daisy nodded. 'And Grandma will too, when she comes around.'

Rachel had wondered. Evelyn had been bitterly disappointed to learn that Rachel was going to marry someone else. It was probably just as well Steve was staying with them, because it had given both of them an excuse for not seeing one another.

But then, Lauren had rung and told Steve she was sorry she'd doubted him. No doubt she'd heard that Joe was going to marry Rachel, too, and had decided to cut her losses. In the event, Steve had taken off back to Miami with only a desultory word of farewell for his daughter, and Evelyn had been forced to accept that what hopes she'd had were never going to be realised.

Another possible obstacle had been removed when Joe decided to take up permanent residence in England. 'This way, Daisy's education isn't going to suffer,' he'd said casually, making Rachel love him even more. 'We can always spend the holidays in the States. Then, when she's old enough, she can choose whether she wants to go to an English or an American university.'

'But won't that interfere with your work?' Rachel asked one morning after Daisy had left for school. Joe was still in bed, reading the morning papers, and she'd brought toast and a fresh pot of coffee upstairs for them to share. 'Your living here, I mean?'

'I've always spent a lot of time in England anyway,' said Joe, moving aside to allow her to climb onto the bed beside him. 'These days, much of what I do can be done by email or video-conferencing, and when I have to travel I'll arrange it so you can come with me.'

Rachel tucked the lapels of the fluffy cashmere dressing gown Joe had bought her closer about her. 'And can you do that?' she asked, sitting cross-legged so she could place the tray on the bed in front of her.

'Hey, I own the company,' said Joe teasingly. 'I get to do whatever I like.'

Rachel drew a trembling breath. 'Do you want coffee first or toast?'

Joe surprised her by lifting the tray and setting it on the bedside table at his side of the bed. 'I want you first,' he told her huskily, pulling her towards him. His hand slid down into the vee she'd made of her legs. 'Mmm, that's better,' he said, encountering warm flesh and damp curls. 'I want to love you,' he added, his tongue tracing the parted contours of her lips. 'Who needs food when I can eat you?'

They honeymooned in Hawaii, choosing one of the smaller islands where the tourists could be trusted to leave them alone. They spent four weeks relaxing and swimming and soaking up the sun. Rachel's skin turned a delicious honey-brown, and her hair was bleached to a flattering lightness.

Daisy spent the time with her two sets of grandparents.

Evelyn had come around, as Daisy had predicted, and she and Howard had been especially thrilled when Joe had flown them both to New York for the wedding ceremony.

'Can you imagine anyone else inviting his wife's ex-in-laws to his wedding?' Rachel had teased Joe when he'd asked her opinion. 'Oh, darling, I don't know what I've done to find someone as wonderful as you.'

'Just lucky, I guess,' Joe had said with a smug grin. Then, as she'd wound her arms about his waist, 'Hey, didn't you say Daisy was due home from school?'

Rachel had ignored him, and the kiss they'd shared had quickly deepened to a sensual assault on her senses.

Joe's parents had taken to Daisy at once. His mother had

told Rachel they were so relieved their son had fallen in love at last, and finding they had a ready-made granddaughter had been a bonus.

As far as Rachel was concerned, she'd loved Joe's parents on sight. His father was so like Joe, and his mother had instantly made her feel as if she was already part of the family.

Consequently, she had no qualms about leaving Daisy in their care for the first two weeks she and Joe were away. Snow was falling in the mountains upstate, and they were planning to take Daisy skiing, with trips to the Statue of Liberty, the Empire State Building, and shopping on Fifth Avenue thrown in for good measure. Then Joe's sister, Rosa, would escort her back to England for a two-week stay with Steve's parents.

On their last night in Hawaii, they went out to one of the small fish restaurants that were so popular in the resort where their hotel was situated. They ate lobster and clams, and Rachel was irresistibly reminded of the first meal they'd shared together in Miami.

She was gazing reminiscently into the distance when Joe captured her hand and brought it to his lips. 'Penny for them,' he said lightly. 'Or shall I guess?'

Rachel's green eyes softened as they turned to his dark face. 'Can you?'

'I think so.' His eyes darkened. 'We ate fish at the Sea House, and then I made love to you for the first time.'

'Hmm.' Rachel kissed his knuckles in her turn. 'It was the most perfect experience I'd ever had. I'd never felt like that before.'

'Not even with Steve?'

'No.' Rachel was definite.

Joe pulled a wry face. 'I used to think I'd never hear that guy's name without wanting to sock him on the jaw. But you know, I have so much to thank him for.'

Rachel dimpled. 'Do you think so?'

'Oh, yeah.' Joe's knee rubbed sensuously against hers. 'He did me the greatest favour in the world. He allowed me to meet you.'

Rachel took a deep breath. 'I doubt if he sees it that way.'

'Tough.' Joe was unrepentant. 'Now, I've got something to tell you.'

Rachel frowned. She had something to tell Joe, too, and she wondered for a moment if he'd guessed her secret.

But no. As he started to speak, she realised that what he had to tell her was just going to add to their happiness.

'You remember what I said about us needing somewhere larger to live now that I'm going to be working at home as well as you?' he asked, and she nodded.

'Well, I wonder how you'd feel about us buying a small estate just outside of Westlea. Melton Hall is up for sale, and I've got first refusal, if you're interested.'

Rachel caught her breath. 'Melton Hall?' she echoed. 'But that's enormous!'

'Not very.' Joe gazed at her appealingly. 'It has just eight bedrooms. And Charles says he'll come and organise the place for us, which is quite a concession. He's always insisted he'd never move out of London, but I think you and Daisy have won him over.'

'Oh, Joe.' Rachel stared at him in disbelief. 'I don't know what to say.'

'You could say you'll at least give the idea some consideration,' he murmured gently. 'What do you think?'

Rachel shook her head. 'I hope you're not thinking we'll be able to fill all those bedrooms!' she protested, and he gave a soft laugh.

'No. As I say, that's up to you. But there'll be you and me and Daisy. And Charles, of course. And my parents, when they come to stay.'

Rachel moistened her lips. 'Would you mind if there was someone else? Fairly soon, actually.'

Joe's brows drew together. 'You don't mean…?'

'Hmm.' She felt a ridiculous wave of colour sweeping up her throat. 'I'm pregnant.' She took a breath and then added quickly, 'I was going to tell you tonight. You—you just beat me to it.'

'Oh—my—God!' Joe gazed at her, his lips parting in stunned disbelief. Then his eyes dropped intimately to where her stomach disappeared beneath the rim of the table. 'You're going to have a baby. *My* baby. Oh, my God!'

Rachel swallowed. 'Are you pleased?'

Joe's fingers gripped hers so tightly she winced. 'Am I pleased?' he breathed, and ignoring the other diners, he leant across the table and gave her a long, lingering kiss. 'I'm ecstatic,' he told her at last. 'I love you, Rachel Mendez. And when we get back to our suite, I'm going to show you exactly how much.'

* * * * *

BEDDED FOR THE
ITALIAN'S PLEASURE

CHAPTER ONE

JULIET wondered what it was like in the Caymans at this time of year. Pretty much like Barbados, she assumed. They were all islands in the Caribbean, weren't they? But she'd never been to the Caymans.

Still, whatever they were like, they had to be better than this gloomy employment agency, whose sickly green walls and wafer-thin carpet were a poor substitute for the comfort she was used to. Had been born to, she amended, fighting back the tears of self-pity that formed in her eyes. Beautiful violet eyes, her father used to call them. They reminded him of her mother, who'd died when she was just a baby. How long ago it all seemed.

One thing she knew, her father would never have allowed her to be duped by a man like David Hammond. But her father, too, had died of a brain tumour when Juliet was just nineteen and a year later David had seemed like a knight in shining armour.

If only she'd realised that his main interest in her was the trust fund her father had left her. That just a handful of years after their society wedding he'd take off with the woman he'd introduced to Juliet as his secretary. With her stupid indulgence, he'd taken charge of her trust fund. By the time she'd realised what was happening, he'd transferred the bulk of it to an offshore account in his own name.

She'd been so naïve. She'd let David's good looks and boyish charm blind her to any faults in his character. She'd believed he loved her; ignored the advice of friends when they'd told her he'd been seen with someone else. Now the few pounds he'd left in their joint account were running out fast.

Of course, those friends that had stuck by her had been sympathetic. They'd even offered to help her out financially, but Juliet had known their friendship couldn't last under those circumstances. No, she had to get a job; though what kind of a job she could get with no qualifications she dreaded to think. If only she'd continued her education after her father died. But David's appearance in her life had blinded her to practical things.

She glanced round the waiting room again, wondering what sort of qualifications her fellow applicants had. There were five other people in the room besides herself: two men and three women, all of whom seemed totally indifferent to their surroundings. If she didn't know better, she'd have said they were indifferent to being offered employment, too. At least two of them looked half-asleep—or stoned.

Which could be good news or bad, depending on the way you looked at it. Surely after interviewing someone dressed in torn jeans or a grungy T-shirt, or that girl whose arms were covered with lurid tattoos, Juliet, in her navy pinstripe suit and two-inch heels, would be a relief. Or perhaps not. Perhaps unskilled jobs were more likely to be offered to people who didn't look as if they could afford to be out of work.

'Mrs Hammond?'

It's Ms Lawrence, actually, Juliet wanted to say, but all her means of identification were still in her married name. Not that everyone who got divorced reverted to their previous identity. But Juliet had wanted to. She'd wanted nothing to remind her that she had once been Mrs David Hammond.

Now she got nervously to her feet as the woman who'd called her name looked expectantly round the room. 'That's me,' she said, aware that she was now the centre of attention. She tucked her clutch bag beneath her arm and walked tentatively across the floor.

'Come into my office, Mrs Hammond.' The woman, a red-head, in her forties, Juliet guessed, looked her up and down and then led the way into an office that was only slightly less unprepossessing than the waiting room. She indicated an upright chair facing her desk. 'Sit down.' Juliet did so. 'Did you fill in the questionnaire?'

'Oh—yes.' Juliet produced the sheet of paper she'd been rolling into a tube as she waited. When she laid it on the woman's desk—Mrs Maria Watkins' desk, she saw from a notice propped in front of her—it remained in its half-curled position and she offered a little smile of apology as Mrs Watkins smoothed it out. 'Sorry.'

Her apology was neither acknowledged nor accepted. Mrs Watkins was too busy reading what Juliet had written, pausing every now and then to glance at her as if she couldn't believe her eyes. So what? Had the slick business suit fooled her? Or was she admiring Juliet's dress sense? Somehow, she didn't think so.

'It says here that you're twenty-four years old, Mrs Hammond.' Mrs Watkins frowned. 'And you've never had a job?'

Juliet coloured a little. 'No.'

'Why not?'

It was straight question, but Juliet had the feeling she shouldn't have asked it. She had some pride. Did this woman have to rob her of every single drop?

Taking a deep breath, she said, 'Is that relevant? I need a job now. Isn't that enough?'

'No, I'm afraid it's not, Mrs Hammond. Would-be employers require CVs; references. It's important for me to understand why a would-be applicant has none of these things.'

Juliet sighed. 'I was married,' she said, deciding that was the least controversial thing she could say.

'Yes, I see that.' Mrs Watkins consulted the sheet again. 'Your marriage ended some nine months ago, did it not?'

Nine months, eight days, recited Juliet silently. 'That's right.'

'But no job?'

'No. No job.'

Mrs Watkins sucked in a breath through her nostrils that was clearly audible. It was the kind of sound her father's butler, Carmichael, used to make when he disapproved of something she'd done. That Mrs Watkins disapproved of her lack of experience was obvious. Juliet wondered if she would have fared better if she'd come in a grungy shirt and jeans.

'Well,' Mrs Watkins said at last, 'I have to tell you, Mrs Hammond, it's not going to be easy finding you employment. You have no discernible qualifications, no employment history, nothing in fact to convince an employer that you're a good worker. And trustworthy.'

Juliet gasped. 'I'm trustworthy.'

'I'm sure you are, Mrs Hammond, but in this world we don't work on word-of-mouth. What you need is an erstwhile employer to vouch for you, someone who is willing to commit his opinion to paper.'

'But I don't have an erstwhile employer.'

Mrs Watkins gave a smug smile. 'I know.'

'So you're saying you can't help me?'

'I'm saying that at the present time, I don't have a vacancy you could fill. Unless you wanted to wash dishes at the Savoy, of course.' She chuckled at her own joke. Then she sobered. 'You'll find details of courses you could take at the local college—classes for everything from cookery to foreign languages—in the waiting room. I suggest you take a few of the leaflets home and decide what it is you want to do. Then, come back and see me when you feel you have something to offer. Until then, I'd advise you not to waste any more time.'

Waste *my* time, was what she meant, Juliet decided gloomily, getting to her feet. 'Well—thank you,' she said, the good manners, which had been instilled into her since birth by a series of nannies, coming to her rescue. 'I'll think about what you've said.' She paused. 'Or find another agency.'

'Good luck!' The latter was said with some irony and Juliet left the office feeling even more of a pariah than before. But what had she expected? Who had she imagined would employ someone without even the sense to recognise a con man when she saw one?

Outside again, she looked up and down Charing Cross Road, considering her options. Although it was only the beginning of March, it was surprisingly warm, though a light drizzle had started to dampen the pavements. She lifted a hand to hail a taxi and then hastily dropped it again. The days when she could swan around in cabs were most definitely over.

Sighing, she started to walk towards Cambridge Circus. She would catch a bus from there that would take her to Knightsbridge and the tiny one-bedroom apartment where she lived these days. The large house in Sussex where she'd been born and lived for most of her life had been sold just after her marriage to David. He'd said the house he'd found in Bloomsbury was much more convenient. It wasn't until he'd left her that she'd found out the house had been rented by the month.

She knew her friends had been appalled at her naïvety, but, dammit, she'd never encountered David's kind of ruthlessness before. It was just luck that the apartment had been in her name and David couldn't touch it. It had been her father's *pied-à-terre* when he'd had business to attend to in town, and she'd hung on to it for sentimental reasons.

Halfway to her destination she passed a pub and on impulse she went in. It was dark and smoky in the bar, but that suited her. She hardly ever drank during the day and she'd prefer it if no one recognised her in her present mood.

Slipping onto one of the tall stools, she waited for the bartender to notice her. Short and fat, with a beer belly that hung over his belt, he managed to look both businesslike and cheerful. Much different from Mrs Watkins.

'Now, then,' he said, sliding his cleaning cloth along the bar, 'what can I get you?'

Juliet hesitated. It didn't look as if it was the kind of place that had a bottle of house white waiting to be poured. But who knew?

'The lady would like a vodka and tonic, Harry,' said a voice at her shoulder and she swung round, ready to tell whoever it was that she could choose her own drinks, thank you very much.

Then her eyes widened in surprise. She knew the man. His name was Cary Daniels and she'd known him since they were children. But she hadn't seen him for years. Not since her wedding, in fact.

'Cary!' she exclaimed. 'Goodness, fancy seeing you here.' The last she'd heard he was living in Cape Town. 'Are you on holiday?'

'I wish.' Cary slid onto the empty stool beside her, handing a twenty-pound note to the bartender when he brought their drinks. He'd apparently ordered a double whisky for himself and he swallowed half of it before continuing. 'I've got a job in London now.'

'Really?'

Juliet was surprised. Although they'd lost touch for a few years, when his parents died and he'd had to go and live with his paternal grandmother in Cornwall, he had attended her wedding. At that time he'd been excited about the great job he'd got with the South African branch of an investment bank and everyone had thought he was set for life. But things had changed, as they do. Didn't she know it?

'So how have you been?' he asked, pocketing his change and turning on his seat to face her. Although the dim light had prevented her from noticing before, now she saw how haggard he looked. There were bags beneath his eyes, his hair was receding rapidly, and his thickening waistline told of too many double whiskies over the years. She knew he was twenty-eight, but he looked ten years older. What had happened to him? she wondered. Was he suffering the after-effects of a bad relationship, too?

'Oh—I'm OK,' Juliet said lightly, lifting her glass in a silent salute and taking a sip. It was much stronger than she was used to and she just managed to hide a grimace. 'Getting by, I suppose.'

'I heard about your divorce.' Cary was nothing if not direct. 'What a bastard!'

'Yes.' There was no point in denying it. 'I was a fool.'

'I wish I'd been around when it happened. He wouldn't have got off so lightly, I can tell you. What's the son of a bitch doing now?'

Juliet pressed her lips together. It was kind of Cary to be so supportive, but she couldn't see him tackling someone like David. He simply wasn't the type. 'Um, David's in the Caymans, or so I believe,' she admitted reluctantly. 'But do you mind if we don't discuss it? There's no point in harbouring old wounds. I was a fool, as I said. End of story.'

'You were gullible, that's all.' Cary was assertive. 'As we all are from time to time. It's easy to be wise after the event.'

Juliet gave a rueful smile. 'Isn't that the truth?'

'So—what are you doing?' Juliet tried not to resent his curiosity. 'And where are you living? I guess the house in Sussex has had to be sold.'

'Yes.' Juliet acknowledged this. 'I've got a small apartment in Knightsbridge. It used to be Daddy's and it's not the Ritz, but at least it's mine.'

'Bastard!' said Cary again. Then, 'I suppose you've had to get a job.'

'I'm trying to,' said Juliet honestly. 'But I've got no qualifications. I don't even have anyone I could apply to for a character reference. Except friends, of course, but I wouldn't do that to them.'

'Ah.' Cary swallowed the remainder of his drink and signalled the barman that he wanted another. He gestured towards Juliet's glass, too, but she shook her head. She'd barely touched the drink. 'So—do you have any plans?'

'Not yet.' Juliet was getting tired of talking about her problems. 'What about you? Are you still working for the bank?'

'No such luck!' Cary reached for his second whisky and

downed a generous mouthful before going on. 'I've been black-balled by the banking community. Hadn't you heard? I'm surprised you didn't read about it in the papers. It was all over the financial pages.'

Juliet was tempted to say that she'd had other things to do than study the financial pages, but she was disturbed by what he'd said. 'What happened?'

Cary grimaced. 'I gambled with clients' funds and lost a packet. The bank was down a few million dollars and I was lucky to escape without being charged with negligence.' He lifted a careless shoulder. 'Apparently Grandmama still has some pull in financial circles. I was just chucked out of the bank with a severe slap on the wrist.'

Juliet was amazed. 'But a few million dollars!' she echoed disbelievingly.

'Yeah. I don't do things by halves.' He took another mouthful of his drink. 'It sounds a hell of a lot more in South African rand, let me tell you. But, dammit, you're encouraged to take risks and I took 'em. I guess I'm not such a clever dealer, after all.'

Juliet shook her head. 'I don't know what to say.' She paused. 'Was your—was Lady Elinor very cross?'

'Cross!' Cary gave a short laugh. 'She was livid, Jules. Positively fire-breathing. She'd never approved of my chosen career, as you probably know, and getting thrown out of South Africa pretty well burnt my boats with her.'

Juliet looked down at the liquid in her glass. She remembered Lady Elinor Daniels very well. Mostly because when Juliet was thirteen she'd been quite a frightening figure. She remembered feeling sorry for Cary, too, whose parents had disappeared while sailing in the Southern Ocean. At seventeen, he'd been taken away from everything and everyone he was used to, forced to go and live in some old house in Cornwall with a woman he barely knew.

Juliet lifted her head. 'But you say you've got another job?'

'A temporary one, yeah.' Cary scowled. 'Believe it or not, I'm working in a casino. Oh, not handling money. They've got more sense than that. I'm what you'd call a meeter and greeter. A kind of—bouncer, with class.'

Juliet gasped. 'I can't believe your grandmother approves of that.'

'She doesn't know. As far as she's concerned I've got an office job. She still hasn't given up hope of me settling down with a good woman and taking over the running of the estate. And that low-life, Marchese, is just waiting for me to put a foot wrong.'

Juliet would have thought he'd already put more than one foot wrong, but she didn't say so. 'Marchese?'

'Rafe Marchese!' exclaimed Cary half-irritably. 'Surely you remember? My aunt Christina's deliberate mistake?'

'Oh, your cousin,' said Juliet, understanding. But Cary took offence at that.

'The bastard,' he corrected. 'A real one this time. Surely you don't expect me to be friendly towards him. He's made my relationship with Grandmama almost impossible over the years. I don't forget how he treated me when I first went to live at Tregellin.'

'He's older than you, isn't he?'

'A couple of years. He must be thirty now. Or maybe a little older. Whatever, he's there all the time, like a thorn in my side, and Grandmama loves to taunt me about leaving the estate to him.'

'To taunt you?'

'Yeah. Not that she would, of course. Leave the place to Marchese, I mean.' Cary laughed again. 'She's far too conventional for that.'

Juliet hesitated. 'If your aunt was never married to his father, why is his name Marchese?'

'Because she put his father's name on his birth certificate.' Cary was dismissive. 'A bit of a joke, that, considering I don't think Carlo even knew he was going to be a father. Christina was such a flake, always taking off for some new destination, finding one distraction after another.'

'I thought she was an artist,' said Juliet, trying to remember what her father had told her.

'She'd have liked to think so,' said Cary, with a sarcastic smile. 'Anyway, like me, Rafe was orphaned at a fairly early age. One too many Martinis for Christina and she fell from the balcony of the hotel in Interlaken where she was staying with her latest conquest.'

'How awful!' Juliet was amazed that he could be so blasé about it. She had been his aunt, after all. She took another sip of her drink, taking a surreptitious glance at her watch as she did so. It was time she was leaving. She needed to buy one or two items of food from the local delicatessen before heading home.

'Anyway, I've got to go down there next week,' Cary went on, apparently unaware that she was getting restless. He grimaced. 'I told her I'd got a girlfriend and she wants to meet her.'

'Oh.' Juliet smiled. 'Well, I hope she likes her. Is it someone you met while you were in Cape Town, or does she live in London?'

'I don't have a girlfriend,' declared Cary flatly. 'I just told her that to get her off my back. You know what I said about her wanting me to settle down and so on? I thought if she believed I was getting serious about someone, she'd lay off for a bit.'

'Oh, Cary!'

'I know, I know.' He scowled and summoned the bartender again to order another drink. 'Where am I going to find a suitable girlfriend between now and next Thursday? I don't even know any "suitable" girls. My tastes run in another direction entirely.'

Juliet stared at him. 'You're—gay?'

'Hell, no!' Cary snorted. 'But the kind of girls I like, you don't take home to introduce to your grandmama. I'm not interested in settling down, Jules. I'm only twenty-eight. I want to have some fun. I don't want some good woman and a couple of sprogs hanging about my feet.'

Juliet shook her head. He'd changed so much from the shy boy he'd been when they were children. Was this his grandmother's doing, or had he always had this streak of selfishness in him? Perhaps he wasn't so different from David, after all.

She was suddenly aware that he was staring at her now. There was a distinctly speculative look in his eyes, and she hoped he had no designs as far as she was concerned. She might be desperate, but Cary simply wasn't her type. Sliding down from her stool, she nodded pointedly towards the door.

'I've got to go.'

'Go where?'

Was it any of his business? 'Home, of course.'

Cary nodded. 'You wouldn't fancy having dinner with me, I suppose?'

'Oh, Cary—'

'It was just a thought.' He chewed vigorously at his lower lip. 'I wanted to put a proposition to you. But I can do it here, just as well.'

'Cary—'

'Hear me out.' He laid a hand on her sleeve and, although Juliet badly wanted to pull away, she had accepted a drink from him and that made her briefly in his debt. 'Would you consider coming down to Tregellin with me? As my *pretend* girlfriend,' he added swiftly, before she could object. 'You say you need a job. Well, I'm offering you one. Well-paid, of course.'

Juliet couldn't believe her ears. 'You're not serious!'

'Why not? We're friends, aren't we? We're male and female. Where would be the harm?'

'We'd be deceiving your grandmother. And—your cousin.'

'Don't worry about Rafe. He doesn't live at the house.'

'All the same—'

'You'd be doing me the greatest favour, Jules. And

Grandmama is bound to believe it when she sees it's you. You know she's always liked you.'

'She hardly knows me!'

'She knows *of* you,' persisted Cary. 'And when we get back, I'll be able to write you a reference you can use to get another job.'

'A real job, you mean?'

'This is a real job, Jules, I promise you. Oh, please. At least say you'll think it over. What have you got to lose?'

CHAPTER TWO

THE tide was in and the mudflats below Tregellin were hidden beneath a surge of salt water. There were seabirds bobbing on the waves and the sun dancing on the water was dazzling. For once, the old house had an air of beauty and not neglect.

It needed an owner who would look after it, Rafe thought, guiding his mud-smeared Land Cruiser down the twisting lane that led to the house. Though not him, he reminded himself firmly. Whatever the old lady said, she was never going to leave Tregellin to the illegitimate son of an olive farmer.

Not that he wanted her to, he reflected without malice. Now that the studio was up and running, he hadn't enough time to do what he had to do as it was. Oh, he collected the rents and kept the books, made sure the old lady paid her taxes. He even mowed the lawns and kept the shrubbery free of weeds, but the house itself needed a major overhaul.

The trouble was, he didn't have the money. Not the kind of money needed to restore the place to its former glory anyway. And if Lady Elinor was as wealthy as the people in the village said she was, she was definitely hiding it from her family.

He knew Cary thought his grandmother was a rich woman. That was why he seldom refused an invitation, ran after her as if her every wish was his command. It was pathetic, really. If Rafe had had more respect for the man he'd have told him the old lady was just using him to satisfy her lust for power. If she did intend to make Cary her heir, she was going to make him work for it.

Whatever happened, Rafe doubted Tregellin would survive another death in the family. Unless Lady Elinor had some hidden cash that no one knew about, when she was gone the estate would have to be sold. It was probably Cary's intention anyway. Rafe couldn't see his cousin moving out of London, giving up the life he had there. Nevertheless, with death duties and lawyers' fees, Rafe suspected he'd be lucky to clear his grandmother's debts.

Rafe was fairly sure the old lady had been living on credit for some time. The tin mines, which had once made the Daniels' fortune, had been played out and dormant for the past fifty years. The estate, with its dairy farms and smallholdings, had struggled in recent years. Things were improving but, like everything else, they needed time.

Time they might not have, he acknowledged. It was sad, but the old lady wasn't as robust as she'd once been. He hated to think of what might happen when she died. Tregellin deserved to be resurrected. Not sold to fund another loser's debts.

He skirted the tennis court and drove round to the front of the house. Tregellin faced the water. It occupied a prime position overlooking the estuary. When he was a kid he used to love going down to the boathouse, taking out the old coracle Sir Henry had taught him to use.

He pushed open his door and got out, hauling the bag of groceries he'd bought at the local supermarket after him. Lady Elinor wouldn't approve of him spending money on her, but Josie would. Josie Morgan was the old lady's housekeeper-cum-companion, and was almost as old as Lady Elinor herself.

Although he'd parked the Land Cruiser at the front of the house, Rafe followed the path that led round to the kitchen door. Hitchins, the old lady's Pekinese, was barking his head off as usual, but when Rafe came through the door he stopped and pushed his snub nose against Rafe's leg.

'Noisy old beast, aren't you?' Rafe chided him, bending to scratch the dog's ears with an affectionate hand. Hitchins was almost fourteen and blind in one eye, but he still recognised a friend when he saw one. He huffed a bit, wanting to be picked up, but Rafe dropped his bag on the scrubbed-pine table and started to unpack it instead.

Josie bustled through from the hall, carrying a tray, and Rafe saw an empty cafetière and two cups, and a plate that still contained three chocolate digestives. He picked up one of the biscuits and bit into it as Josie welcomed him, making light of her thanks as she examined what he'd brought.

'Fillet steak!' she exclaimed with some enthusiasm. 'You spoil us, Rafe, you really do.'

'If I don't, who will?' he retorted philosophically. 'How is the old girl this morning? I intended to get over yesterday evening, but then I got caught up with something else.'

'The something else wouldn't be called Olivia, would she?' she teased him, putting the steak and other perishables he'd brought into the ancient fridge.

'You've been listening to too much gossip,' retorted Rafe, stowing a warm loaf in the bread bin. 'Where is the old lady, anyway? I'd better go and say hello.'

'Shall I bring another pot of coffee?' Josie paused in what she was doing, but Rafe just shook his head.

'I'll take one of these,' he said, picking up a can of ginger ale he'd bought for his own use when he was here. 'No. No glass,' he deterred her, when she would have taken one from the cupboard. He paused. 'The conservatory, right?'

'Oh—yes.' Josie pulled a rueful face and tucked a strand of iron-grey hair behind her ear. 'She'll have heard the car, I don't doubt for a minute. She may be old but her hearing's as sharp as ever.'

Rafe grinned, and with Hitchins at his heels he walked across the mahogany-panelled hall and into the morning room opposite. Beyond the morning room, a vaulted conservatory basked in sunlight. It was built at one side of the old house, to take advantage of a view of the river. Weeping willows trailed their branches in water that mirrored their reflection, while kingfishers dived from the river bank, their speed only equalled by their success.

Lady Elinor was seated in a fan-backed basketwork chair beside a matching table. The morning newspaper resided on the table, turned to the crossword that was almost completed. It was the old lady's boast that she could finish the crossword before eleven o'clock every morning and, glancing at his watch, Rafe saw she still had fifteen minutes to go.

'Don't let me keep you!' she exclaimed shrewishly, noting his momentary distraction, and Rafe pulled a face before bending to kiss her gnarled cheek.

'I won't,' he assured her. 'I was just checking the time, that's all. It looks like it's in danger of defeating you today.'

'If you're talking about the crossword, that fool, Josie, has kept me gossiping again. She brings my coffee and then thinks she has to keep me entertained. I've said to her a dozen times, I don't need her company.'

'You love it really.' Rafe was laconic. He picked up the Pekinese and walked across to the French windows, gazing out across the river to the meadows beyond. 'So—what have you been talking about? Or am I not supposed to ask?'

'Since when has that stopped you?' Lady Elinor was impatient. 'I was telling her that Cary's bringing his fiancée to meet me on Thursday. I'm hoping they'll stay for a few days. At least over the weekend.'

'His fiancée, eh?' Rafe turned, and put the dog down again. Ignoring its complaints, he pushed his hands into the pockets of his leather jacket, a heavy strand of night dark hair falling over his eyes. 'That must please you. Him settling down at last.'

'If it's true.' The old lady massaged the handle of the malacca cane that stood beside her chair and Rafe thought how difficult it would be for Cary to put one over on his grandmother. Her brain was as sharp as it had ever been, despite the many wrinkles that lined her patrician features. 'I've met the girl, actually. She and her family lived in the same road as Charles and Isabel, when they were alive. Her name is Juliet Lawrence—well, it used to be Lawrence, but she's a divorcee, so who knows what she calls herself now? She's younger than Cary. Her father used to work in the City. Her mother died when she was just a baby and I believe her father died five or six years ago.'

'A comprehensive history,' remarked Rafe drily, and Lady Elinor gave him a darkling look.

'I need to know these things, Raphael,' she said irritably. 'I don't want Cary marrying some strumpet. At least this girl is from a decent family.'

Rafe shrugged. 'You don't think entertaining Cary and his girlfriend might be too much for you right now?' he ventured, and saw the look of indignation that crossed the old lady's face.

'I've had a cold, Raphael. Not pneumonia. It's the time of year. I always catch a cold in the spring.'

'If you say so.' Rafe knew better than to argue. 'OK. If that's all, I'll go and see if Josie needs any help. If you're putting them in the Lavender Room, I'd better check the bathroom for leaks.'

Lady Elinor looked positively offended. 'I'm not putting *them* anywhere,' she declared, laying great emphasis on the pronoun. 'Cary will stay in his own room, as usual, and Miss Lawrence can use Christina's apartments.'

Rafe's jaw tightened. 'I've never heard you call them that before.'

'Haven't you?' The old lady was dismissive. 'Christina was my daughter, Raphael. Just because she chose to live the kind of life I could never approve of doesn't mean that I've forgotten her.'

'Or forgiven her?'

'I'm too old to bear grudges, Raphael.'

'OK.' He inclined his head and strolled towards the door. 'Is there anything else you need?'

Lady Elinor pursed her lips. 'Josie told me that you had a reception at the studio last night,' she ventured, with some reluctance. 'Why wasn't I informed?'

Rafe sighed, pausing in the doorway, one shoulder propped against the frame. 'I didn't think you'd be interested.'

The old lady scowled. 'And why would you think that?'

'Why would I think that? Let me count the ways,' he misquoted mockingly. 'Because you don't approve of my painting portraits for a living? Because you don't want me to turn out like my mother? Because my independence sticks in your craw? Am I getting close?'

'I don't approve of some of the people you mix with,' conceded Lady Elinor testily. 'But I never stopped your mother from doing what she wanted, and I shan't attempt to stop you. Remember, it was she who chose to live in all those exotic places, hauling a small boy around whose existence I knew nothing of. When she died, however, I didn't hesitate in offering you a home here with me.'

Rafe's shoulders rounded. 'I know.'

'Just because we don't always see eye to eye—'

'Look, I'm sorry, OK?'

'—doesn't mean I don't care about you, Raphael.'

'I know.' Rafe closed his eyes for a moment and then said wearily, 'I should have told you about the reception. You're right, I was thoughtless. The local paper took some pictures, so when I get copies I'll show them to you. It wasn't a very grand affair. Just a glass of wine and a chance to view the studio.'

'I'm sure it was very exciting,' said Lady Elinor, but Rafe could hear the reluctance in her voice. 'Before long, you won't be spending any time at Tregellin at all.'

'I'll always have time for you, old lady,' retorted Rafe harshly. 'Look, I've really got to get moving. I'm meeting Liv Holderness at half-past twelve.'

'Olivia Holderness?' Lady Elinor's eyes narrowed. 'Would that be Lord Holderness' daughter?'

'Lord Holderness doesn't have a daughter,' said Rafe flatly. 'Or a son either, as you very well know. Liv's his wife. She wants to discuss having her portrait painted as a gift to her husband on his sixtieth birthday.'

'I see.' The old lady frowned. 'You seem very familiar with her. I seem to remember Holderness hasn't been married to her for very long.'

'Eighteen months, I think.' Rafe's tone was sardonic. He knew nothing went on in the surrounding area that Lady Elinor didn't hear about sooner or later. 'She's his third wife. The old guy turns them in at regular intervals for a new model.'

'Don't be coarse.' Lady Elinor was disapproving. 'And you be careful what you're doing, Raphael. It seems significant to me that she'd choose a local studio over any number of more famous establishments she and her husband must know in London.'

Rafe grimaced. 'Damned with faint praise,' he said drily. 'Don't worry, I've known Liv for a few years. Her father owns the Dragon Hotel in Polgellin Bay.'

'Ah.' The old lady nodded. 'So she's one of the Melroses?'

'The youngest daughter,' agreed Rafe, wishing the old lady didn't make them sound like the Doones.

'So she's a lot younger than Holderness?'

Rafe nodded. 'About thirty years, I think. But they seem happy enough.'

'Well, you keep what I've said in mind,' declared Lady Elinor, unexpectedly getting to her feet and coming towards him. She was tall, though not as tall as he was, and leaning heavily on her cane. She was wearing her signature pleated skirt and silk blouse, with a heather-coloured shawl draped about her shoulders, and her once dark hair was now liberally threaded with grey. She laid a hand on his sleeve and looked up at him with eyes as blue as the gentians that grew higher up the valley. 'You take care,' she added, reaching up to kiss him. 'I may not always show it, but I'm very fond of you, Raphael.'

It was the electric bill that had done it.

It had been waiting for her when she'd got back to the apartment and she'd stared at the figure she owed with wide dis-believing eyes. She couldn't believe she'd used that much elec-tricity. For heaven's sake, she'd rarely used the oven and she'd religiously turned out lights as she'd gone from room to room.

But she had used the microwave, she'd acknowledged. And the underfloor heating system was expensive. A neighbour had warned her of that. But seeing what she'd owed in black and white had really scared her. The fact that it had been the heaviest season of the year had been no consolation at all.

That was why, when Cary had rung two days later, asking her if she'd reconsidered, she'd given in to his persuasion. The figure he'd offered her for four days work had been impossible to refuse. She'd known it would pay her immediate bills and leave her a little bit over. Possibly enough to survive until she got a proper job.

All the same, as Cary turned off the A30 just beyond Bodmin on Thursday afternoon, Juliet couldn't deny the butterflies in her stomach that were telling her she'd made a terrible mistake. She liked Cary; of course she did. Or perhaps she'd used to like the boy she'd known all those years ago. These days, she knew very little about him. His attendance at her wedding hardly consti-tuted grounds for a friendship.

And, despite the fact that he kept telling her she was going to love the area where his grandmother's house was situated, the idea of being introduced to Lady Elinor Daniels as Cary's fiancée left an unpleasant taste in her mouth. When he'd first broached the idea, he'd said he needed a girlfriend. Now it had metamorphosed into a fiancée, which was a whole different ball game.

'Not long now,' Cary said, taking her silence for tiredness. 'We could still stop for lunch, if you like. That would give us a break.'

Juliet, who didn't want to spend any more time alone with him than was necessary, managed a faint smile. 'We don't want to be too late arriving,' she said, keeping her eyes on the road ahead. 'Besides, didn't you say your grandmother is expecting us for lunch?'

Cary's mouth compressed and Juliet got the feeling that he wasn't looking forward to this visit any more than she was. Which was understandable, she supposed, if the old lady kept interfering in his private life. But, let's face it, she thought, without Lady Elinor's intervention he could be languishing in a South African prison. She'd read enough stories about rogue dealers who'd almost bankrupted the banks they'd worked for.

'I suppose it is a bit late now,' he conceded at last, and she realised he was responding to her question. Then, pointing away to the west, 'Have you ever seen sea that colour before? In England, I mean. It's almost tropical. It reminds me of a holiday I had in Mauritius. God, that was some hotel we stayed in. A whole floor given over to our suite.'

'Expensive,' murmured Juliet drily, and Cary turned to glance at her.

'Yeah, I wish I had that kind of cash now,' he agreed, without a trace of remorse. 'That's why I have to be so careful how I treat the old girl. Without her money, I'd be taking a package holiday in Spain every year.'

Juliet's eyes widened. 'Does she know you spend the money she gives you on expensive holidays?'

Cary frowned. 'Hey, that information's not for public consumption,' he said. 'Don't you be discussing my financial arrangements with her. If she chooses to sub me sometimes, I'm not going to refuse it, am I? The old girl's loaded! You might not think it to look at the house, but, believe me, I know she's got a fortune hidden away somewhere.'

Juliet was feeling less and less enthusiastic about her part in this deception. She told herself that if Cary had been totally honest with her from the beginning, she'd never have agreed to come. Or was she being totally honest with herself? she wondered. Damn it all, she was doing it for the money, too.

'Tell me about your cousin,' she said, trying to distract herself. 'What's he like? Does he look like you?'

Cary scowled. 'As if.' And then, when she was obviously waiting for him to go on, he muttered irritably, 'He looks like a gipsy, if you must know. Swarthy skin, greasy black hair and an attitude you could cut with a knife.'

Juliet's brows ascended. 'You really don't like him, do you?'

Cary shrugged. 'I've told you what he's like. Always ingratiating himself with the old woman. I've no doubt she'll sing his praises while you're here. She does it just to wind me up.'

'Oh, Cary—'

'I mean it. I've got better things to do than mend light switches and plug leaks. I'm a banker, Jules, not a labourer. Or rather I was until the futures market stuffed up.'

Juliet chose her words with care. 'He probably only does these things to help your grandmother. I mean, it isn't always easy to find a plumber or an electrician when you need one.'

'Yeah, well, he needn't think that doing all these things gives him some claim on the estate when the old lady snuffs it. As soon as the will's read, I'm going to tell him I don't want him trespassing on the place in future. Tregellin's mine. I'm the only legitimate heir and he knows it. But that doesn't stop him from hanging around, pretending he's helping her out.'

Juliet shook her head. 'You're so bitter!'

'No.' Cary wouldn't have that. 'Just practical. Anyway, we're almost there. That's the chimneys of the house you can see over the treetops. It's set on a promontory overlooking the Eden estuary. The River Eden, I mean.' He grimaced. 'It may be a beautiful spot, but it's no Garden of Eden.'

They approached the house down a winding track between hedges of rhododendron and acacia. Juliet guessed that in late spring and early summer these same hedges would be a riot of colour. Right now, the glossy leaves hid the buds of any blossoms, and because there were lowering clouds overhead it was rather gloomy.

The grounds of the house seemed quite extensive. A tennis court and a croquet lawn, a vegetable garden behind a lichen-covered stone wall. They circled the building and Juliet saw that it was the back of the house that faced the road. The front looked out across the river estuary, the water shallow now as the tide receded.

There was a big SUV already parked on the forecourt and as Juliet thrust open her door and got out she heard Cary give a grunt of irritation. Turning to see what had caused his annoyance, she saw that a man had just appeared from around the side of the house. He was a big man, tall and powerfully built, wearing a worn leather jacket and jeans that clung to lean muscular thighs. Scuffed boots completed his attire and Juliet didn't need a sixth sense to know that this must be the infamous Rafe Marchese.

He looked across the width of the courtyard towards her and she felt a disturbing flutter of awareness in the pit of her stomach. But goodness, he was attractive, she thought, realising that Cary's scornful description hadn't done the man justice.

His hair was dark, yes, and needed cutting, but it wasn't greasy. His skin was darkly tanned and there was the stubble of a beard on his jawline, but she wouldn't have called him swarthy either. He wasn't handsome. His features were too hard, too masculine for that. And she'd bet her last penny that it wasn't only for his technical skills that Lady Elinor liked having him around.

'Cary,' he said evenly, as the other man got out of the car, and Cary was obliged to acknowledge him in return.

'Rafe.' His voice was tight and he turned at once to take their luggage from the back of the car, making no attempt to introduce Juliet.

Which really annoyed her. More than it should, probably, she admitted, but dammit, she was supposed to be his fiancée. Deciding she didn't care what Cary thought, she walked around the bonnet of the car and held out her hand.

'Hi,' she said with a smile. 'I'm Juliet. Cary's—girlfriend.'

CHAPTER THREE

THE lunch had been cold, but Juliet knew they couldn't blame the housekeeper for that. They'd been expected at one; they'd actually arrived at a quarter-past two. However expert the cook, no one could have kept a mushroom risotto hot indefinitely.

Not that she'd been particularly hungry. The encounter between Cary and Rafe Marchese had robbed her of her appetite somewhat. The two men obviously disliked one another, but Cary had behaved like a boor and she'd been sucked into his game.

Perhaps some of the blame was hers. She'd initiated his anger when she'd introduced herself to his cousin. But, dammit, she'd been angry with Cary for ignoring her and she hadn't thought about the possible consequences of her actions when she'd approached the other man.

The truth, however unpalatable, was that she'd wanted Rafe Marchese to notice her. Which was weird, considering that since David had walked out on their marriage over a year ago she'd had no interest in other men.

Not that she flattered herself that Marchese had felt the same way. He'd been polite, but distant, his first words succinctly delineating her reason for being there. 'Ah, yes,' he'd said. 'Cary's fiancée.' He'd paused. 'Lady Elinor was beginning to think you'd changed your minds.'

All the same, when he'd touched her hand she'd reacted as if she'd accidentally touched a hot wire. The heat that passed from his hand into hers shocked her to the core. Then she'd looked up into eyes that were as dark and brooding as the storm clouds massing over Tregellin and known that, whatever happened, she was already out of her depth.

Of course, she'd snatched her hand away, rather rudely, and Cary had come charging over, like some mad bull defending his mate. 'What's going on?' he'd demanded, laying a possessive hand on Juliet's shoulder. 'What have you been saying to my fiancée? As you apparently knew we were coming, I thought you'd have had the decency to stay away.'

Rafe Marchese didn't seem at all perturbed by Cary's bluster. 'It's good to see you, too, Cary,' he'd said, as faultlessly polite as before.

'Well…' Cary had been indignant. 'Grandmama told me how you're too busy for her these days. Spending time with your artsy-craftsy friends, was how she put it. But I might have known you'd be around when I was here.'

Rafe's lips had tilted humorously. 'I shouldn't take what the old lady says too seriously,' he'd remarked, his eyes lingering on Juliet's now burning face. 'You know she likes to play us off against each other. If you weren't such an easy mark, she'd never get away with it.'

'Oh, and you know her so well,' Cary had sneered, but Rafe had only lifted his shoulders in a self-deprecatory shrug.

'I'd say I see more of her,' he'd declared mildly. 'Whether that constitutes knowing her better remains to be seen.'

'Well, don't think I don't know what you're trying to do,' Cary had continued. 'You think that, because I live in London and you live here, you've got the advantage.' His hand had squeezed Juliet's shoulder. 'Once we're married, I think you can kiss any chance of changing her mind goodbye.'

Dear God, Juliet had wanted to die, she thought now as she unpacked her suitcase. For heaven's sake, it was bad enough pretending to be Cary's fiancée without him talking about them getting married as if it were going to happen in the next few weeks. She had no idea what Rafe Marchese had thought. If his mocking smile was anything to go by, he was used to Cary's bombastic behaviour and he didn't take offence from it. But she wished she hadn't been a part of it all the same.

The altercation had been thankfully brought to an end by the advent of a small dog. It was a little yapping Pekinese that had made straight for Cary and dug its teeth into his trouser leg. 'Damn stupid mutt!' Cary had exclaimed, kicking out angrily, sending the dog scuttling across the yard.

'He's actually quite intelligent,' Rafe had remarked coolly, bending to rescue the little animal, massaging its ears with a long-fingered brown hand that was lightly covered with dark hair. Juliet had felt a momentary envy for the dog, which was ridiculous. But then Cary had hauled their bags out of the car and headed for the house and she'd been obliged to follow him.

She guessed now that he hadn't wanted to argue with the animal. It was Lady Elinor's dog and Juliet doubted she'd appreciate learning that her grandson had kicked the Pekinese. It was to be hoped Rafe Marchese wouldn't tell her. Though after the way Cary had behaved, she wouldn't blame him if he did.

Meeting Lady Elinor again had been a bit of an anticlimax after the confrontation outside. She was a lot older than Juliet remembered, naturally, but she was still an intimidating figure. If anything, Juliet would have said that Rafe resembled her far more than Cary. He had her height and that same air of cool breeding.

During lunch, Juliet had had to fend off quite a number of questions about her failed marriage to David. The fact that it was only nine months since her divorce was finalised had elicited the opinion that in her position Lady Elinor wouldn't have been in any hurry to rush into marriage again.

Of course, Cary had come to her rescue, assuring the old lady that the reason Juliet's marriage hadn't worked was that she'd married the wrong man in the first place. 'Hammond was only after her money,' he'd said contemptuously, and Juliet had been glad Rafe Marchese hadn't been there to see the faintly amused expression that had crossed Lady Elinor's face at his words.

But at least it had given her a breathing space and, when the meal was over, she'd been relieved to hear her hostess bid Josie show their guest to her room. Evidently the old lady had wanted to spend some time alone with her grandson and Juliet prayed he wouldn't make any more promises he couldn't keep.

With her unpacking completed, Juliet contemplated the apartment she'd been given. It was much bigger than the rooms she was used to. Even the rooms at her father's house couldn't have competed with this. But the whole place was incredibly shabby, the high ceilings badly needed attention and the thick paper that must have once decorated the walls was now scuffed and peeling from neglect.

It was no wonder, really, if Josie was the only help Lady Elinor had. She was almost as old as her mistress, and Juliet doubted she had time to dust all the rooms, let alone attend to any repairs. Everything here was on a grand scale, including the furniture, and the bathroom next door sported a claw-footed tub and a lavatory that was elevated on a small dais.

Still, from the brief bounce she'd permitted herself on the bed, the mattress was comfortable. And the sheets were clean and smelled sweetly of a lavender-scented rinse. It was only for three nights, she assured herself. And Lady Elinor was unlikely to have anything more to say to her. Perhaps she could borrow Cary's car and drive into the nearest town. She had little money to do any shopping, but at least it would keep her out of the way.

The room was at the front of the house and she had a magnificent view over the river estuary. At present the tide was out and there were dozens of birds strutting over the mudflats, looking for food. She saw gulls and waders; she even recognised a pair of sandpipers. She was no expert, but she guessed you could get really interested in stuff like this if you lived here.

It was still only about half-past four and, deciding she couldn't stay in her room until suppertime, Juliet thought she'd go in search of the housekeeper. Perhaps Josie would tell her a little more about the history of the house—or the history of its occupants, she conceded, aware that she was more interested in Rafe Marchese than she was in anything or anyone else.

She rinsed her face at the crackled marble basin in the adjoining bathroom and then regarded her reflection in the spotted mirror. She still looked flushed, but that was probably just the cold water she'd washed with. Clearly Lady Elinor didn't believe in heating the water during the day.

In her bedroom again, after assuring herself that the cream silk jersey top and matching linen skirt she'd worn to travel in would do for her explorations, she reapplied eyeliner and mascara, brushing a bronze gloss over her generous mouth. She wasn't beautiful, she thought, but her heart-shaped features did have a certain appeal. Thankfully her hair, which was naturally curly, didn't require much more than a brush running through it. It bobbed just below the level of her shoulders and, although it was some time since she'd been able to afford highlights, there were still golden streaks in its honey-brown mass. Or were they grey? she fretted, leaning closer to the mirror. After what she'd been through, she wouldn't have been surprised.

She made her way to the head of the stairs and started down, keeping a wary eye open for either Cary or her hostess. She would prefer not to run into either of them just yet and, as the gloomy hall appeared to be deserted, she headed swiftly towards what she hoped was the kitchen. And found Rafe Marchese lounging on a corner of the pine table, sharing a pot of tea with the housekeeper.

Juliet didn't know who was the most surprised, herself or Josie. 'Why—Miss Lawrence,' she said awkwardly, getting up from her place at the table to face her. 'I was just about to bring up your tea.'

'My tea?'

Juliet now saw the tray that had been prepared and left on one of the cabinets. There was a cup and saucer, milk and sugar, and a plate containing wafer-thin cucumber sandwiches and tiny butterfly cakes. Only the teapot was missing and she guessed Josie had been interrupted by her visitor.

If Rafe was disconcerted by her sudden appearance, he didn't show it. He didn't even get up, she noticed, merely raised the mug he was drinking from to his mouth and regarded her enigmatically across the rim.

'Yes, your tea.' Josie was anxious to assure her guest that it was all ready for her. 'But as you're down, would you like me to serve it in the drawing room instead?'

'Oh—um—' after the fiasco of lunch, Juliet had no desire to repeat the experience '—couldn't I just have it here? With you and—Mr Marchese.'

'Rafe,' he said flatly, putting his mug down on the table. He had no desire to get to know this young woman any better than he did already, but he couldn't ignore her. 'I think Josie would prefer it if you allowed her to serve you in the drawing room.'

Juliet's lips pursed. 'And I'd prefer to have it here,' she insisted smoothly. 'Is there a problem with that?'

'Of course not, Miss Lawrence.' Josie was clearly disturbed by the sudden hostility between them. 'If you'll just give me a minute to boil the kettle and make some fresh tea—'

'What you're having is fine.' Juliet sent Rafe a challenging look. Then, with what he thought was a reflection of his cousin's arrogance, 'I thought you'd left, Mr Marchese.'

'I came back,' said Rafe calmly. Then, mimicking her defiance, 'Do you have a problem with that?'

Her cheeks darkened with becoming colour, proving she wasn't as confident as she'd like to appear. 'It's not my place to comment,' she retorted tartly, but he couldn't let her get away with that.

'But you have,' he pointed out, picking up his mug again, and Josie clasped her hands together in dismay.

'Rafe, please,' she said, her eyes wide and appealing. 'I'm sure Miss Lawrence was only making conversation.' She hurriedly took the cup and saucer from the tray and lifted the teapot she'd been using. 'How do you like your tea, Miss Lawrence? With milk and sugar or a slice of lemon?'

Juliet felt embarrassed. There'd been no tension in the room when she'd arrived, but there was now. And it was all her fault.

Well, maybe not entirely her fault, she defended herself, as Josie added to her cup the milk that she'd requested. She was beginning to wonder if Cary might have some justification for his resentment after all. There was no doubt that Rafe was being deliberately awkward with her.

'Is your room comfortable?' Josie asked, offering Juliet a seat—and a way out—and, although she would have preferred to remain standing, she realised the old woman wouldn't sit down again unless she did.

'Um—very comfortable,' she said, casting another glance at Rafe as she pulled out a chair and sat down. 'It has a marvellous view of the estuary.'

Rafe watched her through narrowed eyes, wishing the old lady hadn't put her in his mother's old room. Wondering, too, what a girl like her would see in a loser like Cary. What had Lady Elinor told him? That she'd already been married and divorced? She didn't look old enough to have had so much experience of life.

Juliet was aware of him watching her, lids lowered, lashes to die for shading those disturbing dark eyes. What was he thinking? she wondered. Did he assume that like Cary she was only interested in the old lady's money? For, despite what he'd said to his cousin, she'd seen the expression on Cary's face when he'd thought Lady Elinor wasn't looking, and it hadn't been pleasant.

The silence had gone on too long and Josie, who had evidently been trying again to think of something non-contentious to say, turned appealing eyes to Rafe. 'Your grandmother's having a small dinner party on Saturday night. Did she tell you?'

Rafe's mouth compressed. 'Now why would she tell me a thing like that?' he queried drily. 'I'm not invited, am I?'

'N—o.' Josie had to be honest. 'But the Holdernesses are coming.'

'Are they?' He pulled a wry face. 'The old girl must be pulling out all the stops.'

'Well, that's the thing…'

But Josie belatedly seemed to realise she'd gone too far in a guest's presence and, meeting her troubled eyes, Rafe took his cue and said, 'Well, don't worry. I'll be around if you need me.'

'Oh, Rafe!'

The words were said with such heartfelt emotion that Juliet realised that, whatever she thought of him, the housekeeper didn't share her view. In fact, there seemed to be a genuine affection between them and Juliet permitted herself another look in his direction.

Only to encounter his reflective gaze.

She looked away immediately, but not before she'd gained the impression that his opinion of her was no less critical than hers of him. He evidently did think she was some empty-headed bimbo who'd only latched on to Cary because of his expectations.

As if!

Deciding it was up to her to try and change that impression, she forced herself to meet his gaze again and say politely, 'Cary said something about you being an artist, Mr Marchese. Should I have heard of you?'

'I believe what he actually said was that I had artsy-craftsy friends,' murmured Rafe rather maliciously, and heard Josie's sudden intake of breath.

'Rafe!' she exclaimed again, barely audibly, but Juliet wasn't listening to her.

'And do you?' she countered. 'Have artsy-craftsy friends, I mean?'

Rafe sighed, putting down his empty mug and regarding her tolerantly for once. 'No,' he said flatly. 'That's just Cary's way of denigrating anything he doesn't understand.'

'Please, Rafe…'

Josie was getting desperate and this time Juliet did hear her. 'Oh, don't worry, Mrs Morgan,' she said, giving the housekeeper a quick smile of reassurance. 'Mr Marchese doesn't like me. That's obvious. Well, that's OK. I'm not especially fond of him either.' She finished her tea and set down her cup. 'If you'll excuse me, I think I'll take a look outside, if that's permitted?'

When she emerged into the hall again, Cary was just coming down the stairs. Oh, great! she thought. That was all she needed. And the situation wasn't improved when the door behind her opened again. For some reason, Rafe had chosen to follow her.

Someone—Cary, she assumed—had turned on some lights and the hall didn't look half as gloomy as it had done when she'd come downstairs. In fact, with what appeared to be a Waterford crystal chandelier picking out the reddish grain in the panelling, a little of its former grandeur had been restored.

The angle of the stairs meant that Cary didn't immediately notice his cousin. 'Where've you been, Juliet?' he demanded peevishly. 'I've been looking for you for ages. I went to your room, but you weren't there. Obviously.' He waved an impatient hand. 'What the hell have you been doing?'

If Juliet had hoped that Cary's words might deter Rafe from interfering, she was mistaken. 'She's been having tea in the kitchen, with me and Josie,' he drawled lazily, stepping into the light. 'I assume you have no objections?'

'Like hell!' Cary had reached the bottom of the stairs and now he looked suspiciously from Juliet to the other man. Then, scowling at his supposed fiancée, 'How did that come about?'

Juliet sighed. 'By accident,' she said tersely, flashing Rafe an exasperated look. 'I was looking for—for someone to talk to. I thought Josie might be able to tell me a bit more about the house.'

'So what was he doing?' Cary cocked his head towards Rafe.

'I was having tea with Josie, if it's any business of yours,' replied Rafe before Juliet could answer. 'This isn't your house yet, Cary. I come and go as I please.'

'Don't I know it?' Cary sounded aggrieved. 'So where's the old girl? In the conservatory, as usual.'

'I imagine she's resting.' Rafe spoke with evident reluctance. 'She usually rests in the afternoon, as you'd know if you spent more time at Tregellin.'

Cary didn't bother answering him. Instead, he placed an arm about Juliet's shoulders, causing a rather unpleasant shiver to ripple up her spine. He bent his head towards her. 'How about you and me taking a walk in the grounds?' he suggested. 'I'd like to show you around.'

'Oh—no.' With some discretion, Juliet managed to ease herself out of Cary's reach. 'I—er—I was just thinking of taking a bath.'

She heard Rafe's disbelieving exhalation of breath and determinedly avoided his gaze. It wasn't anything to do with him if she chose to change her mind.

'A bath, eh?' Was Cary being deliberately provocative? she wondered. 'Oh, yeah, that sounds like a plan. We could take a bath together, baby. Have you noticed how big the tubs are here? It makes you wonder what the people of Great-Grandmama's generation used to get up to when Great-Great-Grandpapa used to throw those wild house parties between the wars.'

'Not what you're imagining, Cary,' declared a cool, aristocratic voice from the direction of the morning room. Lady Elinor was standing in the open doorway, the little dog, Hitchins, tucked under her arm. 'Rafe.' She nodded towards her other grandson. 'A minute before you leave, if you please.'

CHAPTER FOUR

JULIET had a bath, but it was a fairly cold one. The only shower was hand-held, and she used it to sluice herself down before stepping out onto the marble floor. Fortunately, she'd laid a towel beside the bath before getting into it. She was already shivering, and imagining bare feet on cold marble didn't bear thinking about.

There was no hair-drier, but she'd washed her hair that morning, so that didn't worry her. Nevertheless, she wished she'd brought her own drier with her. She'd been spoiled, she thought. She was used to staying in hotels where every amenity was provided.

Not any longer, of course, she told herself, the spectre of the electricity bill briefly rearing its ugly head. And, however awkward it was for her here, at least it would provide her with enough money to pay it. If she could just ignore Rafe Marchese, it wouldn't be all that bad.

With the knowledge that Lady Elinor was giving a dinner party for her grandson on Saturday evening, Juliet studied the clothes she'd brought with her rather critically. It wasn't that she was short of clothes. On the contrary, until David had cancelled her credit cards, shopping had been something she enjoyed. But she hadn't brought a lot of clothes with her. Cary's complaint that his grandmother never spent any money hadn't prepared her for the real situation at Tregellin. Although the old lady might not have a lot of money, she lived in some style. The upkeep of the house alone had to be excessive, but there seemed to be no question of her leaving it and moving to smaller premises.

Which meant Juliet had to save her little black dress until Saturday. It was the most formal thing she'd brought, and when she'd tucked it into her case back in London she'd had real doubts about bringing it. She was glad she had now. Cary would expect his 'fiancée' to wear something suitable.

That evening she decided to wear a pair of cropped trousers in aubergine silk, whose low waist exposed a generous wedge of creamy skin. She'd wear a mauve and green patterned top with the trousers, its smock style successfully covering the breach.

It was a little after seven when she went downstairs. Cary had told her before they'd parted in the hall that his grandmother usually had supper at half-past. Although she would have preferred to stay in her room until it was time to eat, that would have been impolite, and, hearing the sound of voices from the drawing room, she headed in that direction.

The housekeeper was on her way out as Juliet entered the room, and after wishing their guest a good evening she hastened on her way. Expecting to find Cary with his grandmother, Juliet was perturbed to find it was just the two of them, though the old lady was graciousness itself as she offered her guest a sherry before the meal.

'Oh…' Juliet had never liked sherry, finding it too sweet, usually, but good manners dictated that she accept Lady Elinor's offer. 'Thank you.'

'Perhaps you'd help yourself,' added the old lady, gesturing with her cane towards the tray on the nearby bureau. 'I have a little arthritis in my hands and I don't find it easy lifting the decanter.'

Juliet nodded and went to do as she'd been asked, grateful that she need only pour herself a small amount. 'My father suffered from arthritis in his hands, too,' she said, coming to sit on the leather sofa opposite the old lady's armchair. 'He used to say it was with holding a pen for so many years.'

Lady Elinor acknowledged this. She was looking particularly elegant this evening in an ankle-length black skirt and a cream silk blouse. Once again, a shawl was draped about her shoulders, a Paisley pattern this time in autumn shades.

'Your mother died before your father, didn't she?' she remarked, and Juliet conceded that this was so.

'She died just after I was born. My father was devastated, as you can imagine.'

'Of course.' Her hostess absorbed this. 'And your father was considerably older than your mother, I believe,' she went on, startling Juliet by her knowledge. 'But at least he had you. You must have been very close.'

'Yes, we were.' Juliet felt a twinge of the distress she'd suffered when her father had died. Then, frowning, 'Did you know my father, Lady Elinor?'

'No.' The old lady shook her head. 'But I remember my son and his wife talking about Cary's friendship with Maxwell Lawrence's daughter. And I know Cary was dismayed when I removed him from all the friends he'd had in the village.'

Juliet took a tentative sip of her sherry and found it wasn't as sweet as she'd anticipated. 'That seems such a long time ago.'

'Well, of course, it is.' Lady Elinor sighed. 'It's easier to look back when you're my age.' She paused. 'But you married someone else. Cary attended your wedding. Did you realise you'd married the wrong man?'

Juliet pulled a wry face. 'You could say that.'

'You'd prefer not to talk about it?'

'No.' Juliet bit her lip. 'It was just a stupid mistake, that's all. David never loved me. As Cary probably told you, he was only interested in my money.'

Lady Elinor's brows drew together. 'And your father didn't insist that he sign some kind of agreement before you became his wife?'

'My father died a year before I met David,' explained Juliet ruefully. 'And as I say, I believed him when he said that money didn't matter to him.'

'Money always matters,' declared the old lady firmly. 'Except perhaps to someone like Rafe.' She paused. 'You've met Rafe, haven't you? He's my daughter Christina's son. Unfortunately she was never married to his father.'

'Ah.' Juliet pressed her lips together for a moment. 'May I ask what you meant when you said Rafe wasn't interested in money?'

It was a personal question, but happily the old lady didn't appear to take offence. 'Perhaps I should amend that to *my* money,' she said, with a wry smile. 'He does extremely well without it. The small gallery he's just opened in Polgellin Bay has proved quite a success.'

Juliet's eyes widened. 'So he is a painter?'

'He paints,' agreed Lady Elinor consideringly. 'He also teaches art at a comprehensive school in Bodmin.'

'Really?' Juliet realised Rafe had been deliberately vague on the subject. 'How interesting!'

'You think so?' The old lady sounded as if she had her doubts. 'His mother broke my heart with her—reckless disregard for propriety. She painted, too, and look what happened to her.'

'Cary said she—fell from the balcony of an hotel.'

'Well, that's the official story, anyway.'

Juliet stared at her. 'It's not true?'

Lady Elinor smiled a little drily. 'Ah, that would be telling, wouldn't it, Miss Lawrence? Why don't you tell me how you and Cary came to meet again? It seems such a coincidence. Do you visit the casino, by any chance?'

'The casino?' Juliet was taken aback.

'Yes. That is where my grandson works, isn't it?' She pulled a wry face. 'I can't imagine how he persuaded them to employ him after the fiasco he was involved in in South Africa. You know about that, I suppose?'

'Well, yes.'

Juliet didn't know what else to say and for once she was relieved to hear heavy footsteps crossing the hall. A moment later Cary appeared in the doorway, somewhat overdressed in satin-seamed black trousers and a dark red dinner jacket.

He came into the room with a slight swagger, as if he expected to be complimented on his appearance. But all Lady Elinor did was raise her dark eyebrows at him. And when Hitchins, who had been asleep in his basket at her feet, awoke and started growling, she bent and lifted the little animal onto her lap.

'Grandmama.' Cary greeted her politely, gave the dog a less-friendly look and then came to seat himself beside Juliet. 'You're looking delectable this evening,' he said, bestowing an unwelcome kiss on her neck just below her ear. 'Hmm, and you smell delectable, too. Is it Chanel?'

'No.' Juliet refrained from saying that it was a simple herbal essence that wasn't half as expensive. 'Your grandmother and I have been waiting for you.'

'Sorry.' Cary would have kissed her again, but Juliet managed to avoid it. 'If I'd known you were missing me, I'd have been much quicker, believe me.'

'She didn't say she'd been missing you, Cary,' observed the old lady a little maliciously. 'As a matter of fact, Juliet and I have been having a very interesting conversation.'

'You have?' Cary looked a little uneasy now.

'Yes.' His grandmother smiled her satisfaction. 'She was just about to tell me where the two of you renewed your acquaintance.'

Juliet sighed, aware that Cary had stiffened beside her. This was an eventuality they hadn't covered, though she realised in hindsight it had been foolish not to do so. 'We—er—we met at the home of mutual friends,' she lied, the glance she cast in Cary's direction warning him not to contradict her. 'It was the Bainbridges, Cary, wasn't it? John and Deborah. We've both known them for years.'

'Yes, the Bainbridges,' agreed Cary gratefully, but Juliet,

hearing the falseness in his tone, could well understand why
Lady Elinor had chosen to investigate his employment for
herself. It was to be hoped the old lady wasn't a friend of the
Bainbridges, too. Debbie would be most confused to hear that
Juliet was planning on getting married again without telling her.
Not to mention meeting her future fiancé at her house.

'And that was when?'

The old lady wasn't finished yet and this time Cary intervened. 'Oh—it must be over six months ago!' he exclaimed ex-
pansively, inspiring a silent groan from Juliet.

'Over six months?' queried his grandmother at once, as
Juliet had known she would. 'So why haven't I heard anything
about it? When you were down—let me see, six weeks ago—
you made no mention of the fact that you were thinking of getting engaged, Cary.'

Cary looked blank-faced now and Juliet knew that, once
again, she'd have to come to his rescue. 'That was my fault, Lady
Elinor,' she lied, hoping her smile would hide her blushes. 'I'm
afraid I asked Cary to keep our relationship to himself. With it
being such a comparatively short time since my divorce, I didn't
want anyone to think I was rushing into marriage again.'

The older woman's lips thinned. 'Even though you are,' she
commented drily, and Juliet gave a rueful shrug. But, fortunately, Josie returned at that moment to say that supper was
ready and Cary got gratefully to his feet.

The rest of the evening progressed without further embarrassment. Juliet couldn't decide whether Lady Elinor had been satisfied with the answers they'd given her or merely biding her time
until morning. Whatever, the meal—roast beef and Yorkshire
pudding with a fruit compote for dessert—passed without incident,
and afterwards Juliet had the perfect excuse to retire early.

'It's been a very long day,' she said, when Cary chose to
question her departure, and, meeting her narrowed gaze, he evidently decided not to push his luck.

'Yeah, you get a good night's rest,' he said, catching her hand as she passed him and raising it to his lips. 'I'll see you in the morning, darling. Sleep well.'

In fact, Juliet slept only fitfully. Although the bed was comfortable, it was a strange bed, and the knowledge that there were still three more days to go weighed heavily on her mind. After tossing and turning for hours she eventually rose just as the sky was lightening, padding barefoot across to the windows and peering out.

The view was calming. Sunrise on the estuary, and the mudflats were a veritable hive of activity. She'd never seen so many birds in one place before, cackling and squawking as they vied with one another for the grubs the receding tide had left behind.

It looked as if it was going to be a fine day. The clouds, such as they were, were thinning, and a delicate haze was lifting to reveal a pale blue horizon. Juliet knew a sudden urge to be outside, far from another round of interrogation. For no matter how amiable Lady Elinor had been the night before, she was fairly sure her curiosity hadn't been totally assuaged.

In the bathroom, the hand shower ran lukewarm, but it was better than nothing. Chilled, but refreshed, Juliet dressed in jeans and a V-necked olive-green sweater, pulled on Converse boots, and left her room.

As on the night before, there seemed to be no one about, which wasn't really surprising. It was barely seven o'clock. Much too early for Lady Elinor to want breakfast.

The kitchen was chilly. The Aga, which had evidently kept the place warm the afternoon before, was cold now and blinds still covered the windows. Juliet opened the blinds and, locating the kettle, set it to boil. If she could just find a jar of instant coffee, she thought, she'd be happy.

She found what she was looking for in the third cupboard she opened, and by then the kettle was boiling. She put two teaspoons of coffee in a mug and then filled it with hot water. Then she turned to a rather elderly fridge, looking for milk.

She had her back to the door when a key turned in the lock and it opened. She swung round in surprise to find Rafe Marchese letting himself into the house. He was carrying a couple of bags and the delicious aroma of newly baked bread came to her nostrils. She had thought she wasn't hungry, but she'd been wrong.

'Making yourself at home?' he remarked lazily, putting the bags down on the pine table. He was wearing khaki cargo pants this morning and a navy body-warmer over an open-collared Oxford shirt. There was a disturbing glimpse of dark body hair showing in the opening, and his shirtsleeves were rolled back to display forearms that were deeply tanned and also spiced with hair.

Juliet felt herself going red as she looked at him. Honestly, she thought with annoyance, you'd think she was a foolish virgin who'd never dealt with men before. Which was so untrue. What was it about Rafe Marchese that made her think about things any decent girl would be appalled by?

'Um—do you want some?' she asked, trying to sound cool and collected, when she was anything but, and Rafe's lips curved in amusement.

'It depends what you're offering,' he said, watching as the hot colour flamed in her cheeks.

She was certainly easy to watch, he thought. Easy to disconcert, too, which was interesting. This morning she was wearing jeans that hugged the sexy contours of her hips, and, although she persistently pulled her sweater down, it kept inching up to display a tantalising glimpse of creamy skin.

She was certainly nothing like the woman he'd expected when the old lady had told him that Cary was bringing his fiancée to Tregellin. And, although common sense told him it would be unwise to bait her, there was something about her that aroused a malicious desire to see how far he could go.

For her part, Juliet knew he was being deliberately provocative, and she wondered why. Dammit, she was a divorced

woman, and supposedly Cary's fiancée besides. Did he know she
was hopelessly out of practice when it came to men like him?

'Coffee,' she replied now, with heavy emphasis, and, as if taking pity on her, he grinned.

'If you mean that—stuff—you're drinking, I'll pass,
thanks,' he said, pulling various bakery products out of the
bags. 'Josie makes filter coffee. The equipment's around here
somewhere.'

'I hope you don't expect me to make you special coffee!' exclaimed Juliet indignantly, and he arched a mocking brow in her
direction. 'What are you doing here, anyway?' she persisted, refusing to let him daunt her. 'Isn't it a bit early to be making a
social call?'

Rafe sucked in a breath. 'This is your idea of being sociable?'
He propped his lean hips against the drainer, crossed his feet at
the ankles and folded his arms. Then, regarding her with dark, assessing eyes, he added, 'Remind me to avoid you when you're
feeling touchy. Or is that tetchy?' He grimaced. 'One or the other.'

Juliet pursed her lips. 'You didn't answer my question.'

'What question was that?'

Juliet knew he knew damn well what question, but she played
along. 'I asked what you were doing here so early in the
morning. Did Lady Elinor send for you?'

Rafe looked down at the toes of his boots before answering
her. Then he said, 'In a manner of speaking,' not wanting to
explain exactly why he was here.

'Why?'

'Why what?'

'Why did she send for you?' If he could be provocative, so
could she. Then a thought occurred to her. 'She's not ill, is she?'

Rafe's lids lifted and he looked at her again with those dark,
disturbing eyes that caused such an insistently hollow ache in
the pit of her stomach. 'Not that I know of, anyway,' he
remarked. Then, casually, 'Did you have a pleasant evening?'

Juliet blew out a breath. She felt as if she'd been running fast and not getting anywhere. He was being purposely obtuse and she didn't know how to penetrate his mocking façade.

'It was—very pleasant,' she said at last, resisting the urge to expand upon her words. She took a sip of her coffee. 'Hmm, this is good.'

'Yeah, right.'

Rafe didn't believe her, but he really didn't have the time to prove it to her right now. Rubbing a hand over the incipient beard on his jawline, he straightened away from the unit and said, 'D'you want a croissant? They were made fresh this morning and I can vouch for that.'

Juliet was tempted, but she wasn't sure it would be wise to take anything from him. Her tongue circled her lips. 'Did you make them?'

Rafe gave a short laugh. 'No,' he said, for once being straight with her. 'I didn't get to bed till one a.m., so I certainly wasn't up at five o'clock making pastry.'

One o'clock! Juliet would have loved to ask what he'd been doing until that time, but she didn't have the courage to go that far. Besides, he'd probably been with some woman, and did she really want to know?

Instead, she said, 'OK,' unable to deny the lure of the delicious-smelling roll. It was so long since she'd been able to afford such a treat.

The pastry crumbled in her fingers and tiny flakes flecked her lips as she struggled to get it into her mouth. She looked incredibly sexy and Rafe knew an unexpected desire to lick the pastry from her lips with his tongue. She wasn't wearing any make-up this morning, and he sensed her mouth would be soft and wet and sweet-smelling—

Dios! He arrested his thoughts at that point. She was Cary's girlfriend, for pity's sake. What was he thinking of, allowing himself to get a hard-on when there was absolutely no chance of him easing it with her? If he had any sense, he'd keep her at arm's length.

Juliet had put down her cup to take the pastry and now she

pulled a paper towel from the roll and wiped her lips. 'That was—fantastic!' she said, and meant it. 'Thank you.'

'My pleasure,' Rafe returned, aware that she was looking at him with much less hostility now. Evidently his generosity had had the opposite effect on her and it would be fatally easy to change his mind.

But, to his relief, he heard the sounds of activity from upstairs. Josie's rooms were above the kitchen and dining room, and Rafe guessed she'd either heard his car or their voices. Probably the latter.

Keeping his tone deliberately light now, he said. 'So—what are you and Cary planning on doing today?'

Juliet picked up her cup, took a sip, and set it down again. 'I don't know.' She pulled a wry face. 'Believe it or not, before you arrived I was intending to go for a walk. Maybe along by the river.'

Rafe regarded her assessingly. 'In those boots?'

Juliet glanced down at her feet. 'They're very comfortable.'

'But not exactly waterproof,' observed Rafe drily. 'You need rubber boots. The river bank is very muddy at this time of year.'

'Oh, well…' Juliet shrugged her slim shoulders, causing her hair to bounce against her neck. 'I suppose I'll just have to confine my explorations to the garden.' She paused. 'Are you—teaching today?'

Rafe's brows drew together. 'The old lady told you that, I suppose?'

'That you teach? Yes.' Juliet frowned. 'It's not a secret, is it?'

'No.' But she could tell he didn't like the idea that they'd been talking about him. 'You'll find that Lady Elinor prefers the thought of me pursuing regular employment to making my living in some other way.'

'Painting, you mean?'

He grinned without malice and her stomach twisted in response. He was so damn attractive and she wouldn't have been human if she hadn't been aware that being single again had definite disadvantages. It was so long since she'd either had, or wanted to have, sex with a man, least of all David. But the idea of Rafe's hands on her body caused goose bumps to feather her skin.

Not that it was likely to happen, she reminded herself. Apart from the fact that he wasn't interested in her, she was supposed to be Cary's girlfriend. There was no way he was going to forget that, however much she might wish he would.

'Yeah, painting,' he said now, just as Josie came into the kitchen. Her sharp eyes took in their presence and the bakery bags lying open on the table. And Rafe found himself feeling guilty. As if the thoughts he'd been having were somehow visible on his face.

'You're up early, Miss Lawrence,' she said, addressing herself to Juliet first, and Juliet gave a rueful smile.

'It was such a lovely morning,' she said, even though she'd had no idea what it was like when she'd first got out of bed. 'I thought I might go for a walk.'

'And I delayed her,' put in Rafe pleasantly. 'She needs rubber boots and she doesn't have any.'

'What size shoes do you take, Miss Lawrence?' asked the housekeeper, bending to open what appeared to be a flue. Juliet realised then that the Aga hadn't been dead, as she'd imagined. As soon as Josie opened the vents, it roared to life again.

But they were waiting for her answer, and forcing herself to concentrate, she said, 'Um—five-and-a-half, I think.'

'Then you can borrow my boots, if you want to,' declared Josie triumphantly. She straightened, resting a hand on the curve of her spine as though it pained her. 'They're a six, but if you add a couple of pairs of socks, they should do.'

Juliet didn't know what to say. She'd never had to borrow anyone's boots before, but this was not the time to be choosy. 'That's awfully kind of you,' she said. 'And, please, call me Juliet. Yes, I'd like to borrow your boots, if you don't mind?'

CHAPTER FIVE

RAFE arrived home soon after noon. His apartment was over the small studio where he exhibited his own, and occasionally other artists' work. It had been a dream of his when he was growing up to open his own premises. And, although the rewards were small, he got a great deal of satisfaction out of it.

He'd had a class at the school where he worked part-time that morning. But this afternoon, Liv Holderness was coming to the studio so he could make some provisional sketches for her portrait. He sometimes used a camera to get a perspective on his subject. He needed to assess height and depth and the kind of lighting that would be needed. Photography was another subject he'd become fairly expert in, though painting was his first love.

In his apartment, which comprised a large living and dining area, a small kitchen, bedroom and bath, he flung off his body-warmer and went to make himself some coffee. Spooning the grounds into the filter, he was reminded of his early-morning encounter with Juliet Lawrence. Irritation stirred in his gut. Dammit, what was it about that woman that bugged him so? She'd been reasonably polite, friendly almost, but he'd behaved like a jerk.

To begin with, anyway, he amended, remembering how he'd provoked her. And, really, he'd prefer not to think about the way he'd reacted later. Letting her get under his skin had been pathetic. Apart from anything else, she was Cary's fiancée. And from what he'd learned from Lady Elinor, it didn't sound as if she'd done a decent day's work in her life.

According to the old lady, she'd been the pampered only child of a wealthy businessman. She'd gone straight from finishing-school into marriage, apparently becoming a pampered wife. The reasons the marriage hadn't worked out weren't so easy to fathom. Irreconcilable differences, he assumed, switching on the coffee-maker. Wasn't that the current jargon when couples got bored with one another and wanted to move on?

Why she would attach herself to Cary Daniels was another mystery. Unless she was one of those females who needed a masculine hand to hold. After all, she was—what?—twenty-something, with no evident desire for independence. Didn't she care that Cary went through money like a knife through butter?

Whatever, it was nothing to do with him, he reminded himself. Thank God, he had his own life and could make a comfortable living without anyone's help. That was one of the things that annoyed the old lady. Lady Elinor would have much preferred him to be like his cousin. As it was, she could rarely catch him on the raw.

He'd brought a ciabatta sandwich home with him. Shades of his father, he thought wryly. He'd always liked Italian bread. It was filled with smoked ham and cheese and he was enjoying it with his second mug of coffee when Olivia arrived. Shoving its remains into his small fridge, he put down his mug and went to answer the door.

Olivia Holderness was nothing like Juliet Lawrence. Though, once again, why he should be making a comparison annoyed the hell out of him. Just because Liv was a busty blonde, who liked to wear short skirts and high heels to draw attention to her shapely legs, was no reason to criticise her. Yet that was what he was doing, he recognised. Comparing her with a woman who might be tall and slim and classy, but didn't have half Liv's charm.

Nevertheless, he wasn't in the best of moods when he

escorted Liv downstairs again and into his studio. The place was closed to the public when he was working. Unlike some painters, Rafe didn't like an audience. Besides, any serious collectors tended to make an appointment, and Rafe's main source of income was commissioned stuff.

'I can only stay an hour,' Olivia was saying conversationally as he seated her in the chair he intended to use to get perspective. 'Bobby thinks I'm at the hairdresser's,' she added as Rafe adjusted the lights he was angling to expose her face. She giggled. 'I'm going to have to make some excuse when he notices my hair still looks the same as it did. What do you think?'

Rafe was still getting his head round the fact that 'Bobby' was Lord Robert Holderness. It was easy to forget that Liv was Lady Holderness now, despite the way she looked. She'd confided that Bobby had fallen in love with her because she was so different from his other wives. And that Rafe could readily believe.

'My hair looks all right, doesn't it?' She was persistent. 'I mean, I want it to look good in the portrait.' She giggled again. 'Imagine me having my portrait painted! I mean, who'd have thought it?'

Rafe found himself smiling. 'Who indeed?' he remarked drily, and she gave him a flirtatious look.

'You don't think I'm silly?'

'No. Why would I? You're paying me very well and I need the work.'

'Now, I happen to know that's not true.' Olivia pressed her lips together thoughtfully for a moment. 'Poppy—that's Poppy Gibson,' she added, mentioning the name of the wife of the local member of parliament, 'she told me she'd been at your reception last week and you'd been offered quite a few commissions. I just wish Bobby and I had been able to come. But he wasn't feeling so good—he has blood pressure, you know—and I couldn't leave him on his own, could I?'

'Definitely not.'

'And you think my hair looks all right?' She touched the straightened strands that dipped provocatively to the exposed curve of her breast. 'Connie—that's Conrad Samuels at Batik in Bodmin—thinks I suit this colour. But I'm not sure. I'm a natural blonde, you know?'

'Yeah, right.' Rafe was sarcastic. He'd known her long enough to be aware that her hair was naturally brown. Like Juliet's, he thought, though without the shine he'd noticed just that morning. He scowled. God, he had to get that woman out of his head.

'There's no need to look like that.' Olivia had taken his scowl for a response to what she'd been saying. 'Anyway, Bobby thinks I'm a natural blonde and that's what matters.'

'Does he?' Rafe's mouth quirked up at the corners. 'Now, that surprises me.'

'You devil!' Olivia jumped up from the chair and punched his arm. 'I bet you can't remember what I look like. It was dark that night and you were—well—'

'Drunk,' supplied Rafe drily, pushing her back onto the seat. 'Now, sit still, will you? We're wasting your time and mine.'

'But it was good, wasn't it?' Olivia was determined to continue their conversation. 'I remember waking up the next morning and thinking I was in love.'

'In lust more like,' countered Rafe, not wanting to have this conversation. His association with Liv had been short and not especially sweet. He remembered waking up with a hangover. Much like the one he'd got this morning, he thought, but with a legitimate cause.

'But we were good together,' she persisted. And when he didn't answer, she shook her head in annoyance. 'Rafe, are you listening to me?'

He'd just lined up his camera when she shifted and ruined the shot. 'I'm listening,' he said through his teeth. 'But I'm trying to work here. If you'd wanted to chat, you should have asked me out for a drink.'

Olivia's jaw jutted. 'I'm sorry if I'm being a nuisance,' she said huffily, and Rafe only just managed to suppress his groan.

'You're not a nuisance,' he assured her. 'Take no notice of me. I had too many glasses of wine last night.'

'Wine?' Olivia arched neatly plucked brows. 'Since when do you drink wine, Rafe?'

'Since I discovered it's a cheaper analgesic than Scotch,' he informed her flatly. Then, after studying her through the lens of his camera for a moment. 'Are you sure about this? You really think your husband will approve?'

'Me being painted in the nude?' Olivia looked smug. 'Oh, yes. Bobby's nuts about my body.'

'OK.' Rafe knew better than to argue, but he hoped she was right. 'So—you want the whole shebang? Belly button, boobs and butt?'

Olivia grimaced at him. 'You have such a charming way of putting it.' She folded her hands in her lap, tugging at the hem of her skirt, pretending that she didn't want him to notice her legs. And they were very attractive legs, Rafe had to admit. He hoped he could do them justice.

'Fine.'

He adjusted the camera again, taking several shots from different angles. This was useful to learn the structure of her face, the shape of her head, the curve of her neck. He was aware of her watching him, following his movements with her eyes, a look of anticipation on her face. And wondered, not for the first time, if accepting this commission had been entirely wise.

'OK,' he said after a few minutes, stowing the camera on a side-table and tugging a velvet couch into the middle of the floor. 'Come and make yourself comfortable on this. I want to make a few sketches, just to get an idea of how it's going to look.'

Olivia got immediately to her feet. 'Shall I take all my clothes off?' she asked eagerly, her fingers going to the buttons of her skirt.

'No!' Rafe's response was emphatic and Olivia gave him a resentful look. 'That is,' he hastened on in an effort to redeem himself, 'it's not necessary today. These are just preliminary sketches. I'll fill in the details later. It's amazing how much can be done without the subject's participation.'

Olivia pouted. 'Won't I have to take my clothes off at all?'

'Not initially, no.' Rafe sighed. 'You should be grateful. This is a draughty old place at the best of times.'

'I suppose.' But Olivia still looked disappointed and Rafe realised she'd wanted to strip for him. Oh, God, he thought, surely the old lady wasn't going to be proved right. When Lady Elinor had poured scorn on the credentials of the new Lady Holderness, perhaps he should have listened...

Juliet spent a pleasant couple of hours trudging along the river bank. Upstream, she'd discovered that it wasn't a particularly wide river. Indeed, in places the trees growing on the opposite bank hung so far across the water that they almost touched those on this side. The ground, as Rafe had warned her, was thick with mulch, the accumulation of last autumn's windfall and months of heavy rain.

The air near the estuary was salty, but further upstream it was overlaid with the smell of rotting vegetation. Yet, spring was definitely stirring. She wished she knew more about the wild flowers that grew in such profusion along the stream.

When she got back to the house, she discovered that Cary and his grandmother were having morning coffee in the conservatory. Juliet, who'd changed out of Josie's boots in the mudroom, would have preferred to hurry upstairs and tidy herself before meeting her hostess again. But Cary had evidently been looking out for her and he came to the door of the morning room as she was hastening across the hall.

'Where've you been?' he asked at once, just as he'd done the evening before. 'If you'd planned on going out, you might have told me.'

'I didn't exactly plan it,' said Juliet, not wanting to get into how she had come to go out in the first place. She ran a hand over her tumbled hair. 'I just went for a walk, that's all. And, as you can tell, the wind was fairly strong.'

'Even so, you should have told me,' Cary insisted in a hushed voice. 'I'd have appreciated the chance to get a breath of fresh air after the atmosphere in this mausoleum.'

'I'm sorry.'

'Well, never mind. You're here now. Come on in. We're having coffee in the conservatory.'

'Oh, well—I was just going to tidy up,' she protested, but Cary didn't seem to care about her feelings. Or her appearance, for that matter.

'Later,' he said, taking hold of her elbow and guiding her into the morning room. 'Here, take off your coat. We don't want the old girl thinking you were about to make a break for it.'

'As if!'

Juliet gave him an impatient look, but Cary was intent on his objective. 'Here she is, Grandmama!' he exclaimed triumphantly, leading her into the conservatory. 'I thought she was still in bed, but apparently she's been for a walk.'

Before Juliet could speak, however, Hitchins came hurtling across the floor. He'd apparently been sleeping in his basket, as usual, but Cary's loud voice had disturbed him. As before, he made straight for Cary's trouser leg, and she could see his frustration at not being able to do anything about it.

'Hey…' With a smile of greeting for Lady Elinor, Juliet bent and detached the Pekinese from his quarry. Evidently he had no quarrel with her, because when she lifted him into her arms he immediately licked her chin. 'Now, you won't get around me that way,' she said, even though she was touched by the little dog's affection. 'That was naughty. We don't go around biting people, do we? It's not polite.'

The old lady had been watching this exchange with some interest. 'He likes you, Miss Lawrence,' she said. 'He's usually a good judge of character, I find.'

Which Cary evidently didn't find easy to deal with. The smug smile he'd been wearing while Juliet was holding the dog now gave way to a petulant scowl. But he didn't say anything, she noticed. He just shoved his hands in his trouser pockets and pretended he hadn't understood what the old lady was saying.

Deciding it was up to her to answer, Juliet scratched the dog beneath his chin. 'I used to have a golden retriever,' she said. 'When I was much younger. And, please—my name is Juliet. I'd be happy if you'd use it.'

'Juliet.' Lady Elinor nodded and pointed to the wickerwork armchair adjacent to her own with her cane. 'Come and sit down, Juliet. And I think you can put Hitchins down, too. If Cary will just stop waffling about, the dog will simply ignore him.'

'I'm not waffling about, Grandmama.' Cary's tone was defensive, if anything. He paused. 'Shall I go and ask Josie for another cup for Juliet? Then you and she can have a nice chat.'

Juliet, who'd just sat down, raised horrified eyes to his face. But there was nothing she could say that wouldn't sound rude, and he knew it.

'Yes, go and make yourself useful, Cary,' his grandmother agreed, which once again caused him some irritation, Juliet could see. 'And bring a fresh pot of coffee when you come back. It will save Josie's legs.'

'I'm not a servant, Grandmama.'

For once he seemed prepared to stick up for himself, but Lady Elinor soon put him straight. 'Nor is Josie,' she retorted, waving her cane like a magic wand. 'Off you go. And don't be too long.'

To Juliet's amazement, Cary didn't argue. He merely inclined his head before walking meekly to the door. It astonished her that he'd let the old lady walk all over him. Was he prepared to take any amount of humiliation just to ensure his inheritance? It seemed so.

'And did you enjoy your walk?' asked Lady Elinor as soon as Cary was out of earshot, and Juliet nodded.

'Very much.'

'Where did you go? Along the river bank? Didn't Josie warn you it's very wet at this time of year?'

'Um—Mr Marchese did, actually.'

'Rafe?' The old lady frowned. 'Rafe was here?'

Juliet felt the colour entering her cheeks. 'Yes. I think he brought some—things—for Mrs Morgan. I was up early and I happened to be in the kitchen when he arrived.'

'Ah.' Lady Elinor looked thoughtful. 'So—what is your opinion of Rafe?'

'Oh…' Juliet was nonplussed. She didn't even want to think about Cary's cousin. 'He—er—he seems very nice. Does he live near here?'

Lady Elinor gave a short laugh. 'My dear, there is nothing remotely nice about my eldest grandson. Aggravating, provocative, fascinating, even. But not *nice*. That is such a namby-pamby word.'

Juliet pressed her lips together. 'He's—not much like Cary, is he?'

'No. Thank God!' The old lady reached for her cup of coffee and took a drink before continuing, 'So—I gather Rafe didn't tell you where he lives.'

'No.' Juliet shook her head. And then, wanting to explain herself, 'We didn't talk for long.'

'Well, he lives in Polgellin Bay. Above his studio, actually. Though he works at a school in Bodmin, as I believe I told you before.'

Juliet nodded. Then, in an effort to keep the conversation moving, 'Do you have any of his paintings, Lady Elinor?'

There was silence for a short while and Juliet was beginning to wonder if she'd said the wrong thing, when the old lady answered her. 'Rafe doesn't believe I'm interested in his work,' she said, somewhat obliquely. 'But I'd be interested to hear your opinion, Juliet.'

Like that was going to happen, thought Juliet wryly. Even if Rafe's studio were open to the public, that was the last place Cary would take her.

'Have you and Cary set a date for the wedding?'

The question was so unexpected after what they'd been discussing, Juliet was briefly at a loss for words. Then, 'Oh, no. We—er—we've just got engaged. We're not thinking of getting married for some time.'

'I thought not.'

The old lady's words were disturbing and, realising Cary wouldn't thank her if she created doubts in his grandmother's mind, Juliet hurried on. 'Maybe—maybe we'll think about it later in the year.'

'You're not wearing a ring.' Lady Elinor was far too shrewd not to have noticed.

'No.' Juliet had no answer for that either, and she wished Cary were here to share the grief.

'I imagine my grandson is fairly short of funds, as usual,' the old lady continued. 'Remind me to look in my jewellery box, Juliet. I may have just the ring for you to wear.'

Oh, God!

Juliet couldn't meet her eyes. This was so much worse than anything she could have anticipated. Imagining herself wearing a ring that Lady Elinor might once have worn when she was a young woman was mortifying. She'd never felt so despicable in her life.

It was hardly a relief to hear Cary coming back. The damage had been done, and there was no way her 'fiancé' was going to turn the old lady down. Indeed, as soon as they got back to London he'd probably take the ring and have it valued. If it was worth more than a few pounds, she doubted Lady Elinor would see it again.

Naturally, his grandmother told him of her suggestion. 'As I'm giving a small dinner party tomorrow evening to celebrate your engagement, I can hardly have Juliet turning up without an engagement ring, can I?'

'You're a brick, Grandmama!' exclaimed Cary at once, giving her an enthusiastic hug that almost caused Hitchins to renew hostilities. 'What would we do without you?'

CHAPTER SIX

JULIET was getting ready for dinner when Josie tapped at her door.

At first she was tempted to ignore it, to pretend she hadn't heard the knock. She was uneasily aware that it could be Cary. And while he knew that her being here was simply as a favour to him——OK, he was paying her to pretend to be his fiancée, but that was all——no one else did. And she didn't altogether trust him not to try and take advantage of it. Particularly after what had happened that afternoon.

Juliet had hoped that Lady Elinor might forget about her offer to give her a ring. But, immediately after lunch, she'd asked Josie to bring her jewellery box and she'd spent the next half-hour poring over its contents.

Juliet had been aware that Cary had been dying to see what was in the velvet-lidded box his grandmother guarded so fiercely. But the old lady had made sure he was sitting at the opposite end of the table while she examined its contents. A man shouldn't be too curious, she'd told him. He'd see the rings she'd chosen for Juliet to choose from in the fullness of time.

Juliet herself hadn't wanted to have any part of it, but in that she'd had no choice. Even without Cary's arm lying possessively about her shoulders, Lady Elinor had expected her to be involved, and that was that.

The rings the old lady had eventually laid out on the crisp linen tablecloth sparkled in the sunlight. They were obviously very old, but remarkably contemporary in design. There was a diamond solitaire, an emerald dress ring, surrounded by rose-cut diamonds, and a single ruby, set in a circle of what Juliet suspected were semi-precious gems.

Juliet heard Cary's greedy intake of breath when he saw the rings. She was almost able to guess what he was thinking, could hear the calculator in his brain working out their exact value to him.

'Which do you find appealing, Juliet?' Lady Elinor asked, inviting her to sit beside her. 'As you can see, they're all practically antique. The diamond belonged to my grandmother, the emerald was a gift to my mother from the Brazilian cultural attaché, while the ruby was given to me when I was presented at court.'

Juliet shook her head. 'They're all very beautiful.'

'Yes, they are.' Cary spoke in her ear, apparently unable to resist joining them and picking up the diamond solitaire. She'd seen him pretending to admire the ring, when in actual fact he'd been assessing its potential. 'This is awfully kind of you, Grandmama. I know both Juliet and I are very grateful, aren't we, darling?'

Juliet's smile was forced as she looked up at him. 'Very,' she agreed through clenched teeth. Then she whisked the diamond out of his hand and set it back on the cloth. 'I don't know which to choose.'

'Oh, I think the solitaire is the most appropriate,' Cary declared tightly. 'It looks the most like an engagement ring to me.'

It would, Juliet thought scornfully, knowing exactly how his mind was working. 'Actually,' she said, picking up the ruby, 'I think this is the one I like best.'

'But—'

'I'm sure you'd agree that, as Juliet is going to wear the ring, she should be the one to make the decision,' his grandmother had interposed smoothly. 'I must say, I like the ruby myself. It's a Burmese stone and it's flawless.'

And small, Juliet had reflected gratefully before going for

her shower. She would not be a party to Cary's taking his grandmother for every penny he could get.

Now, hearing someone at the door, she wondered if he'd decided to challenge her on it. She knew he hadn't been pleased when they'd left the dining room but, pleading tiredness, she'd been able to avoid a confrontation. Almost two days over, she thought, wrapping her silk robe tightly about her. She just had to get over tomorrow and then they'd be heading home.

But there was still tonight and, pulling open the door, she prepared herself to face his wrath. After all, he'd had all afternoon to feed his resentment, and something told her Cary wasn't the type of man to forget a grievance.

So she was pleasantly surprised when she saw who her visitor was, even though Josie looked rather harassed. 'Oh, Miss Lawrence,' she said, apparently forgetting that Juliet had asked her to use her first name, 'I was beginning to think you and Mr Cary must have gone out.'

'Oh—no. I was just in the bathroom.' Juliet felt guilty now for keeping the old woman waiting. 'Is something wrong?'

'Well—just a hiccough.'

Josie was decidedly flustered, and although Juliet suspected she wouldn't take her up on it she invited the housekeeper into the room and offered her a seat. In fact, the woman seemed grateful for her consideration, perching on a chair by the door and twisting her hands together in her lap.

'It's just—well, Lady Elinor won't be joining you for dinner this evening,' she said. 'She's not at all well. I've had to call Dr Charteris.'

Juliet was genuinely concerned. 'Is there anything I can do?'

'I doubt it.' Josie pulled a face. 'She hates being incapacitated. And she wouldn't thank you for visiting her right now, I can tell you. She's not going to be pleased with me when she hears I've called the doctor as it is.'

'But, if she's not well—'

'I know.' Josie grimaced. 'But that's the way she is.' She

paused. 'Anyway, I was wondering whether you and Mr Cary would mind having a cold meal this evening? What with the doctor coming and all—'

'Of course.' Juliet couldn't let her go on. 'Don't worry about us, Mrs Morgan. A sandwich would do.'

'Oh, I don't think Mr Cary would agree—'

'I'll make sure that Mr Cary agrees,' Juliet assured her firmly, ignoring the fact that only minutes before she'd been feeling apprehensive of seeing him again. 'Perhaps I could help you?'

Josie looked at her, wide-eyed. 'I don't think Lady Elinor would approve of that.'

'Lady Elinor doesn't need to know, does she?' Juliet smiled encouragingly. 'Actually, I'd enjoy it.'

Josie got to her feet again. 'I don't know what to say, Miss Lawrence.'

'You can start by calling me Juliet,' Juliet told her firmly. 'Now—when is the doctor due?'

About three-quarters of an hour later, Juliet was in the kitchen grating cheese when Cary put his head round the door.

'Oh, there you are!' he exclaimed, not noticing what she was doing for a moment. 'You must be the most elusive woman I've ever met. You're always disappearing somewh— What the hell are you doing?'

Juliet put down the grater. 'What does it look like I'm doing?'

'It looks as if you're doing Josie's job,' he retorted coldly. 'Where is she? Wasting time, as usual?'

'I don't think Josie has any time to waste,' said Juliet tersely. 'Have you any idea how much work is entailed in running a place like this? No, I thought not.'

Cary scowled. 'I still don't understand what you're doing here. Do you want the old girl to think I'm marrying a scrubber?'

Juliet caught her breath. 'No one's likely to think that but you, Cary. And what's wrong with being a scrubber anyway? It's a job of work, isn't it, and in my situation beggars can't be choosers.'

'Oh, come off it. You wouldn't dream of cleaning people's houses for a living. And, besides, it's only an expression. What I really meant was, I don't think Grandmama would approve of her guest preparing her own dinner.'

'Your grandmother isn't well,' said Juliet shortly. 'Didn't Josie tell you? She's had to call the doctor.'

'Charteris.' Cary said the man's name almost consideringly. Then, 'No sweat! But no. No one told me anything.'

Juliet frowned, suddenly noticing that Cary was still wearing the grey trousers and tweed jacket he'd been wearing that afternoon. 'What have you been doing?'

'Oh…' Cary looked a little furtive now. 'This and that.' And then, as if he had something of importance to tell her, he let the door close behind him and came across to the table where she was working. 'Actually,' he went on in a low voice, 'I've been checking the books.'

'The books?' Juliet looked confused.

'The estate books,' whispered Cary, his excitement barely controlled. 'God, you'll never believe what I found!'

Distaste showed on Juliet's face, but she couldn't help the obvious question, 'Did your grandmother ask you to look at them?'

'The old girl?' Cary scoffed. 'Not likely.'

'So she doesn't know what you've been doing?'

'No.' Cary was impatient. 'But never mind that now, I saw this letter—'

'I don't think you should be reading your grandmother's correspondence,' said Juliet severely. 'Her letters are private.'

'Oh, for pity's sake.' Cary snorted. 'She lets that bastard, Marchese, keep her accounts.'

'Don't call him that.'

'Oh, hello, are you a fan of his, too?'

'No.' But Juliet knew she'd gone red. 'I just don't think you should call him that.'

'Yeah, right.' Cary was scornful. 'Anyway, forget about him. The old girl's had an offer for Tregellin. Can you believe that?

I doubt if even that—Marchese knows about it. Some property developer from Bristol wants to buy the house, the farms, everything. He wants to build an estate of luxury homes on the site, with a golf course, clubhouse, the whole works. The offer's probably worth millions!'

Juliet stared at him in dismay. 'You're not serious!'

'I am.'

'I can't believe that Lady Elinor would consider selling out to a developer.'

'Well, of course she wouldn't!' exclaimed Cary irritably. 'That's why I've never heard about it. The offer was made months ago. My guess is, she rejected it outright.'

'Thank goodness.'

Juliet's response was heartfelt. She might have only been here a couple of days, but she already cared about the place. The house might need renovating and she was sure it fairly devoured the cash for its upkeep, but its position was incomparable. She shuddered at the thought of a string of wealthy investors buying second homes on the land where the house and grounds used to be, polluting the air with their gas-guzzling cars and frightening the birds away.

'What do you mean, thank goodness?' Cary was impatient. 'It's the chance of a lifetime. I wouldn't turn it down. I'd grab it with both hands.'

'Which is probably why you haven't heard about it.' Juliet was scathing. 'And you haven't even asked how your grandmother is. She could be dying for all you know.'

'No such luck,' muttered Cary, barely audibly, but Juliet heard him and her lip curled in contempt. 'Anyway, what are you doing?' he demanded, changing the subject. 'Playing housemaid?'

'I'm helping Josie,' retorted Juliet, returning to her grating. 'With your grandmother being unwell, she asked if we'd mind having a cold meal tonight, but I thought I might improve on that. What do you think?'

'You're making the meal?' Cary was aghast. 'You're not a cook!'

'No.' Juliet conceded the fact. 'But I found some kidneys in the fridge and I'm planning on sautéing them with some bacon. I thought we might have baked potatoes, too, topped with grated cheese. Does that sound good to you?'

Cary grimaced. 'Kidneys! I don't eat offal!'

You would if your grandmother offered it, thought Juliet irritably, but she held her tongue. 'So—you'll have sandwiches, right?'

'Sandwiches!' Cary gave her a scornful look. 'You have got to be joking.' He paused. 'How about going out?'

'Going out?'

'Yeah. We could go into Bodmin, meet up with some friends of mine, find a club, get something to eat there. They might even have a casino. What about it?'

'What about your grandmother?'

'Oh, please.' Cary groaned. 'She won't want to see me.' Then he frowned. 'Where's your ring?'

'In my pocket.' She was wearing navy linen trousers this evening with a warm pink angora sweater, whose V neckline was lower than she could have wished. She shook her head. 'Don't you ever think about anything else but money?'

'Give me a break.' Cary turned towards the door. 'So that's a no, is it? You're not coming?'

'Correct.'

Juliet refused to look at him, and with a grunt of resignation he left the kitchen. She half hoped he might change his mind and go and see his grandmother, but a few minutes later she heard the sound of a car being started and then the distant roar of the engine as he drove away.

Dammit!

She didn't usually swear, but Cary's selfishness really got to her. She wanted to put down the grater and abandon any attempt at making a meal.

But a few minutes later, when Josie came into the room, the

smell of cooking food had her wrinkling her nose with pleasure. 'Oh, Miss—Juliet—you didn't have to do this.'

'Why not?' Juliet smiled at her. 'I imagine Lady Elinor can eat something, can't she? Kidneys are supposed to be good for the digestion, I believe.'

Josie came to squeeze her arm. 'You're a kind girl,' she said fiercely. 'Who'd have thought Mr Cary would find himself a nice girl like you?'

'Who'd have thought it?' agreed Juliet drily, but she kept her real feelings to herself.

With Josie's approval, Juliet ate her supper in the conservatory. She did consider taking her tray upstairs, but now that Cary had gone out she felt more at ease and the conservatory was still warm after being bathed in sunshine for most of the day.

She was pushing a slightly burned kidney round her plate when she became aware that she had company. The conservatory was lit by patio lights, only a couple of which were actually illuminated, and she got quite a start when she saw a tall dark figure standing in the doorway to the morning room.

'Hi,' said her visitor, making no attempt to come further into the room. 'Josie said I'd find you here.'

Juliet took a steadying breath. 'Were you looking for me?'

'I came to see the old lady,' Rafe corrected her drily. 'Josie rang and told me she'd called the doctor.'

'Ah.' Juliet nodded. Despite her reservations about him, she was fairly sure that Rafe thought more of his grandmother than Cary ever had. 'So—how is she tonight?'

'Frustrated.' Rafe propped a shoulder against the frame of the door. 'She dislikes having Charteris telling her to look after herself.'

'But she should.' Juliet didn't know whether to get to her feet or stay where she was. 'And if there's anything I can do to help…'

Rafe inclined his head. He was wearing black pleated trousers this evening and a white silk shirt. The cuffs of his shirt were rolled back to his elbows, and her eyes were drawn to the contrast between the fabric and the dark tan of his skin. She wondered if he'd been planning on going out when Josie phoned. Whether he'd had a date with some young woman he was interested in.

'In the normal way, she doesn't have a problem,' Rafe said at last, aware that his own motive for coming to find Juliet was hardly commendable. When the old lady had told him what had happened, that their visitor had made a meal for them all, he'd felt a compelling desire to thank her. But now, standing here, looking at the attractive picture she made in the lamplight, he wondered if gratitude had really been at the top of his list.

'You mean you think our being here might be too much for her?' Juliet had interpreted his words to mean that she and Cary were the real reason Lady Elinor had had to take to her bed.

'No.' Rafe shook his head. 'She had a bad dose of flu in February. Charteris warned her to take things easy for a while, but you must have realised by now that the old lady doesn't play by anyone's rules but her own.'

Juliet frowned. 'Are you worried about her?'

'No more than usual.' Rafe's tone was dry. 'By the way, she asked me to tell you, the kidneys were delicious.'

Juliet's cheeks turned a becoming shade of pink. 'She didn't really say that.'

'She did.' Rafe hesitated a moment and then left the door and walked slowly across the tiled floor. He knew he was tempting the devil by being here, but Josie had also told him that Cary had gone out and he enjoyed baiting his fiancée. She was such an easy target. 'So where's the boy wonder this evening?' he asked casually, pausing beside her chair. 'Checking out the local talent?'

'No!' Juliet had hoped they could have a conversation without resorting to sarcasm. 'He's gone into Bodmin to meet some friends, I believe. If it's any business of yours.'

Rafe dropped down into the chair opposite her, and she immediately felt as if the room was too small. Or perhaps it was just that he was too close, the cooling atmosphere in the conservatory making her overly aware of his heat.

'So why didn't you go with him?' he asked, spreading his thighs and allowing his hands to hang loosely between his knees. 'Or didn't he ask you?'

'He asked me!' Juliet was defensive, even though she was telling the truth. 'I didn't want to go out.'

Rafe's dark brows formed a V, but he didn't argue with her. Instead he contented himself with just looking at her, apparently waiting for her to say something else. He had the unnerving ability to create tension between them when she had no earthly reason to be apprehensive of him. Heavens, she'd hoped this morning that he was beginning to accept her, but now she sensed another attitude entirely.

And, thinking of the morning, she finally thought of something she could say. 'I—er—I enjoyed my walk,' she said, trying to control the breathy element in her voice. 'This morning, I mean. And—and you were right about it being wet. Without Mrs Morgan's boots, my feet would have been soaked to the skin.'

Rafe's eyes narrowed on her suddenly animated face. He knew she was nervous of him. He'd sensed that from the first time he'd met her, but he couldn't decide whether it was a sexual awareness or something else. One thing was certain—she didn't act like any divorced woman he'd ever known. She seemed far too innocent in his opinion, although again he could be wrong. It might all be an act gauged to arouse his sympathy. Despite his reservations, he was tempted to find out.

'How long have you and Cary been engaged?' he asked, without warning, and Juliet looked momentarily like a rabbit caught in the headlights of his car.

'Um—a few weeks,' she said vaguely. Then, as if inspired, 'We've known one another since we were children.'

'Yeah, I know that.' Rafe smoothed one lean brown hand over his knee. 'The old lady told me.'

'Lady Elinor tells you a lot.'

The words were out before she could prevent them and Rafe gave her a wry smile before saying, 'Does that bother you?'

'Of course not.' Juliet swallowed. 'Obviously, you're very close to her.'

Rafe shook his head. 'I doubt if the old lady is close to anyone. Except Josie, maybe.'

'That's not true.'

'You don't think she's close to Cary, do you?'

'He's her grandson.' Juliet was defensive again.

'He's also a selfish creep. Even you must know that.'

Juliet's lips parted and she got jerkily to her feet. 'You have no right to say things like that to me!'

'No?' To her dismay, Rafe stood also, and although she was a tall girl, she still had to tilt her head to look up at him. 'You're not going to tell me that with your experience you can't recognise his faults? I thought they must be part of his charm.'

Juliet gasped. 'That's insulting!'

Rafe knew he had gone too far, but he couldn't seem to control this totally negative desire to provoke her. 'How have I insulted you? By assuming that, as you've been married before you must have some experience of men? Or by doubting Cary's charm?'

'You know what you said,' she retorted, stung into retaliation. 'Is that what you tell Lady Elinor? That—that Cary's a selfish— what you said?'

'A creep! I said he was a creep, and he is,' said Rafe harshly, but he was aware she'd scraped a nerve. 'And if you think I need to tell the old lady that, then you don't know her at all.'

'I don't.' But Juliet knew her words had been as unforgivable as his. However, she couldn't back down now. 'I don't know her or you,' she added tersely. 'If you'll excuse me, I'd like to take my tray back to the kitchen.'

'And if I won't? Excuse you, I mean?' Rafe stepped in front of the table where she'd left the remains of her meal. 'We haven't finished our conversation.'

'I have,' said Juliet, aware that the anger she'd summoned so bravely was rapidly draining away. She held up her head, though she avoided those dark, disturbing eyes. 'Why are you doing this, Mr Marchese? You don't even like me.'

Rafe almost gasped. 'I didn't say that.'

'You didn't have to.' Juliet decided to abandon her plan to return the tray, but she didn't feel she could just storm out of the room. 'If I've offended you, Mr Marchese, I'm sorry. For some reason, we seem to rub one another up the wrong way.'

Rafe wanted to groan with frustration. Her choice of words was so formal, so *prim*. God, he was the one who ought to retract his words. She was hopelessly inexperienced for her age. What kind of a man had she married? What kind of a marriage had it been?

Later on, he told himself he hadn't intended to touch her. He'd wanted to provoke her, yeah; to get her to shed that prissy way of talking to him and behave like any other woman of his acquaintance. But she was still Cary's fiancée, for pity's sake, and he had some sense of honour beneath the tough exterior he showed to the world. Besides, he'd never seduced another man's woman, and he'd had no intention of doing so now.

Yet he stopped her when she would have turned away from him, imprisoned her beside him with one slightly cruel hand about her wrist. And then, when she'd stared up at him with shocked, indignant eyes, he'd cupped her nape with his free hand and brought her mouth to his.

CHAPTER SEVEN

JULIET huddled under the covers of her bed knowing she'd done something totally stupid. No matter how she tried to justify what had happened, nothing could alter the fact that she was supposed to be Cary's fiancée and she'd let Rafe Marchese kiss her.

Kiss her!

Was that really all he'd done? Was that a genuine description of his hungry possession of her mouth? Dear God, she felt as if he'd ravaged her. How else to explain the searching pressure of his tongue against her teeth, the pitiful defence she'd put up before she'd let him have his way with her?

Well, to be honest, he hadn't actually had his way with her, she reassured herself. He'd kissed her, yes; he'd thrust his tongue down her throat. He'd even pushed his leg between hers to bring her closer. But he hadn't actually touched her intimately. Not really. Even if she was still wet and throbbing from her own pathetic arousal.

How on earth had it happened? she asked herself for the umpteenth time. One minute she'd been preparing a dignified exit, and the next he'd grabbed her and pulled her into his arms. Why hadn't she stopped him? Why hadn't she slapped him or said something to wipe that predatory look off his face? Why had she behaved as if he held all the cards?

But, heavens, her limbs had turned to jelly as soon as he'd put his arms around her. He'd held her so close to him that she'd felt the taut muscles of his thighs against her legs. Her breasts had been crushed against his chest in a way that must have left him in no doubt as to their reaction, and when his hand had cupped her bottom she'd felt an unfamiliar wetness in her pants.

Touching her breasts now, she discovered they were still hot and heavy. Much like his erection, she remembered, shivering convulsively. He'd felt so big, so powerful, pushing against her stomach with an insistence she'd never experienced before. David had made love to her, but she'd never responded so violently. And, God help her, she'd wanted Rafe to show her exactly how satisfying making love with him might be.

Which was unforgivable on all counts. What was wrong with her, for goodness' sake? What had happened to the cool, controlled individual she'd always believed herself to be? Heavens, she hadn't even caused a scene when David had walked out on her. Was that because she'd felt she deserved it or because she hadn't really cared?

And why was she having this crisis of identity now? Just when she was supposed to behave with the style and confidence for which she'd once been famous? What was it about Rafe Marchese that made her act in a way that was totally unfamiliar to her? What she did know was that if Rafe had been the one to ask her to *act* as his fiancée, she'd be in deep trouble now.

Even deeper than the trouble she was already in, she acknowledged. Dear heaven, the man had only kissed her and already she was a quivering wreck.

Looking back, from the safety of her bed, Juliet wondered now what might have happened if Josie hadn't interrupted them. Fortunately they'd heard her footsteps as she crossed the hall, and by the time she'd appeared in the doorway Rafe had put half the width of the conservatory between them. But she was sure he must have been glad of the comparative darkness to conceal his frustration. Juliet knew she'd been flushed and breathless, limp with relief or disappointment. She wasn't sure which.

* * *

On Saturday morning, Cary suggested they take a trip into Polgellin Bay.

Juliet had no idea what time he'd returned the night before and she didn't really care, but she did think he ought to spend some time with his grandmother instead of going out again.

'Oh, she's OK,' he said when she broached the subject with him. 'I went to see her earlier on and she said she was feeling much better.'

Juliet wasn't sure whether this was the truth or not, but her own conscience was still pricking her and she didn't feel she had the right to criticise Cary's behaviour when her own was so much less than perfect. But she suspected his information had come from Josie. When she'd seen Lady Elinor earlier, she'd said nothing about her grandson. Only Rafe.

The old lady had sent word with Josie that she'd like to speak to Juliet after breakfast. She'd been eating in the dining room. Cary hadn't come down yet, and, although Juliet had offered to have her meal in the kitchen with the housekeeper, Josie had been adamant.

'We don't want you going away with the idea that a visit to Tregellin means doing for yourself,' she'd declared firmly. 'Now, you sit yourself at the table, and I'll fetch you some coffee and toast.'

It was when Josie came back to see if Juliet needed anything else that she delivered Lady Elinor's summons. 'She'll be getting up later on,' she confided, 'but I think she's concerned that you might feel you have to hang about here until she appears. She's feeling much better this morning. Quite looking forward to the dinner party tonight. Now, I'll show you to her room. She should have finished her breakfast by now.'

Lady Elinor lay propped on lace-edged pillows in a bed as big, if not bigger, than the one Juliet had slept in. Her room was huge, too, with the kind of antique furniture Juliet had only ever seen in a saleroom. But for all its faded grandeur, there was something impressive about it, and the view from the windows was worth a king's ransom.

Or a developer's fortune, thought Juliet unwillingly, remembering what Cary had told her. If she were Lady Elinor, she'd do everything she could to hang on to this place. It wasn't just a house. It was a family tradition.

'You saw Rafe last night.'

After giving an impatient response to Juliet's concerned questions about her health, Lady Elinor got straight to the point.

'Um—yes.' Juliet hoped her face wasn't as revealing as her uncertain stomach. Already the coffee she'd had for breakfast was threatening to return. 'I believe you spoke to him, too.'

'Well, of course. He came to see me.' The old lady was complacent. 'He worries about me. Or so he says.'

'I'm sure we were all concerned about you yesterday evening,' said Juliet carefully. Dammit, she owed Cary her support. 'Rafe—Rafe said you'd had flu earlier in the year and perhaps you were doing too much.'

'Rafe should keep his opinions to himself,' retorted Lady Elinor shortly. 'Who was it that called Charteris? Was it him?'

'No, I think that was Josie,' said Juliet, hoping she wasn't treading on anyone's toes. Then, appealingly, 'It's always best to have a professional judgement.'

'Humph.' The old lady regarded her dourly. 'It comes to something when you can't make a decision for yourself.' She frowned and then changed the subject entirely. 'Did you tell Rafe I'd given you a ring?'

Juliet caught her breath. 'No.'

'Why not?' She frowned. 'I'm surprised he didn't ask you about it.'

Juliet moistened her lips. 'Well, actually, I wasn't wearing it.' She paused and when it became apparent that something more was required, she added awkwardly, 'I'd put it in my pocket while I was helping Mrs Morgan prepare supper, and I'm afraid I forgot about it. Until—until later.'

Until she'd escaped from the conservatory, actually. Uneasily she remembered running up the stairs, scolding herself for what had happened, feeling like a scarlet woman. She'd pulled the ring out of her pocket then and rammed it onto her finger. As if it might act as some kind of talisman and erase the mistakes she'd made.

It hadn't, of course. But its glowing heart had sobered her. Reminded her that whatever happened here, she was not at all what either Rafe—or Lady Elinor—believed her to be.

'I see.' If she hadn't been feeling so ashamed, Juliet might have wondered at the faintly smug gleam that entered the old lady's eyes at her words. 'Well, you're wearing it this morning.'

'Oh—yes.' Juliet couldn't prevent the index finger of her right hand from circling the flawless stone. 'It's so beautiful! Naturally I'll give it back before we leave.'

'Give it back?' Lady Elinor stared at her disapprovingly. 'Of course you won't give it back. The ring is yours.'

'But—' The words stuck in her throat but Juliet knew she had to say them. 'If—when—Cary buys me an engagement ring, I won't need it any more.'

'You don't like it?'

'Of course I like it.'

'Then we'll hear no more about it.' The old lady flapped a dismissive hand. 'It pleases me to think that my grandson's wife will wear the ring. That in time she'll pass it on to her granddaughter. Now, I don't want you spending the day worrying about me. Get out and enjoy yourselves. I'll see you later.'

And that was how Juliet had had to leave it. But she wasn't happy about the situation and she determined that when her 'engagement' to Cary ended, she'd return the ring to Lady Elinor with her gratitude.

Now, aware that Cary was still waiting for an answer to his invitation, Juliet gave in. If they were out of the house for a few hours, Lady Elinor would have time to get more rest. Besides, she would enjoy seeing a little more of the surrounding area. So far, apart from her walk along the river bank, she'd spent all her time in the house.

Telling Josie what they were doing, they left Tregellin a few minutes later. It was already after ten o'clock and, although it had rained earlier, a watery sun was breaking through the clouds as they drove down the valley towards the coast. The road twisted and turned, high hedges giving glimpses of the sea in places, the salty breeze blowing strongly from the west.

Polgellin Bay was bigger than Juliet had expected. They'd followed the coastal road into the resort, passing pretty villas with palm trees growing in their back gardens, the lushness of the vegetation an indication of how temperate the climate must be. A narrow main street angled down to a harbour, with fishing boats and fancy yachts protected by a sea wall.

Cary parked by the harbour. At this time of year it was nowhere near as busy as it would be in the season, he told her. At present, it was possible to walk into the shops and cafés without difficulty. In late spring and early summer, the crowds made getting around at all a nightmare.

Juliet doubted anywhere so pretty could be deemed a nightmare whatever the season. Now that the sun had come out it was quite warm, and she was glad she'd shed her jeans in favour of low-rise cotton trousers. Teamed with a hot-pink camisole and a white cotton shirt, they made her feel as if she was on holiday. Maybe for a few hours she could forget the duplicity of her role.

A harbourside pub offered outdoor tables, and Cary suggested they have a drink before going to explore the town. 'Just coffee for me,' said Juliet firmly, but she appreciated the opportunity to sit and enjoy the activity around them. A fishing boat had just come in and she could see dark grey lobsters and wriggling crabs being tossed into an ice-filled trough.

Afterwards, they strolled up the steep street they'd driven down earlier. Many shops with famous names vied with local dealers for trade. There were numerous cafés and lots of gift shops, as well as several art galleries, with canny stacks of posters outside to lure the customers in.

Juliet found herself saying, 'This is where—your cousin has his studio, isn't it?' and then cursed her impulsive tongue when Cary gave her a knowing look.

'Yeah,' he said flatly. 'Well, not here, exactly. It's up one of these side-streets. He can't afford the rents on these premises with what he makes from his daubings.'

Juliet sucked in a breath. 'I gather you're not interested in art.'

Cary snorted. 'Art, yes. What he produces, no.' He sneered when he saw how his contemptuous words had affected her. 'Come on, then. I'll show you. I'm sure Rafe won't turn you away.'

'Oh—no…'

The last thing Juliet wanted was to see Rafe this morning. Dear lord, he was going to think she'd arranged this outing. That, in spite of the way she'd scuttled away last night, she couldn't wait to see him again. Which was patently untrue, she told herself, as Cary took her arm to guide her up another steep street running parallel with the harbour. Indeed, she'd been hoping she wouldn't see him again before they left.

'Honestly, I don't think this is a good idea,' she protested, pulling herself free of his hand and surreptitiously wiping her damp palms on her trousers. 'The studio may be closed.'

'It may,' agreed Cary without sympathy. 'But I'll get him to open it up. He just lives over the place, after all, and he's not likely to be teaching on Saturday.'

The door to the studio was closed and blinds were half-drawn against the glare of the sun. There didn't seem to be anybody about and Juliet was about to suggest that they should leave it when a woman got out of a sleek Mercedes coupé across the street and walked towards them.

'Are you looking for Rafe?' she asked, with the kind of confidence that could only come from knowing him well. 'Hey, you're his cousin, aren't you?' she went on, staring at Cary. 'I remember seeing you around when you lived at Tregellin.'

Juliet saw at once that Cary didn't like being associated with Rafe. And, from his expression, he didn't care for her familiarity either. Though, looking at her deep cleavage and short pleated skirt, Juliet guessed she was just the sort of woman he usually preferred.

'I'm Cary Daniels, yes,' he said at last, realising he couldn't ignore her. Not in Juliet's presence, anyway. 'And you are?'

'Liv. Liv Holderness. Well, Liv Melrose, don't you remember? As I recall it, you used to be quite a regular at my dad's hotel.'

'My God!' Cary looked stunned. 'You're *Lady* Holderness?'

'One and the same,' agreed the woman nonchalantly. 'Bobby and I are having dinner with you and your grandmother this evening. Didn't she tell you?'

'I— She may have done.' Cary was clearly finding it difficult to come to terms with this development and Juliet wondered if his relationship with the woman had been as casual as he'd obviously like to pretend. He licked his lips. 'Are you here to see— Rafe?'

'That's for me to know and you to find out,' she declared playfully. Her gaze drifted over Juliet with a calculated interest. 'Who's this? Another relation?'

'Er—this is Juliet Lawrence. My fiancée,' said Cary swiftly, and Juliet saw the way Liv Holderness' eyes widened.

'Your fiancée?' she echoed, a faint smile hovering about her full lips. 'I bet your grandmother approves.'

'She does.' Juliet was stung into answering for herself. Then she looked at Cary. 'We ought to be going.'

'You've seen Rafe?'

The woman arched narrow brows, and Juliet knew an uncharacteristic urge to make some scathing comment about his choice of visitor. But, of course, she didn't, and it was left to Cary to admit that no, the studio didn't appear to be open.

'Well, it won't be,' said Liv Holderness impatiently. 'Rafe never works with an audience. Besides, he's probably up in his apartment. Have you rung the bell?'

'No.' Cary cast Juliet a helpless glance and then watched as
the woman brushed past them and pressed a scarlet-tipped finger
to the bell-push beside a painted door that hadn't seemed to Juliet
to have any obvious connection to the studio. 'I didn't think he'd
be in.'

Which was so patently untrue that Juliet could only stare at
him in disbelief.

'Oh, he will be,' asserted Liv Holderness confidently. 'He's
expecting me.'

Juliet's mouth was dry and she looked longingly over the
rooftops towards the harbour. She so much didn't want to be
here. Particularly not now she'd discovered that Rafe was apparently having some sort of relationship with this woman.
Heavens, what was he going to think? That they were spying on
him?

But it was too late. The door was swinging open and Rafe
appeared, dark and disturbingly male in a cotton T-shirt and
khaki shorts. He was wearing trainers, too, and, judging by the
V of sweat that stained the front of his sleeveless T-shirt—and
outlined every taut muscle—he'd either been running or doing
some other physical exercise. And Juliet, who'd always believed
she didn't like men in shorts, realised her opinion had been
vastly under-researched.

'Darling!' Liv Holderness wrinkled her nose at him. 'What
have you been doing?'

Rafe's expression mirrored his frustration. For God's sake,
he thought, what the hell was Cary doing here? And Juliet. He'd
have expected her to steer well clear of him from now on.

'You're early,' was all he said, totally ignoring his cousin's
scornful face. 'I was just about to have a shower.'

'Not before time, I'd say,' declared Cary, giving Juliet a
sardonic look. 'I didn't know splashing a paintbrush around
could bring you out in a sweat!'

Juliet wanted to die with embarrassment, but Rafe just pulled
a wry face. 'How would you know, Cary?' he enquired mock-

ingly. 'I doubt if you've ever broken sweat in your life! Oh, except when the South African authorities were on your tail. I bet you weren't so smug then.'

'Why, you—'

Juliet didn't know what Cary might have done if Liv Holderness hadn't stepped forward at that moment. But whatever it was, she doubted her 'fiancé' would have come off the winner. Seeing them close together only made the difference between the two men so much sharper. The terrier and the tiger, she thought fancifully. There'd be no contest.

'Can we come up?'

It was the other woman who spoke and Juliet put a hand on Cary's arm, urging him to make some excuse for them to leave. But for some reason Cary wouldn't respond to her silent pleas. 'Yeah, how about it, Marchese?' he said. Then, in an aside to Juliet, 'I want to see where he lives. I bet it's a dump!'

Rafe wanted to refuse. Apart from the fact that he objected to spending any more time with Cary than he had to, he didn't want Juliet invading his space. She'd already invaded far more of his thoughts than was sensible in the circumstances. Dammit, she was his idiot cousin's fiancée. He had no right to be remembering how soft and responsive her mouth had been when he'd kissed her.

But Liv was no fool, he knew, and she'd soon suspect something was up if he acted out of character. So, with a gesture of resignation, he said, 'Yeah, come on up. Liv, you can make us some coffee.'

Juliet glared at Cary, but he only urged her forward. 'Hurry up, baby,' he said. 'You know you wanted to see where the great painter lived.'

If Rafe heard, he ignored it, and, cursing herself for creating this situation in the first place, Juliet followed Liv Holderness up a narrow flight of stairs. The other woman was wearing high heels and wobbled precariously on the worn treads. Juliet thought cynically that Cary's eyes were probably glued to the hem of the other woman's skirt which bobbed provocatively near the apex of her thighs.

The apartment they entered was surprisingly spacious. Or at least the living room was, Juliet amended, unable to deny her interest as she looked around. Compared to Tregellin, it was intensely modern, with an arrangement of chocolate brown leather sofas and armchairs at one end of the room and a wrought-iron dining set at the other. There was a comprehensive entertainment centre enclosed within a teak console and the positioning of various vases and small sculptures gave the room an elegant appearance. More elegant than Cary had expected, Juliet suspected, aware of his eyes assessing the room's tasteful appointments. Probably estimating how much they were worth, she thought, her cynicism asserting itself again, and she determinedly looked away.

And met their host's dark appraising gaze. She stiffened, almost instinctively, wondering if he intended to get his own back by mentioning their encounter the night before. But all he said was, 'If you'll excuse me...' and headed lazily towards an inner door that evidently led to the bathroom.

CHAPTER EIGHT

OR HIS bedroom, Juliet reflected tensely, looking anywhere but into those magnetic eyes. But when he turned away she couldn't prevent herself from watching him, her gaze drawn to his tight buttocks and the hairy length of those long, powerful legs.

She swallowed and then became aware that her interest hadn't gone unnoticed. Cary was looking at her now with a mocking, speculative stare. Oh, God, she thought, how had she got herself into this situation? If Cary thought she was attracted to Rafe, heaven knew what mischief he might do.

Liv Holderness, meanwhile, had teetered her way across to where a breakfast bar hid a small kitchen. Limed-oak units with granite working surfaces gave the place a sophisticated look. There were spotlights in the ceiling and copper-bottomed pans hanging below wall cupboards, with earthenware bowls on the window sill, where spider ferns and other greenery tumbled to the floor.

Liv was obviously familiar with the kitchen's layout because she found the coffee-maker and grains without much effort. Juliet tried not to let her own feelings about Rafe impinge on her opinion of the woman, but the image of them together—in his bed—kept popping into her mind.

'Have you known Cary long?' Liv asked, and Juliet guessed she was trying to define their relationship. She didn't fool herself that the woman considered her any competition. Why should she? But she wanted to know what she was dealing with; if Rafe was involved.

'Since we were kids,' replied Cary at once, turning from the painting he'd been studying. 'So, what's going on with you and Marchese? Or is that a leading question?'

She smiled, but it didn't quite reach her eyes. 'I think that's our business, don't you?' Then she turned to Juliet. 'So what do you do when you're not spending time with Lady Elinor?'

Juliet swallowed, wishing Cary would answer that, too. To avoid doing so, she gestured towards a group of four water colours that hung on the wall beside the dining table. 'Is this Mr Marchese's work, Lady Holderness?'

'Call her Liv, for God's sake!' Cary scowled and the woman came out from behind the breakfast bar and gave Juliet a considering look.

'As if Rafe would hang anything of his in his apartment!' she exclaimed scornfully. 'No, these are Susie Rivers. She's what you might call a protégée of his.'

'He has a lot of them,' remarked Cary slyly, earning another acrimonious glare from Liv. He put his arm around Juliet, ignoring her resistance. 'Let's sit down, darling. I'm sure Rafe will be only too happy to show you his work, when he's cleaned up.'

To Juliet's relief, there were no more questions about her background and when Rafe came back into the room, they were all sitting down, drinking the coffee Liv Holderness had made. There were specks of water sparkling on his night-dark hair, a dark blue shirt and tight jeans accentuating his lean, muscled frame. He was barefoot, and in those first few seconds Juliet felt as if she knew everything about him. Well, about his appearance, anyway, she amended, wondering what it was about him that disturbed her so much.

'I'll get you a cup,' said Liv at once, but before she could get up Rafe waved her back into her seat.

'I can do it,' he said, going to pour himself some coffee.

Then, coming round the bar, he rested his hips against the granite counter. 'I'm so glad you've made yourselves at home.'

'No, you're not.' Liv was sardonic. 'I know you prefer your privacy when you're working.'

'I hope you don't expect us to believe he'd been working earlier,' Cary admonished. 'For heaven's sake, we're not morons.'

Rafe was tempted to make some cutting comment, but Juliet would be bound to get the wrong impression if he did. Just because he'd had a crisis of some sort the night before didn't mean he wanted to repeat the exercise.

'I'd been running,' he said, by way of an answer. 'I'm sorry if my appearance offended your sensibilities, Cary, but some of us get off our backsides from time to time.'

'Makes a change from crawling, I suppose,' retorted Cary derisively, and Juliet stifled a groan. For pity's sake, did he want to start a fight with the other man? She could sense the cold hostility in Rafe's narrow-eyed gaze.

'Just shut the hell up, will you, Cary?' Liv had evidently come to the same conclusion, but, unlike Juliet, she wasn't afraid to speak her mind.

'Who do you think you're talking to?' demanded Cary at once, but Liv wasn't listening to him. Instead she turned to Rafe again, her smile warm and familiar.

'I think Juliet wants to see some of your work, darling,' she said, as if Juliet was incapable of speaking for herself. 'Would you like me to take her down to the studio? Then you can finish your coffee in peace.'

'I don't think—' Juliet was beginning, when Rafe put down his cup.

'If Juliet wants to see the studio, I'll show it to her,' he said flatly. 'Is that what you want?' He looked directly at her. 'Make up your mind. I've got work to do.'

Juliet could hear Cary muttering about ignorant bastards and knew that any moment he was going to make some other remark that would further sour Rafe's mood. And, although she told herself that the last thing she wanted to do was be alone with him, what could it harm to see his studio and the work he was doing?

'Um—yes, I'd like that,' she said, ignoring Cary's outraged expression. 'Thanks.'

'I'll come with you,' said Liv at once, swallowing the last of her coffee and getting to her feet, and Rafe sighed. He guessed that if Liv accompanied them, Cary would, too, and he didn't want his cousin anywhere near his studio at present.

'The place isn't big enough for all of us,' he said, regarding her warningly. 'I've got work in progress that I don't want anyone else to see yet.'

'Oh…'

She got the message at once, he saw. Letting Cary see the sketches Rafe had been making for her portrait wasn't the wisest thing to do in the circumstances. It would be like him to drop that tasty little morsel into the conversation at dinner that evening and then pretend to be mortified when her husband expressed his surprise.

'Well—OK,' she said, and Juliet stared at her. Why had she suddenly changed her mind? 'Cary and I will have another cup of coffee. We can reminisce about old times.'

Cary wasn't at all suited. 'I didn't come to Polgellin Bay to sit in this apartment drinking coffee,' he grumbled, but Liv put on her most persuasive expression.

'Just for five more minutes,' she cajoled appealing. 'You can tell me what you've been doing since you left Tregellin.'

She'd taken hold of his arm now, and Juliet couldn't decide whether he was disgruntled or flattered. Either way, Rafe ushered her towards the door and other considerations took the place of curiosity.

There were two doors at the foot of the flight of stairs that led up to Rafe's apartment. One to the outdoors, she knew, and the other led into his studio. Rafe went ahead of her, switching on a couple of spotlights to illuminate an area bigger than she'd expected from what he'd said to Cary. But she didn't really blame him for not wanting his cousin to join them. They weren't exactly the best of friends.

The door closed behind her and Juliet struggled to concentrate on why she'd come here. She and Rafe were alone, it was true, but she didn't kid herself that this had been his idea. On the contrary, as he lifted a canvas off an easel that had been set up to one side of the studio, and stowed it at the back of the studio, she guessed he didn't want her to see his 'work-in-progress' either.

'It's very—impressive,' she said, looking about her. And it was certainly more professional than she'd imagined when Lady Elinor had spoken of it. Sketches littered a side-table and dozens of canvases were stacked against a wall. There were palette knives and brushes, drawing equipment, charcoal, chalk and varnish, as well as jars and jars of paint in every colour imaginable scattered about the floor.

'It's adequate,' he said, without pretension, turning to give her a narrow-eyed stare. 'But you didn't really want to see my work, did you?'

'Yes.' Juliet answered without thinking, unaware of how revealing her answer might sound. 'I really did. It's very—interesting.'

Damned with faint praise. Rafe's jaw compressed. 'If you say so.'

Juliet sighed. 'Why should it surprise you that I'd like to see your work? If you're thinking about what happened last night, forget it. I have.'

'It's good to know I'm so forgettable.'

Rafe spoke mockingly and Juliet wished she wasn't so aware of him in the confined space. The studio was filled with the mingled aromas of oil and other painting supplies, but she still couldn't ignore the subtle scent of man.

Licking her lips, she said, 'Do you want to talk about it? Is that what you're saying?'

Rafe made an indignant sound. 'Hey, you brought it up, not me.'

'I know I did, but—well, it shouldn't have happened. You know that as well as I do.' She glanced about her in an effort to change the subject. 'So may I see something?'

'Do you always switch from one thing to another like this?' His brows arched. 'I'm still trying to get my head round the fact that you didn't engineer this invitation just to spend some time alone with me.'

Juliet stared at him in frustration, the colour ebbing and flowing in her expressive face. 'Don't lie to me, Mr Marchese,' she said hotly. 'I'm engaged to Cary. That might not matter to you, but it matters to me.'

'Does it?' He couldn't prevent the amused retort. 'You know, I didn't get that impression last night.'

'No, well…' Juliet gave a careless shrug. 'You took me by surprise, that's all. I wasn't expecting it.'

'Believe it or not, neither was I,' remarked Rafe drily. Then, with cool deliberation, 'Did Cary tell you where he spent his evening? Did he meet up with the, in quotes, "friends" you spoke about?'

Juliet pursed her lips. 'I didn't ask him.'

'No?' Rafe couldn't help feeling pleased with her answer. 'Don't you care?'

Her colour deepened again. 'It's none of your business.'

'So—what are you saying? That you have an open relationship?' He paused and, when she didn't answer, he went on, 'That's when—'

'I know what an open relationship means,' she interrupted him fiercely. She wrapped her arms about herself. 'Can we talk about something else?'

'Your call.'

But he couldn't help wondering about her relationship with his cousin. Was she just humouring him until something better came along? It seemed likely, but he didn't care for the idea. And he despised himself for wanting something he couldn't—and shouldn't—have.

Forcing himself not to think about how her crossed arms pushed her small breasts into a prominent position, he abandoned his stance and walked across to where several canvases were propped against the brick wall. Swinging one around, he displayed a painting of an elderly fisherman sitting on a capstan by the harbour, his head bent over his nets.

Juliet, who'd been wishing she'd never come here, couldn't prevent an automatic gasp of admiration. 'Is this yours?' she asked, coming a little nearer and gazing raptly at the painting. 'My God, it's so lifelike! Is this a real person?'

'It was.' Rafe came to stand beside her, telling himself it was to get her perspective on the canvas. A faint scent came to his nostrils, warm and flowery and essentially feminine, like her. 'His name was John Tregaron. His family have lived in Polgellin for as long as anyone can remember.'

'That's amazing!'

'What? That his family have lived here for hundreds of years?'

Juliet gave him an impatient look and then wished she hadn't been so foolhardy when she met the disturbing darkness of his gaze. 'No,' she said, jerking her chin down again. 'You know what I mean. People must have complimented you on your work before.'

Rafe shrugged. 'Thank you.'

Juliet shifted a little uncomfortably. 'My father was a great admirer of certain painters' work. What little I know about art, I learned from him.'

Rafe wondered if she realised that was a double-edged comment. He guessed not. She was doing her best to normalise their relationship and he had to squash this unforgivable urge to bait her.

'I have my favourites, too,' he conceded, concentrating on the painting to avoid looking at her. 'When I was younger, I used to attend any exhibition I could get to. I started out by liking Turner and a contemporary of his, Thomas Girtin. Have you heard of him? Unfortunately he died when he was in his twenties. There's an anecdote about Turner saying that if Tom Girtin had lived, he'd have starved.'

'Do you believe that?'

Rafe shook his head. 'No, Turner was unique. But they did train together, and their earliest work was similar.'

Juliet was impressed and once again she made the mistake of looking up at him. But this time she couldn't look away. She was mesmerised by his eyes, by the sudden heat in his expression. She rubbed her elbows with her palms, trying to ignore the goose bumps that were feathering her skin.

This time, however, Rafe broke eye contact. Despite his determination not to pursue this unhealthy infatuation, there was an insistent hunger in his gut. He tried to tell himself it was because he hadn't had anything to eat before he went for his run, but his senses told him his need wasn't for food but something less admirable.

'Do—do you have anything else to show me?' Juliet ventured nervously, and Rafe ignored the innocent sexuality of her question and moved forward to replace the painting with a life-size sketch of Lady Elinor herself. It was roughly done, something he'd been working on without her knowledge. The old lady wouldn't sit for him. It would have smacked of giving him her approval.

'Oh—wow!' Juliet was entranced by his offering. 'I had no idea Lady Elinor had been here.'

'She hasn't.' Rafe's tone was flat. 'I did that from memory.'

'Well, it's very good.'

Rafe shrugged. 'I'm glad you approve.'

She smiled then, the corners of her mouth lifting to give her face a dangerous beauty. Dangerous, because she was such a temptation and she didn't know it.

'I approve of your work,' she said lightly. 'That's not to say I approve of you.'

'I'm wounded.' He paused, and then, as a thought occurred to him, 'Did your father approve of your husband?'

'My father?' She was taken aback. 'I— He never met David. He died soon after I left school.'

'I'm sorry.'

'Yes, so am I.' Juliet spoke philosophically. 'If he'd lived, I might not have made so many mistakes.'

Rafe hesitated. 'Because your marriage didn't work out?'

'You could say that.' Juliet pulled a face. 'He certainly wouldn't have trusted David with all *his* money.'

'You did that?'

It was a personal question but having come so far, Juliet couldn't back off. 'Yes,' she said, flushing with embarrassment. 'I know I was a fool. You can't despise me any more than I despise myself.'

'Why would I despise you?' Rafe was vehement. 'He sounds a complete bastard!'

Juliet grimaced. 'Tell me about it.'

'But charming, I guess. Was that why you married him?'

'I'm not sure why I married him now.' Juliet twisted her hands together at her waist. 'My father had just died and I have no brothers or sisters.' Then she broke off. 'But you don't want to hear this. I made a mistake. A lot of mistakes, actually. I'll get over it.'

Rafe half turned to look at her. 'And you think Cary's going to help you?'

Oh, God! Juliet closed her eyes for a moment. For a short while there, she'd actually forgotten why she was here. Thank goodness, she hadn't said anything too revealing. But it wasn't easy to lie, particularly to Rafe.

Which was another mistake.

'Um—I hope so,' she said now, trying to keep her voice light. 'Well, I don't have any money, so I can be sure he's not marrying me for that.'

'So why is he marrying you?' Rafe asked, unable to prevent himself, and Juliet caught her breath.

'Because he loves me, I suppose,' she said, wishing she sounded more convincing. 'Why don't you ask him?'

'I don't need to.' Rafe had reverted to sarcasm. 'Oh, Juliet, when will you ever learn?'

She gasped then. 'You know nothing about it.'

'Don't I?' His conviction disturbed her. 'I'd say I know Cary better than you do.'

'Oh, right.' Juliet knew she had to say something to defend herself. 'So when was the last time you slept with him? I'd be interested to know.'

Rafe scowled. 'I don't get into bed with reptiles.'

'Nor do I.' Juliet hated the smug look on his dark face. Their earlier civility seemed to have evaporated, and she despised herself anew for wishing things could be different. 'Besides,' she added, in an effort to be as objectionable as he was, 'I didn't think you were that choosy. Not judging by your current—what was it you called it—work-in-progress?'

Rafe was incensed. 'I hope you're not implying that I'm sleeping with Liv Holderness?'

'You're not?' Juliet managed to put just the right note of ridicule into her voice. 'Well, she wants you to. The woman can't take her eyes off your butt!'

Rafe's expression darkened with ominous intent, but then the humour of the situation brought an unwilling tilt to his lips. 'Now, I wonder why you noticed that,' he murmured softly. 'Isn't Cary enough for you?'

Her jaw dropped. 'That's a disgusting suggestion!'

Rafe was unrepentant, but he knew he'd already said more than he'd intended. All the same, it galled him that she couldn't see through Cary's lies. Dammit, the man was a walking contradiction.

Abandoning any thought of continuing their conversation, he went to restore the painting and the sketch of Lady Elinor to their original positions. He had to keep his mind on his work and nothing else, he warned himself. In another day or so she'd be gone.

Juliet, meanwhile, was fighting the urge to kick his provocative backside. He'd presented her with the perfect opportunity when he bent to straighten the canvases he'd moved earlier, his jeans outlining tight buttocks and long, powerful legs. Who did he think he was to speak to her like that? If it wasn't such a ludicrous notion, she'd have to wonder if he wanted her himself.

Which was so not true.

'I'm going back upstairs,' she said abruptly, deciding there was no point in trying to reason with him. 'I've seen all I came to see.'

Rafe turned, straightening. 'Well, that's something, I suppose.'

Juliet's lips tightened. 'You just love making fun of me, don't you?'

Rafe's mouth curled. 'Honey, you don't need me to do that,' he retorted harshly, before the reality of what he was saying occurred to him. But hell, she was too naïve for her own good and, if he didn't say anything, it was a fair bet that nobody else would. Particularly the old lady.

'You know—' her voice shook a little, but she carried on anyway '—you criticise Cary but, from where I'm standing, you're not so different.'

'Like hell!'

'I mean it.' She gained confidence from his angry rejoinder. 'You both think you know everything there is to know about women, but you don't.'

Rafe shook his head. 'Is that what you think this is about?'

She held up her head. 'Isn't it?'

'No.' He blew out a breath. 'Face it, Juliet, you know nothing about men. OK, you've been married and divorced and you should have gained some insight into the opposite sex, but you haven't. If you had, I wouldn't feel so bloody responsible.'

Juliet's eyes widened. 'There's no need for you to feel any responsibility towards me, Mr Marchese. I'm quite old enough to know what I'm doing, whatever you may think.'

'Yeah, right.'

He was dismissive and Juliet lost her temper. 'You know what I think, Mr Marchese?' she demanded. 'I think all this sanctimonious talk about responsibility is just a cover for what you really want.'

'Which is?' His tone was icy.

'The opportunity to oust Cary from his rightful place as your grandmother's legitimate heir,' she retorted recklessly and then almost collapsed with fear when his hand shot out and grabbed her wrist.

'Take that back,' he began grimly, but as she pressed her other hand to her throat, his expression grew even more menacing. *'Dios,'* he muttered, his eyes darkening until they were almost black. 'That ring!' He'd noticed her pretend-engagement ring, and now he reached out and pulled her hand towards him. 'Where did you get it?' he grated, his thumb pressing the stone painfully into her finger. 'Did Cary give it to you?'

Juliet swallowed, all her earlier bravado doused by the anguish in his face. 'I— Lady Elinor—g-gave it to me,' she stammered, his hard fingers burning into her flesh. She moistened dry lips. 'I've—I've only borrowed it.'

'Borrowed it?'

Rafe stared down at her with disbelieving eyes and she found herself stammering out an explanation even though he had no earthly right to expect one. 'We— Cary hasn't bought me a ring—yet,' she went on unsteadily. 'And your—your grandmother said that with the Holdernesses coming for dinner this evening I—I should be wearing one.'

'And she gave you this?' Rafe knew he shouldn't question the old lady's actions, but he couldn't deny the swirl of resentment that was building inside him.

'It's only borrowed,' Juliet said again, not understanding his attitude. But something was wrong here, and when she tried to pull away Rafe lifted her hand to study the glowing stone in closer detail.

'You really think Cary will allow you to return this?' he asked harshly. 'Forgive me if I say I doubt that. I doubt that very much.'

Juliet shook her head. 'Surely that's Lady Elinor's business, not yours. It's her ring.'

'It was my mother's,' said Rafe flatly. A bitter smile crossed his dark face. 'The old lady gave it to her on her twenty-first birthday.'

'Oh, God!' Juliet was horrified. 'I had no idea.'

'No.' Rafe believed her.

'She— I— Lady Elinor said she'd been given the ring when she was a girl and I never dreamt—'

'Forget it.' Abruptly Rafe released her, backing off until there was at least an arm's length between them. 'I shouldn't have reacted as I did. The old lady got the ring back when my mother—when she died. I didn't want it and I guess she feels she has the right to do what she likes with it now.'

'But…' Juliet's tongue circled her upper lip. 'I'll give it back,' she said impulsively. 'I don't really need a ring—'

'And have her blame me for ruining her evening? I don't think so.' Rafe was sardonic. 'It's not that important. I shouldn't have mentioned it.'

But it was important and Juliet had the feeling that she knew why Lady Elinor had been so pleased when she'd chosen this particular ring. She'd known Rafe would see it, would recognise it. That was why she'd asked her if he'd seen the ring last night. But Juliet wanted no part of any plan to hurt him.

Shaking her head again, she moved blindly towards the door. She wanted to get out of the studio, out of Polgellin Bay, out of Cary's life and away from Lady Elinor's machinations. The situation was so much more complex than she had ever imagined and she'd had enough.

'I'll see you upstairs,' she said, glancing back at him, and then let out a startled cry when her foot encountered an unexpected obstacle. She'd been so eager to reach the door that led onto the stairs that she hadn't been looking where she was going, and before she knew it she'd stumbled into the canvas he'd placed against the wall when they came in. The canvas teetered, and she grabbed for it, more intent on saving it than herself. And as she did so a handful of sketches fluttered from behind it, spreading themselves decoratively across the floor.

CHAPTER NINE

AFTERWARDS, she wasn't sure whether it was the sight of the sketches or the fact that she was still unbalanced that had caused her to sway towards the wall. Certainly, the images of Liv Holderness nude body had made her feel slightly faint. Dear God, they were having an affair. Why else would she be reclining on his couch completely naked? No wonder she behaved with such a proprietary air towards him. Didn't he care that she was a married woman?

But then, he hadn't cared that she and Cary were supposed to be engaged either, she reminded herself, a feeling of dizziness making her feel really sick. How dared he criticise Cary? Compared to Rafe...

But her head was swimming and the heat in the room made her feel as if there was no air. She turned bewilderedly, her face mirroring her confusion, and with a muffled oath Rafe lunged across the floor.

'Stupid woman,' he muttered, his arm sliding about her waist, stabilising her with the muscled strength of his body. 'Why the hell didn't you look where you were going? I can just imagine what your fiancé would have thought if you'd reappeared sporting a black eye.'

Juliet was trembling so badly, she could hardly find the words to defend herself. And the truth was, without his support she might still have slid bonelessly to the floor. His heavy breathing revealed the effort he'd made to reach her before she lost consciousness, and it was hard not to feel grateful for his help.

'I should think Cary's opinion is the least of your worries,' she managed at last, trying to steel herself to break away. 'Does Lord Holderness know you're making nude sketches of his wife?'

Rafe sighed. He'd known this was coming, of course, and he cursed himself for leaving the sketches lying about. 'No,' he admitted at last, resisting her feeble efforts to get free of him. Then, deciding he had no choice but to trust her, 'I'm painting her portrait for her husband's birthday. It's supposed to be a surprise, so I'd be grateful if you'd keep it to yourself.'

Juliet caught her breath, and this time she managed to turn and face him. 'You expect me to believe that?' she demanded. 'My God, you must think I came down with the last shower of rain!'

'It's the truth,' said Rafe doggedly, and when she would have turned away he caught her wrist and brought her back to him. 'I don't lie,' he told her harshly. 'If I was having an affair with Liv Holderness, do you think I'd be here alone with you?'

Juliet took a deep breath. 'I asked to see your work,' she said.

'And I was reluctant to show you.'

'Because of Liv.'

'No, because of this,' he muttered thickly and, pulling her into his arms, he lowered his head to hers.

He'd taken advantage of her weakness, she told herself later. That was why she didn't stop him when he parted her lips with his tongue. With the unmistakable pressure of his erection pushing against her stomach, it was far too easy to give in to emotions that had been heightened by their argument. And when she felt his thumbs pushing against the undersides of her breasts, she knew an urgent need to push her hips against his.

Her senses were reeling, and somehow the knowledge that she was supposed to be Cary's fiancée got lost in the sensual pleasure he was arousing in her. The force of her own desire overcame any latent outrage. She wanted him to kiss her. Dear God, she wanted him to do so much more than that.

As his mouth ravaged hers, as his tongue pushed deep into her throat, Rafe felt the wild excitement building inside him take possession of his reason. He wanted her, he thought. He wanted her with an urgency he couldn't ever remember feeling before. They were alone here. Could he really rely on neither Liv nor Cary interrupting them? He would like to take her on the couch and wipe the images of Liv's naked body out of her mind.

'I want to make love to you,' he said, his lips finding the moist curve of her neck, his teeth nipping her flesh with sensual urgency. Juliet moaned low in her throat and Rafe's hands shook a little as he peeled her shirt off her shoulders. Her skin was so soft, the narrow straps of her camisole barely concealing the tender peaks of her breasts.

He trailed a finger from her jawline, down across her throat to the dusky hollow just visible above the neckline of the camisole. Then he bent and followed his finger with his tongue, licking her and tasting the slightly salty tang of her damp skin. They were both sweating, he thought. Dammit, his shirt was sticking to his back. He'd never felt such emotional overload, never felt the blood thundering so thickly through his veins.

'You taste so good,' he said, and her hands groped blindly for his face, hot fingers cradling his cheeks, her thumbs moving sensuously against his lips. He couldn't help himself; he opened his mouth and bit on the soft pad until she whimpered, and then he tipped the straps of her camisole off her shoulders and buried his face between her breasts.

Juliet was incapable of resisting. Her body felt hot and alive, alert to every sensual move he made. With his leg braced between her thighs, that sensitive part of her was wet and wanting. His erection pressed against the crotch of her pants, hard and throbbing with a life of its own.

Rafe was aching with the need to be inside her. All he could think about was burying himself in her wet heat and letting her muscles squeeze him until it hurt. He deepened the kiss, backing her up against the wall beside the canvases, bracing himself with his hands on either side of her, pushing his tongue even further into her mouth.

Juliet felt consumed by his hunger. She wound her arms about his neck, pulling him against her, welcoming the carnal rush when his body pinned hers to the wall. She wriggled impatiently, wanting him to touch her everywhere. And particularly that place between her legs that ached for his possession.

'God, keep still!' Rafe muttered hoarsely. He was aware he'd never been so close to losing control in his life. If she didn't stop moving about…

But suddenly, Juliet was stiffening. It was as if the sudden harshness of his words had broken the spell of madness that had gripped them both. 'What did you say?' she demanded unsteadily, her palms now flat against his pectoral muscles, pushing him away, when only moments before she'd been writhing in sexual need.

'Dammit, Juliet—'

'Let me go!'

Rafe gritted his teeth. 'You don't mean that.'

'I do mean it. Let me go!'

'Oh, for God's sake—'

Juliet clenched her teeth. Her shoes weren't stilettos, like Liv's, but he was barefoot, and when she ground her heel into his instep he howled with pain. She felt a moment's remorse as he recoiled and grabbed his foot, hopping on one leg as he sought to restore some feeling to it, but it did give her the opportunity to step away from the wall and straighten her clothes.

'What did you expect?' she asked him bitterly. 'Don't think I don't know what you were trying to do. You thought that by seducing me you could deflect my contempt for the way you're treating Liv's husband. You—you assaulted me. You are totally—totally reprehensible!'

'Oh, grow up!' Rafe was feeling particularly aggrieved at this moment. Apart from the fact that he was suffering the after-effects of her attack, there was a distinct feeling of frustration in his groin. 'My kissing you had nothing to do with those sketches of Liv Holderness. For pity's sake, it's what I do. I'm supposed to be a painter!'

Juliet sniffed. 'All the same—'

'All the same, nothing.' Rafe decided he had nothing to lose by telling the truth. 'You didn't practically cripple me because I kissed you. You just realised you were enjoying yourself and you felt guilty for deceiving Danger Mouse upstairs!'

Rafe was still in a black mood long after Liv had departed.

What he told himself was to his relief Juliet had mentioned nothing of what had passed between them in the studio and she and Cary had left soon afterwards. Liv, however, had been suspicious, but wary, keeping any opinions she might have about their prolonged absence to herself. She knew him well enough to guess that something had happened, but she had more sense than to try and open that particular can of worms today.

Nevertheless, his mood had meant that working was difficult, and with a brief word of apology Rafe had suggested they postpone their appointment until after the weekend was over. 'I've got a headache,' he had said, by way of an excuse, though what he really had was a hard-on that refused to go away.

A cold shower took care of it eventually and he was just stepping out of the cubicle when the phone rang. Grabbing a towel, he wrapped it about his hips, and then strode with some impatience to answer it.

His foot pained him as he paced across the floor and that didn't improve his temper. 'Yes,' he said shortly, hoping it wasn't a client, and then stifled an oath when he heard Lady Elinor's imperious tones.

'Raphael! Raphael, is that you?'

Rafe's jaw tightened. 'As this is my phone in my apartment, I'd say it was a better than average chance that it'd be me,' he

responded tersely. 'What do you want, old lady? I thought you'd
be too busy to talk to me today.'

There was a long silence and Rafe wondered if he'd been too
curt with her. Dammit, it wasn't her fault that he was in danger
of screwing up his life. He didn't know what it was about Juliet,
but she pushed all the wrong buttons. Or were they all the right
ones? Either way, it would be safer if he didn't see her again.

'You sound as if you've been ridden hard and put away wet,'
said Lady Elinor eventually, and he realised, that whatever it was
she wanted, she was prepared to humour him to get it. 'Have you
seen Cary?'

Rafe expelled a sharp breath, the images her words had evoked
causing an unwelcome tightness in his gut. 'Why would you ask
that?' he queried, wondering if Juliet had said something, after
all. But no. She and Cary had hardly had time to get back to
Tregellin, always assuming that was where they had been
heading.

'Because I believe he and Juliet were going into Polgellin Bay
this morning,' Lady Elinor replied smoothly. 'I know Juliet
wanted to see your work.'

'They've been and gone,' said Rafe shortly, deciding there
was no point in prevaricating. If he didn't tell her, Cary surely
would. The fact that Liv had been here, too, would ensure a
discreet—or in Cary's case not so discreet—disclosure.

'And did you show her some of your paintings?' the old lady
persisted. 'She's such a nice girl, isn't she? Not at all what we
expected.'

'You mean, what *you* expected,' Rafe corrected her grimly.
'I didn't have an opinion either way.'

'But you've met her now,' Lady Elinor pointed out. 'You
must have formed some opinion as to her character. Josie tells
me the pair of you spent some time talking together last evening.'

Rafe's teeth ground together. 'What do you want me to say,
old lady? That I like her? That I envy Cary his good fortune?
You like her. Isn't that enough for you?'

'Raphael, Raphael, I'm only asking for your opinion.'

'Really?' Rafe felt driven. Then he said the unforgivable, 'Do you think I want to have sex with her? Is that what you want to hear?'

If he'd expected the old lady to be offended he was disappointed. The peal of laughter that she uttered came clearly over the phone. 'And do you?' she asked, causing him no small measure of frustration. 'Poor Cary. He has no idea what he's up against.'

Rafe's free hand balled into a fist. 'You can be a nasty old woman sometimes,' he said, not caring at that moment what she thought of him. 'Look, is this going somewhere? Because I have to tell you, I'm standing here with just a towel to cover me.'

There was another silence and then Lady Elinor said, 'So you're not going to talk about her?'

'What's to say? You evidently like her.' He scowled. 'Enough to give her my mother's ring.'

'Ah!' Rafe had the feeling that that was what the old lady had been waiting for. 'You noticed.'

Rafe closed his eyes for a moment. 'I couldn't help but notice, could I?'

'If you say so, my dear. Do I take it you object to my generosity? Or is it that you're afraid Cary might pawn the ring before you can get it back?'

Rafe heaved a sigh and opened his eyes again. 'There's no chance of that, is there?' He felt weary suddenly. 'In any case, it was your ring to begin with. You can do what you like with it.'

'Yes, I suppose I can.' Lady Elinor sounded thoughtful for a moment. 'But, in any case, that's not why I rang you. I want you to come to dinner this evening. You've not got a previous engagement, have you?'

Rafe's jaw dropped. 'You're joking!'

'No.' The old lady was annoyingly smug. 'I was going to ask old Charteris to join us, but on second thoughts, I prefer to ask you.'

'No way.'

'Raphael, don't be like that. You wouldn't want your grand-mother to be the odd one out, would you?' She paused. 'The Holdernesses are coming, you know.'

'And that would interest me because…?'

'I understood that you and Lady Holderness were old friends.'

'We are friends. Or, at least, we've known one another for a number of years.' He sighed. 'I've told you what the situation is with Liv. She was here this morning, actually. She and your guests arrived together.'

'How cosy!' Lady Elinor was sardonic. 'Well? What do you say?'

'About tonight?'

'What else?'

Rafe's stomach clenched. He knew that going to Tregellin again while Juliet was there was not a good idea. God, hadn't he just been telling himself that? And seeing her with Cary… His shoulders hunched defensively. He would be all kinds of an idiot if he agreed to the old lady's request…

Juliet prepared for the dinner party without enthusiasm. But, she reminded herself, this was their last evening at Tregellin. In the morning they'd be leaving, and she could put all thoughts of Rafe Marchese out of her head.

And she could forget about what had happened that morning, she added tersely. For heaven's sake, what had she been thinking of, allowing that man to touch her again? Particularly after what she'd just learned about him. The man was totally unscrupulous; totally without shame.

As for that story about him painting Liv Holderness portrait: well, was it likely that Lord Holderness—whoever he was—would want everyone to see a portrait of his wife in the nude? Of course, it was just the sort of idea Liv might have had, to give her an excuse to visit Rafe's studio. But however good the sketches had been, there was no way they were going to be enlarged into a full portrait.

Full-blown portrait, perhaps, she thought maliciously. Yet despite her reservations, she had to admit Rafe's talent was an awesome thing. Just a glimpse of those sketches, and she'd known at once who his subject had been. Which wasn't always easy with a nude.

She sighed, trying not to think about the morning. What she should be worrying about was what might happen if he chose to tell his grandmother her tawdry little secret. Cary would be hopelessly humiliated. He'd never forgive her for making him look a fool.

Yet, would that be such a bad thing? she asked herself. Even before this morning, she'd been feeling bad about deceiving Lady Elinor in this way. If she had half the old lady's character, she'd walk out right now. The trouble was, she didn't have the train fare back to London.

No, she would have to stay until tomorrow. And she supposed she owed it to herself to carry the evening off in a way that would have made her father proud of her. If he could see what she was doing, she hoped he'd forgive her. She wasn't a bad person, she told herself. Just pathetically naïve and weak.

The black dress with its satin lining and chiffon sleeves was attractive. A lace overdress ended some inches above her knees, but sheer black stockings hid her slender thighs from view. Four-inch heels threatened a twisted ankle, but they were the only shoes that matched the rest of her outfit.

She hesitated over what earrings to wear and finally settled on gold loops that complemented her necklace. A handful of narrow bracelets circled one wrist while the watch her father had given her for her eighteenth birthday circled the other. She slipped the ruby onto her finger with some reluctance. Since Rafe had told her whose ring it really was she felt even worse about wearing it.

Still, Rafe wouldn't be present this evening so she could relax. And she might even make a point of forgetting the ring tomorrow morning and face Cary's displeasure once they were safely back in London. He could hardly penalise her then, when she'd done everything he'd asked of her. If he guessed she'd left the ring behind deliberately, so be it. It wasn't his ring and she was unlikely to see him again once this weekend was over.

With one final critical glance at her appearance, Juliet tucked a strand of hair behind her ear and left the room. It was still early. Barely half-past seven, in fact, but she suspected Lady Elinor would be waiting in the drawing room, ready to greet her guests. The Holdernesses might already have arrived. From the little she knew of Lady Holderness, she knew she wasn't the retiring type!

She heard voices as she crossed the hall and her nerves tightened. She'd already lied to four people and she wasn't looking forward to lying to a fifth. What if someone asked a question she couldn't answer? Cary was no help. He'd been pathetically eager to abandon her the night before.

She was so tense that for a moment, when she reached the doorway, she thought she must be hallucinating. The man who was standing on the hearth, one arm resting on the mantel, one foot raised to support itself on the brass fender, was so familiar to her. All in black this evening—black pleated trousers, black turtle-neck and a black velvet jacket—Rafe looked completely at ease in these surroundings. The sweat-stained individual who'd greeted them that morning, or the barefoot artist in jeans and T-shirt with whom she'd shared those devastating kisses, might have been from another planet. This was Rafe Marchese, Lady Elinor's grandson, and anyone who thought differently should definitely think again.

Juliet swallowed and Lady Elinor, who was once again seated on the sofa, raised a welcoming hand. 'Come in, my dear,' she said as Rafe straightened away from the mantel. 'I thought I'd ask Raphael to join us. Raphael, why don't you ask Juliet what she'd like to drink?'

CHAPTER TEN

THE Holdernesses evidently hadn't yet arrived and it was obvious that Lady Elinor expected Juliet to accompany Rafe to the drinks cabinet and tell him what she'd like. In truth, a stiff vodka wouldn't have come amiss but, in the circumstances, she might be wise to keep her wits about her.

'What'll it be?' asked Rafe, aware of her reluctance to be anywhere near him and disliking the connotations. Dammit, he didn't want to be here either. But it had been even harder finding an excuse and the last thing he wanted to do was give the old lady any reason to suspect what had been going on. 'Sherry—or just plain old hemlock over ice?'

Juliet cast a resentful glance in his direction. 'I suppose you're enjoying this, aren't you?' she whispered accusingly. 'Why didn't you tell me you were coming here tonight?'

'Me?' Rafe arched a mocking eyebrow.

'*Us*,' Juliet corrected hastily. 'I meant us.'

Rafe shrugged. 'Would you believe I didn't know myself until later in the day?'

'No.'

'Nevertheless, it's true.' Rafe told himself he didn't care if she believed him or not. 'The old lady likes to keep her guests on their toes. Haven't you realised that yet?'

Juliet moistened her dry lips. 'I haven't been here long

enough to make any assessment of her character,' she replied stiffly, and Rafe gave a reluctant smile.

'Haven't you?' He shook his head. 'I feel as if you've been here for weeks.'

Juliet regarded him defensively. 'Why do I get the feeling that's not a compliment?' She dragged her eyes away from him, trying to concentrate on why she was here. But it was difficult when standing so close to him reminded her so vividly of the heat of his body, the faintly citrus scent that mingled with the clean smell of man.

But then she remembered the sketches...

'What are you two doing?' Rafe wasn't surprised at the old lady's irritation. 'Don't you know it's rude to whisper?'

Juliet swung round. 'I'm sorry—'

'She hasn't decided what she wants yet,' said Rafe obliquely. 'Come on, Juliet. Make up your mind.'

Juliet cast him a venomous look. 'Sherry,' she said abruptly. 'I'll have sherry.' And, reluctantly, 'Thank you.'

'My pleasure.' Rafe sought his own relief in mockery, grateful when Juliet went to sit beside their hostess.

Lady Elinor regarded Juliet closely. 'What has Raphael been saying to you? Is something wrong?'

Juliet felt the colour flooding her throat. 'No,' she denied unconvincingly. 'I— Rafe—I mean, Raphael was just offering suggestions about—about what I should drink.'

'Is that all?' Lady Elinor looked up as her grandson came over to hand Juliet her glass of sherry. 'You haven't been intimidating this young woman, have you, Raphael?'

Rafe straightened. 'Now, why would you think a thing like that, old lady?' He glanced at Juliet's bent head. 'We hardly know one another.'

'But she did visit your studio this morning,' Lady Elinor persisted as Juliet's fingers tightened around the glass. She turned once again to her female guest. 'Did Raphael show you some of his work?'

Juliet couldn't escape an answer. 'Oh, yes,' she said, making
sure she didn't look in Rafe's direction, but the old lady clicked
her tongue with some impatience.

'And?' she prompted. 'What did you think? Has the boy got
any talent?'

The boy! Juliet suppressed a groan. 'I'm—sure he has,' she
murmured uncomfortably. 'But—I'm no expert.' She glanced up
at Rafe, wondering what he'd do if she told his grandmother
what she'd seen. She didn't think she wanted to find out.

'The stock answer,' said Lady Elinor irritably. 'You live in
London, don't you? You must have visited other galleries.'

'I don't have a gallery, old lady,' Rafe intervened, aware of
Juliet's ambivalence. 'And you can't expect Juliet to give you a
report when you won't even come and see for yourself.'

'Of course, you would say that,' retorted Lady Elinor tersely.
'Oh, where's Cary? He must know that the Holdernesses will
be here soon.'

'Actually, I thought one of the paintings he showed me was
amazingly good,' Juliet burst out suddenly, surprising herself,
and then wished she hadn't been so impulsive when her
supposed fiancé sauntered into the room.

'Really?' Despite the fact that moments before she'd been de-
ploring her other grandson's tardiness, now Lady Elinor ignored
him to stare at Juliet with sharp, assessing eyes. 'So why didn't
you say this when I asked you? Why did you let me think that
you hadn't been impressed with Raphael's work?'

'Because she wasn't!' exclaimed Cary scornfully, immediately latching on to the conversation. 'My God, Grandmama, is
that why you sent us there? To act as your unpaid spies?'

'Unpaid?' His grandmother regarded him without liking. 'Be
careful what you say, Cary. For someone who makes his living
hustling at a casino, I don't think you should criticise your
cousin for trying to make a success of his life.'

Cary's jaw dropped in consternation and Juliet saw Rafe turn
away from the younger man's embarrassment. 'Who told you I

worked in a casino?' Cary demanded, his eyes moving suspiciously from Juliet to Rafe and back again. 'If Jules has—'

'It wasn't your fiancée,' replied Lady Elinor contemptuously. 'Or Raphael, before your suspicions turn in that direction. I'm not a complete fool, Cary. I have friends in the City. They keep me informed of what you're doing. And why not? You have nothing to hide, do you?'

'No!'

Cary was indignant, but his reddening face gave the lie to his words, and once again Juliet wished she'd never allowed herself to get involved in his affairs. No matter what she thought of Rafe's behaviour, her own was so much worse.

Relief came with the sound of a car outside and then voices in the hall heralded the arrival of Lady Elinor's other guests. The old lady got to her feet herself to greet Lord and Lady Holderness and, if she considered Liv's slashed neckline and silky harem pants hardly suitable for an informal dinner party, no one would have guessed from her benign expression.

Robert Holderness was a man in his late fifties, whose genial demeanour disguised an evident pride in his young wife. Wearing a dark dinner jacket and tie, he ushered Liv into the room ahead of him, nodding a greeting to Rafe before going to take Lady Elinor's outstretched hand.

'Sorry we're late, Ellie,' he said, and for a moment Juliet didn't know who he was talking to. Then Elinor—*Ellie*—clicked into place, and as she showed her comprehension she saw Rafe watching her from across the room.

'Think nothing of it, Bob,' Lady Elinor assured him pleasantly. 'And this must be your new wife. Olivia, isn't it? Raphael tells me that you and he are old friends.'

Liv looked slightly taken aback for once. 'I— Yes,' she said, clearly not expecting to be welcomed in such a manner. She licked her lips nervously. 'What a—lovely home you have, Lady Elinor.'

'I like it.' The old lady's answer made no allowance for the fact that the place was practically falling about her ears. Rafe thought that only someone of Lady Elinor's breeding could say a thing like that and get away with it. She gestured towards the tray of drinks. 'Raphael, perhaps you'd offer our guests an aperitif?'

'I'll do it.' Cary brushed rudely past his cousin and positioned himself beside the cabinet. 'What'll you have, my lord? Scotch and soda? A Martini?'

'Perhaps you should ask my wife first,' Lord Holderness declared a little testily. He turned to Liv. 'What would you like, my dear?'

'Oh—um, a little white wine, please,' she said, though Juliet noticed her eyes were on Rafe, not Cary. 'I think you should have the same, darling. You know what Dr Charteris said.'

'Charteris is an old woman,' declared her husband shortly, and Lady Elinor, who had resumed her seat, clapped her hands.

'Bravo,' she said. 'I totally agree with you, Bob. But,' her eyes turned towards Juliet, 'I haven't introduced you to my other guest. You haven't met Cary's fiancée, Juliet, have you?'

'Why, no.' Lord Holderness came to shake Juliet's hand warmly. 'How do you do, my dear?' He glanced at the younger man. 'I didn't even know your grandson had a regular girlfriend.'

'Nor did we,' murmured Lady Elinor drily, but her smile for Juliet begged forgiveness.

'Let me introduce you to my wife,' Lord Holderness continued, still speaking to Juliet. 'I'm sure you and she will have much more in common. What do you say, Olivia?'

Juliet thought Liv looked a little sick now, but she couldn't find it in her heart to feel sympathy for her. For heaven's sake, the woman was cheating on her husband. How defensible was that?

'As a matter of fact—' she began, ignoring the plea in the other woman's eyes, but before she could reveal that she'd met Lady Holderness earlier in the day Cary interrupted them.

'That's two white wines, then, is it?' he asked, clearly resent-

ing the fact that he was being sidelined, and Liv turned gratefully in his direction.

'Please,' she said. 'If that's all right with you, Bobby?'

'Whatever Lady Holderness says,' her husband declared,
making it obvious that he expected Cary to treat his wife with
respect. 'I just do as I'm told.'

'Oh, Bobby, that's not true,' Liv protested, once again
jumping in before Juliet could speak, and Lady Elinor took the
opportunity to invite her to sit beside her on the sofa.

'I want to hear all about how you two met,' she said firmly.
'Bob is so shy when it comes to personal details.'

Liv looked decidedly nervous now and Juliet couldn't blame
her on that score. She'd experienced a similar interrogation the first
evening she was here and Liv had so much more to hide than most.

'So—Juliet, is it?—how long have you and Ellie's grandson
been seeing one another?' Juliet was distracted by Lord
Holderness who had evidently decided to conduct his own in-
vestigation. 'Did you meet before he went to South Africa?'

'I—well, yes, we did,' Juliet was fumbling, when to her complete surprise Rafe came to her rescue.

'They met when they were children,' he said, strolling over
to join them. 'Isn't that right, Cary? Before you came to live here,
wasn't it?'

Cary handed out the glasses of wine he was carrying and then
gave his cousin a resentful look. 'You know it was,' he said,
without gratitude, and Rafe's lips tilted in amusement.

'I thought so,' he said drily, making Juliet wonder what else
he knew as well.

But, watching them, she felt powerless to intervene. She
might believe Rafe was only using Cary to protect his own relationship with Liv Holderness, but now that the moment had
gone, she baulked at telling the old man his wife was having an
affair with a younger man. Lord Holderness seemed too genuine
an individual to hurt like that.

Thankfully, Cary seemed more intent on improving the impression Lord Holderness had of him than arguing with Rafe and, slipping a possessive arm about Juliet's waist, he said, 'I consider myself a very lucky man, my lord.'

Rafe, viewing Cary's actions with unjustified irritation, clenched his teeth. Just watching his cousin lay his hands on Juliet aroused a gnawing hunger inside him that wouldn't go away. He badly wanted to tear Cary away from her; to draw her out of there—by her hair, if necessary—and show her she was wasting her time on such a sorry piece of dirt.

Which was so unlike him, he thought, trying to concentrate on the conversation. Keeping his eyes away from Juliet's slightly flushed face, he tried to rationalise what was happening to him. God, he was no caveman, desperate to show how macho he was. But for the first time in his life, he had to accept that Juliet aroused feelings inside him that refused to be rationalised. He wanted her, he acknowledged frustratedly. Or perhaps, less emotively, he wanted to sleep with her. Maybe then he'd be able to get on with his life.

Tuning back into the conversation, he heard Cary saying, 'I'm sure you consider yourself a very lucky man, too,' and Lord Holderness gave a grunt of agreement.

'I do indeed,' he said, taking a sip of his wine. 'Thank you.'

'Yes, Liv's a damn fine woman,' Cary continued, obviously not appreciating that he was treading on dangerous ground. 'I've always thought so.'

As Rafe had anticipated, the old man's eyes narrowed suspiciously. 'You know my wife, Daniels?'

'Oh...' Cary reddened. 'Well, yeah. Everybody knows her!' he exclaimed uncomfortably. And then, compounding his error, 'Only by reputation, of course.'

'By reputation!'

Lord Holderness was fairly breathing fire now and once again Rafe felt compelled to intervene. 'I think what Cary means is that as she's Ken Melrose's daughter, she's naturally met a lot of people,' he said mildly. 'Isn't that right, Cary?'

'Well, yeah,' muttered Cary again, though the look he cast in his cousin's direction was hardly grateful.

'I assume you mean because her father owns the Dragon Hotel,' Lord Holderness said, somewhat mollified. 'But she never worked in the bar, you know.'

Didn't she? Rafe exchanged a speaking glance with the woman in question, but he didn't contradict the old man. Josie's appearance to announce that dinner was waiting was a welcome relief to all of them.

They were eating in the conservatory instead of the somewhat questionable dignity of the formal dining room, but Lady Elinor presided over the table with all the elegance of her ancestors. The fact that on his arrival that evening Rafe had had to help Josie carry the small table out of the morning room and set it up in its present position wasn't mentioned, or that it was he who'd suggested to the housekeeper that a cold starter might be in order, thus saving the old woman from bustling back and forth with hot plates on two occasions.

The seating arrangements were of Lady Elinor's choosing. Significantly, she'd seated herself and Lord Holderness at opposite ends of the table, with Juliet and Cary on one side and Olivia and Rafe on the other. It meant that Juliet was conscious of Rafe's eyes upon her with disturbing frequency throughout the meal, which wasn't tempered by Cary's indignation that his grandmother had placed Rafe opposite him, thus acknowledging his cousin's right to be there.

'What the hell does she think she's doing?' he muttered to Juliet as the other members of the party were debating the pros and cons of Cornwall's bid for independence. 'This is to punish me, isn't it? Because she's discovered that I'm not working at some prissy job in the City.'

'He is your cousin,' pointed out Juliet in an undertone, having no desire to defend Rafe, but aware of the dangers here. 'For goodness' sake, Cary, what does it matter? We're going home tomorrow.'

'I know.' Cary's jaw set belligerently. 'But you have to wonder what he says to her when I'm not here.'

'You're getting paranoid,' protested Juliet impatiently, and then flushed when she found Rafe's eyes on her again. Goodness, she fretted, was reading lips another of his accomplishments? She wouldn't be at all surprised. Lifting her table napkin to her lips, she used it to screen her next words. 'Don't forget, he got you out of a sticky situation earlier on.'

'Yeah. I wonder why.' Cary was unappeased. 'What do you think? Are he and Liv having an affair? She seemed bloody familiar with his apartment, if you ask me. And she didn't like it when you and he went down to his studio on your own, however amenable she might have appeared.'

Juliet's stomach tightened unpleasantly. Hearing her own opinion voiced by another person was so much worse than believing she was the only one who knew the truth. And for all she told herself she hated the way Rafe had behaved towards her, the memory of how she'd felt when he was kissing her was a constant torment.

'You're not eating, Juliet.'

Lady Elinor had noticed that, although she'd taken a few mouthfuls of the chilled consommé that had started the meal, so far she'd barely touched the rosemary-flavoured chicken, whose crisp skin made her feel slightly sick.

'Oh—I'm not very hungry,' she murmured awkwardly.

'You don't like chicken, perhaps?'

'Heavens, yes.' Juliet was conscious of everyone looking at her now. 'It's not the food—'

'Then, what—?'

'You're embarrassing her, old lady.' Rafe regarded his grandmother over the rim of his glass. 'She's not as used to you as we are. Why don't you turn your considerable energies towards ringing the bell for Josie? I'm sure your other guests would like another bottle of this excellent Chardonnay.'

Lady Elinor's lips pursed. 'I'll thank you to keep your opinions to yourself, Raphael,' she declared irritably, and Juliet was aware of Cary's chortle of triumph at what he saw as Rafe's humiliation.

But Rafe's words did have the desired effect and a moment later Lady Elinor reached for the bellpull and gave it a sharp jerk. However, Rafe noticed that it didn't stop her from casting a speculative glance from him to Juliet and back again, and he knew his defence of the girl hadn't gone unnoticed. He just hoped he hadn't overplayed his hand.

After dessert—a delicious summer pudding that Juliet suspected might have been bought in for the occasion—they all retired to the drawing room again for coffee. This time Cary made sure he was seated near Lord Holderness, and when Josie had delivered the tray and departed he started the conversation by saying, ingenuously, 'Grandmama tells me you live in a castle, sir. How exciting! Is it very old?'

Lord Holderness frowned. 'What have you been saying, Ellie?' he asked half-impatiently. 'You know perfectly well that Trelawney is just a country house.'

Lady Elinor's lips tightened. 'I believe what I actually said was that Trelawney looked a little like a castle,' she declared, giving her younger grandson an impatient look. 'Besides, I can't see that it's of any interest to you, Cary.'

'Oh, you're wrong. I'm always interested in old buildings,' he protested with assumed innocence. 'I mean, I'm always amazed at how much it costs for the upkeep these days. I can't imagine how you—all—manage it.'

Juliet was horrified now. She thought she knew exactly where this was going, and she tried to catch Cary's eye to warn him not to say any more. But her 'fiancé' was enjoying himself for the first time that evening, unaware that he might just alienate himself from the one person who cared anything about him.

'Nevertheless, we do,' Lord Holderness responded stiffly. 'It would be a terrible shame if one's heritage had to be sacrificed on the altar of commercialism.'

'I agree.' Cary was endeavouring to sound sincere. 'I know I love this old place, but you must have noticed how it's deteriorating. I wish there was a way I could help you, Grandmama.' He frowned as if he'd just thought of it. 'Have you ever thought of selling some of the land that's at present part of the estate? To give you some working capital, so to speak.'

'That will do, Cary.'

It was Rafe who spoke. He'd been lounging on the sofa beside Lady Elinor, jacket parted, long legs extended and crossed at the ankles. But now he sat up, and Juliet could see he was furious. She was fairly annoyed herself, she thought, and she wasn't even a member of the family. Didn't Cary realise he was in danger of betraying the fact that he'd read that letter from the developer?

'I don't believe I spoke to you,' Cary said now, scowling at Rafe for involving himself in the discussion. He turned to the old lady again. 'You must agree with me, Grandmama. Tregellin is going to collapse about your ears unless something is done.'

'Cary—'

'It's all right, Raphael.' Lady Elinor placed a hand upon his knee, indicating that she didn't need his assistance. 'Cary has his own opinions, of course. And I'm interested in how he feels about Tregellin. I must take his suggestion of selling the property seriously.'

'Not the house,' broke in Cary at once, apparently realising his mistake. 'Just—one or two of the farms, perhaps.' He cast about him for someone to support his argument. 'Jules, you can see the sense in what I'm saying, can't you? No one wants to see the old place fall apart.'

Before Juliet could say anything, Lady Elinor spoke. 'I believe I know what's best for Tregellin, Cary,' she murmured, and, judging from her expression, Juliet didn't think Cary understood his grandmother at all. 'Now,' she turned to Lord Holderness, 'does your wife play bridge, Bob?'

She didn't, but her hostess prevailed upon her to learn and, together with Cary, who was eager to mend fences, they made a four. 'You don't mind, do you, Juliet?' the old lady asked, before they gathered round the table in the conservatory again. 'Raphael, you'll entertain our young guest, won't you? You might show her your mother's paintings. You'll find one or two in the library.'

CHAPTER ELEVEN

RAFE pushed open the library door and allowed a reluctant Juliet to precede him into the room. He was trying hard to hide his frustration at the way Lady Elinor had manipulated him, aware that he was the last person Juliet wanted to spend any more time with.

Not that he'd wanted to join the bridge party. Far from it. But he resented the old lady's machinations almost as much as Cary did. Dammit, he didn't want to spend the rest of the evening with a woman who didn't trust him. Not when being with her was both a betrayal of his own self-respect and an intolerable temptation.

Another source of irritation was the apparent presence of some of his mother's paintings. In all the time he'd lived at Tregellin, he never remembered seeing any of her water colours on public view. In fact, he'd always assumed that the old lady had destroyed any that had come into her possession after his mother's death.

Now, however, when he followed Juliet into the library, which had also acted as his grandfather's study when he was alive, he caught his breath in stunned disbelief. Two walls were, as usual, lined with the books that had been collected over the years, but the others were a veritable art gallery of not just his mother's paintings, but also his own.

Pastel impressions of the shifting light on the canals of Venice mingled with Cornish landscapes that were harsh and rugged, and scarred with old mine-workings; vanilla skies above purple Tuscan hills were offset by a rocky coastline that despite its silvery sands was intrinsically English. Some of his own work, paintings he'd assumed had been sold to anonymous collectors, were his earliest efforts, landscapes that these days wouldn't survive his personal cutting floor.

'*Dios*,' he said succinctly, backing up against the door to close it, leaning against the panels for a moment, too dazed to move.

Juliet turned to give him a resentful look. 'Hey, I don't like this any more than you do!' she exclaimed. And then, noticing his stunned expression, 'What's wrong?'

Rafe grunted. 'Nothing. Everything.' He stared at the paintings. 'I wonder how long the old lady has had these?'

'Your mother's paintings?' Juliet moved closer to the wall. 'I assume these water colours are hers?'

Rafe nodded. 'She loved Italy. Particularly Tuscany.' Then, as if trying to clear his head. 'We spent a lot of time there when I was young.'

Juliet gave him a curious look. 'How old were you when your mother died?' she ventured, and then shook her head. 'Don't answer that. It's nothing to do with me.'

Rafe answered her anyway. 'I was seven,' he said flatly. He bent his head, 'There was no one to look after me, so the authorities sent me to England.'

'To your grandmother?'

'To the old lady, yes,' agreed Rafe, pressing his shoulders back against the door behind him. 'I hated it at first. England was so cold!'

Juliet thought she could imagine how terrifying it must have been for him, a small boy, uprooted from everything he knew and was used to, from his paternal heritage, in fact. She wanted to ask where his father had been at that time, but that would be too intrusive. All the same, she had to know why the pictures had come as such a surprise to him.

Glancing over her shoulder, she said, 'And you didn't know

Lady Elinor had these paintings?' she asked tentatively. 'But if they were here—'

'They weren't.' Rafe raked agitated fingers over his skull. 'I was here, in this room, less than a week ago.' His lips twisted. 'They weren't here then and nor were the others.'

'Your paintings, you mean?'

'If you can call them that.' Rafe was bitter. 'I painted these— oh, maybe fifteen years ago.'

'And what happened to them?'

'I got a call from a solicitor in Bodmin, who said he'd heard about my work through his connections with the school where I was teaching. He came to see them, said he liked them. I considered myself lucky to have found a buyer.' He gave a short, mirthless laugh. 'I even pitied the poor devil for taking them on.'

Juliet stared at him. 'Don't be so critical. I think they're very good. This solicitor must have thought so, anyway.'

'Oh, no.' Rafe pushed away from the door and strode across the room fairly radiating controlled violence. 'Don't you see— there was no solicitor? It was the old lady manipulating me again.' He paused. 'I was still living here, at Tregellin. I didn't have a place of my own, but she knew I'd converted one of the old coach houses into a makeshift studio, and she lost no opportunity to ridicule my efforts, to tell me that I'd never succeed in producing anything worthwhile. She used to tell my mother the same thing. That's why Christina—that was my mother's name—refused to come back to England. The old lady wanted to control her life, just as she'd like to control mine.'

Juliet frowned. 'So why do you think she bought the paintings?'

'Who knows? Another of her games, perhaps. If, by some incredible chance, I became successful, she could produce these and claim she'd always known I had talent.' He snorted. 'If not, no one would be any the wiser.'

Juliet shook her head. 'Do you really believe she's that devious?'

Rafe scowled. 'She can be,' he said, 'so beware.'

Juliet caught her breath. Was he warning her that Lady Elinor might have an agenda for her, too? She'd certainly thwarted Cary's attempt to outwit her. About his job, at least.

'It's nothing to do with me,' she said again, not wanting to take sides, but to her dismay Rafe came to stand directly in front of her.

'It will be when you marry Cary,' he said, lifting a hand and smearing his thumb across her lower lip. It was an incredibly sensuous thing to do and she wondered if his anger had blinded him to his actions. His eyes darkened. 'Are you really going to marry that sorry excuse for a man?'

'He's not a sorry excuse for a man.' Juliet was defensive. 'And you're hardly in a position to judge.' She jerked her head to one side to avoid his intimate caress, but all she did was shift his focus, long fingers curving about the taut muscles at the back of her neck.

She was intensely conscious of him, of the fluid strength with which he held her as he probed the sensitive nerves that bracketed her spine. Her mouth dried, her protests shrivelling in spite of her resistance. All she was really conscious of were his eyes upon her, watching her closely, like a predator preparing to strike.

'Go on,' he taunted at last. 'Say what you have to. You despise me. I can see that. But what is there about Cary that rings your bell? Tell me about him. Tell me how much you love him. What does he have that attracts you? Is it his personality? His good looks? What?'

'I don't have to tell you anything,' retorted Juliet, and Rafe was infuriated by the fact that, once again, she was making him act like a savage. But damn it all, he thought, seeing those paintings had brought out the worst in him. As the old lady had known they would, he guessed bitterly. But even she couldn't have had this scenario in mind.

'Cat got your tongue?' he mocked now, ignoring the insistent voice inside him that kept warning him to end this, while he still could. 'For someone who professes to be engaged to someone else, you're very permissive. Tell me, were you thinking about Cary when I was kissing you, when I was pushing my tongue into your mouth—?'

'Stop it!'

Juliet brought up her hands to push against his chest, but when her fingers spread against the fine fabric of his sweater all she was conscious of was the body beneath the cloth. She could feel his heart beating, a living, breathing force that seemed to surround her, and a trickle of moisture made its way down between her breasts.

'What's he like in bed?' Rafe was relentless, the demon on his shoulder finding pleasure in her weak efforts to escape him. He defended his actions by assuring himself that his grandmother shouldn't have provoked him, but he couldn't help wondering if he was just playing into her hands. 'Is he better or worse than your ex-husband?' he jeered softly. 'I guess he must be *much* better. Why else would you be marrying the poor sod?'

'You have no right to criticise Cary,' Juliet protested unsteadily. 'At least he's not having an affair with a married woman!'

'I'm not having an affair with a married woman!' Rafe shifted to catch her chin in a brutal grip, his fingers digging into her soft flesh. He stared down at her with narrowed eyes. 'If those sketches are still bugging you, I explained what I was doing. Why is it so hard to believe that Liv would come to me?'

'Oh, I have no difficulty in believing that Liv comes to you,' retorted Juliet contemptuously. 'Where else would she go when she wants a younger man in her bed?'

'You're crazy!' Rafe was incensed. 'Liv loves her husband. Just because you got your knickers in a twist when you saw she was naked in those sketches, don't imagine I feel the same.'

'They don't turn you on, then?'

'Hell, no!'

'Oh, please—'

'I mean it.' Rafe swore. 'If I'd been turned on by every nude I'd seen, I'd be in a constant state of arousal.'

'You're disgusting!'

'And you're incredible,' said Rafe harshly. 'If I didn't know better I'd say Cary had dreamed the whole thing up to protect his own sorry ass.' His lips twisted. 'And you're no better. You're prepared to prostitute yourself to get a share of the old lady's cash—'

His words were arrested by the simple fact of Juliet's palm hitting his cheek. She'd pulled her hands free and her fingers stung from their violent contact with his face.

'You—you—' she choked, unable to find an epithet to suit the occasion, and saw the bitter smile that crossed his face.

'Hey, call me a bastard, why don't you?' he taunted. 'You wouldn't be the first.' He pushed her away from him so violently that she almost fell. 'You're just like the old lady, do you know that? You don't like to hear the truth, even when it jumps up and hits you in the face!'

'It's not true!'

Juliet swallowed convulsively, aware that the little she'd eaten at dinner was in danger of making a return appearance. She'd known he had the ability to hurt her, but not how much, and with a muffled moan she turned and headed for the door.

He didn't try to stop her, and upstairs, in her room, she made straight for the lavatory. Her stomach heaved on cue and, after a few exhausting minutes, she transferred to the hand basin.

She was struggling to clean her teeth, to get the unpleasant taste out of her mouth, when there was a knock at the outer door. She stiffened instinctively, but then, realising Rafe was unlikely to come after her, let alone know which room she was occupying, she wiped her mouth with the back of her hand and walked across the sitting room to the door.

'Who is it?' she called, but no one answered. Neither was the knock repeated, and, rueing the fact that the door didn't have a peephole as hotel doors did, she reluctantly cracked it open.

Rafe was standing outside, his hands hanging loosely at his sides, a look of weary resignation on his dark face. She would have slammed the door again, but he put his foot in the opening, pressing it wider with one hand and easing his way inside.

'I'm sorry,' he said simply, her white face and bruised eyes telling it all. Reaching out, he grabbed her hips and pulled her towards him. 'I'm such a fool,' he said, burying his face in the hollow of her neck. 'Please: tell me you forgive me.'

Juliet couldn't speak. She was trembling so badly that she was amazed her legs continued to support her. She needed to sit down, she thought. *Or lie down*, another less virtuous voice insinuated. Which made her no better than Liv.

'Oh, sweetheart.' One hand cupped her nape and her eyes closed as his mouth descended towards hers. Firm lips rubbed gently against hers, his tongue a tender caress now as he parted her mouth and pushed inside. Sensuously, sensually, he coaxed her tongue into a helpless participation and then, as his own needs sharpened, he deepened the kiss until any will she might have had to resist him was totally destroyed.

His kisses drugged her senses, bruised her lips, robbed her of the breath in her lungs. He had a hand at her back, sliding possessively over her bottom, urging her even closer against him until his erection pressed against her mound.

'You knew I'd come to find you, didn't you?' he challenged when his mouth seared her cheek. His tongue found the erratic pulse that beat beneath her ear and which matched his own. He was struggling to hang on to his senses, but with her in his arms it was hard to keep his head.

'N—no. No.' Her response was husky, her voice losing definition as his fingers slid down to her thigh to lift her leg and wind it about his hip. 'I—I didn't even know you knew which room I was sleeping in.'

'Oh, I knew,' muttered Rafe, his hand slipping beneath the short hem of her dress to caress her. 'The old lady told me. But I doubt if even she had anything like this in mind.'

Juliet sucked in a breath as his long fingers moved over the fine silk of her stockings and found smooth bare skin. Between her legs she knew she was wet and vulnerable, and his muffled groan of satisfaction proved he had discovered that, too.

'You want me,' he said, and his words were shaken, as if, in spite of everything, he hadn't been entirely sure of himself, after all.

'Don't talk,' she said, cupping his face in her hands, feeling his stubble against her palms. She brought his lips back to hers. 'This is a much more satisfying use of your mouth.'

'I can think of a better one,' said Rafe harshly, but she noticed he didn't refuse her invitation. Angling her face to his, he captured her lower lip between his teeth, biting the soft flesh with a fierceness that was as sexual as it was painful.

Juliet clung, fisting handfuls of his silk sweater, uncaring that she was pulling his chest hair out by its roots. Only when he stifled a gasp did she realise what she was doing, and, spreading her hands, she murmured 'Sorry' against his lips.

'I forgive you,' he muttered, one hand cupping her bottom, and there was a hungry, carnal urgency in his gaze.

Rafe knew he couldn't wait much longer to be a part of her. His own feelings were getting dangerously out of control. He wanted to tear her clothes from her, to see the breasts that were pressing so provocatively against her bodice. Was she wearing a bra? He didn't think so. And that suspicion alone made him say thickly, 'Let's find somewhere more comfortable, shall we?'

Juliet hesitated, drawing back a little when he would have drawn her closer, and his brows came together in a frown of disbelief. 'You don't want me to touch you?' he asked, allowing one hand to slide down her throat to trace the hollow of her cleavage. 'I thought you did. Because that's what I want, Juliet.' His lips twisted. 'You have no idea how much.'

'I did. I *do*!'

Juliet spoke jerkily and he realised with some amazement that she was nervous. This woman, who'd been married for six years, was nervous. What had that bastard done to her? And he wasn't sure if he was thinking of her ex-husband or Cary...but she definitely wasn't confident about having sex with him.

Moving closer, he lifted her off her feet, and she was forced to put both legs about his waist. He was overwhelmingly aware of how it opened her to his arousal, of how it exposed her legs to her upper thighs and allowed the scent of her essence to rise seductively to his nose.

'Let's stop pretending, shall we?' he said huskily. 'You want me, and God knows, I want you. Am I right?'

'Yes. Yes.' She spoke breathily, a sexy sound that raised goose bumps on his skin. 'But—well—I'm—'

'Engaged,' said Rafe harshly. 'Yeah, I know that.'

'No.' Juliet cradled his face in his hands. 'I just wanted to warn you, I'm not—very good at this.'

Rafe blinked. 'Cary said that?'

Juliet allowed a breath to escape on a sob. 'No, David.'

'Your ex-husband.'

He didn't want to ask, but he had to. 'And Cary?'

'I haven't slept with Cary,' she admitted honestly, and Rafe wanted to howl with delight. She hesitated, and then added uncertainly, 'I don't even know if this is the right thing to do.'

'Trust me, it's the only thing to do,' said Rafe, carrying her across the sitting room and into the bedroom. He laid her on the bed, a single lamp providing the only illumination. 'Believe me, this has gone much too far now for either of us to have second thoughts.'

'Well, yes.' Juliet gazed up at him as he stood looking down at her. 'I—I'm not having second thoughts, but—'

'No buts,' he said, putting one knee on the bed beside her and allowing his hand to trail softly over her cheek. His thumb found the pulse that was racing below her ear and pressed urgently against it. 'Relax, baby. I'm not going to hurt you.'

It was incredibly difficult to take it slowly. Lying there, unconsciously seductive, she made him ache to possess her. All he really wanted to do was take off her clothes and bury his hot flesh between her legs.

Without taking his eyes from hers, he shucked off his jacket and dropped it carelessly onto the floor. He wasn't wearing a tie—which was just as well, he thought gratefully. At least the sweater allowed him to breathe.

Easing down onto one hip, he allowed his hand to move from her ear to the provocative neckline of her bodice. Tracing a line around the rim, he allowed his finger to dip beneath the cloth, discovering, as he'd anticipated, she wasn't wearing a bra.

Fortunately, there was a row of small buttons running from the neckline to her waist. His fingers fumbled, but he succeeded in opening four of the buttons, parting the lace-covered satin to reveal breasts that were full and round and already swollen with need.

'Juliet,' he said hoarsely, bending towards her. He took one ripe nipple between his teeth and heard her take a convulsive gulp of air. His tongue circled the tip, and he tasted its sweetness. Then he massaged the soft flesh with an urgency that was almost painful, before giving up and sucking the areola into his mouth.

Juliet dug her nails into the quilted coverlet, conscious that what he was doing was causing a tightening in her stomach and a throbbing awareness between her thighs. Her breasts ached and she wanted to spread her legs, and have him touch her there, too. But she couldn't tell him that, could she? She wasn't that kind of a girl.

Or was she?

Rafe lifted his head. His eyes were dark and sensual, and she shivered in anticipation of what he might do next. 'Help me,' he said, indicating the tiny buttons, and, although her fingers were slippery with perspiration, she didn't think of saying no.

The buttons opened and she lifted her hands, but instead of trying to cool her hot cheeks she caught his face between her palms and brought his mouth to hers. Her head swam as he kissed her, long, drugging kisses that made her body weak and languid with desire. She couldn't remember ever feeling this way with anyone, particularly David, and she shifted against him restlessly, trying to show him how she felt.

Rafe drew back at last, and she groaned in protest. But all he did was lay a tempting finger across her parted lips. 'We're wearing too many clothes,' he said, stroking her thigh where her dress had been pushed up in her agitation. 'Tell me, how in hell do I take this off?'

'Let me,' she said, too aroused to be reticent. Sitting up, she lifted the hem of the dress over her head. There was something liberating about not being ashamed for him to see her body, and the raw hunger in his eyes made her glad she'd shed her inhibitions.

Nevertheless, when his eyes dropped to the lacy thong that was all she was now wearing, it wasn't easy to prevent the instinctive need to cover herself. At another time, and in another place, she wouldn't have dared to be so shameless. But with Rafe's eyes upon her, she allowed herself to enjoy his admiring gaze.

However, when he hooked a finger into the waistband of the thong and tugged it lower, she couldn't deny a panicky intake of breath. And when that same finger slid down into the curls that hid her womanhood, it took every bit of control to remain where she was without crossing her legs.

But her, 'For God's sake, Rafe,' wouldn't be silenced, and Rafe slanted a look that was defined by a speculative brow.

'What?' he asked, though he knew very well why she was agitated. 'Am I doing something wrong? Perhaps you ought to show me what you like.'

'I like it all,' she confessed chokingly, closing her eyes against the hint of smugness in his face. 'Please, Rafe,' she went on, not entirely sure what she was asking for, and with a smothered oath Rafe bent forward again and buried his face between her legs.

She smelled delicious, and tasted better. The temptation was to slide his tongue into her sheath and feel her come against his mouth. But the ache between his legs forbore such generosity. He couldn't be sure he could wait so long to find his own release.

Forcing himself to be patient, he sat up and hauled off his sweater. Then, he unbuckled his belt and unfastened the button at his waist. He didn't open his zip, aware that if he did so he wouldn't be able to control his erection. He wanted her so badly and there was only so much he could take in his present state.

Juliet felt the draught as he discarded his sweater. She opened her eyes to the sight of his lean brown torso with its distinctive triangle of hair. She saw that the hair arrowed down past his flat navel, disappearing into his waistband, tempting her to discover where it had gone.

Rafe's tugging away her thong caused her to reconsider. She wasn't used to any man undressing her, had never shared the pleasure to be found in participating in her own seduction. David had expected her to take her own clothes off, even when they were on their honeymoon. And then his lovemaking had lacked any kind of foreplay. He'd taken her with as little care as he'd done everything else.

In those days Juliet had found the experience downright unpleasant, not to say painful. And later on, she supposed she'd been stiff and unresponsive whenever he'd wanted sex. She'd even wondered if that was why David had tired of her, always ready to blame herself for his mistakes.

Now, however, she knew it hadn't been all her fault. When Rafe peeled off her stockings and bestowed a trail of kisses from her instep to her inner thigh, her anticipation became intense. She could hardly wait for him to remove the other stocking and repeat the experience. She spread her legs intuitively, her palms between her thighs, holding them apart.

Rafe groaned, her innocent enticement causing an actual pain between his legs. She was so responsive, so ready for him, it was incredible. Had she any idea of what it was doing to him?

Holding her eyes with his, he quickly divested himself of his trousers and boxer shorts. Then, aware of her watching him, too, he stretched his length between her legs. 'You're very big, aren't you?' she breathed, and Rafe gave a muffled groan.

'Size isn't everything,' he whispered, trying to hang on to his sanity. But when she reached for him, he could feel his control slipping away.

Juliet was instantly aware when the smooth, rounded head of his erection probed her vagina. And, although she'd been totally relaxed a few moments before, suddenly what she was about to do didn't seem so easy, after all. Perhaps she was frigid, she thought in panic, just as David had insisted. Foreplay was one thing, but actually letting a man possess her was definitely something else.

Rafe sensed the moment when her response turned to rejection. God, he thought again, what had her ex-husband done to make her so afraid to give in? 'It's OK,' he said, putting his hand between them and finding the swollen nub that he'd tasted earlier. Massaging it gently, he felt her body relax and he took the opportunity to ease inside her. She stiffened again, but then her muscles seemed to act without her volition, expanding and enfolding him within her slick sheath.

Juliet let out a shuddering sigh as he filled her. Apprehension was giving way to anticipation and the excitement she'd felt earlier started to build once more. This wasn't David, she reminded herself, as if any reminder were necessary. This was Rafe and—God help her!—she wanted to share this pleasure with him.

'Dear God,' she moaned, giving in to her emotions. She clutched his shoulders, gazing up at him with wide, appealing eyes. 'Just—do it, hmm? Please, Rafe, I need you now.'

As if he had any choice, thought Rafe wryly. But he'd never had sex with a woman yet without giving her as much pleasure as she was giving him. 'If you're ready,' he breathed, aware that he was trembling. 'Take it easy, baby. I want to show you how good it can be.'

He moved slowly at first, withdrawing almost to the point of separation and then slowly pushing into her again. She moaned as he did so, and he bent to silence her mouth with kisses. Then, caressing her, he repeated the exercise, and felt her muscles tighten around him with obvious intent.

The response she'd shown when he'd first kissed her showed now in the urgency with which she arched against him. And, just as he'd hoped, her nervous breathing quickened to match his own. With a little cry, she wound her legs around him, and he sank so deeply into her that he was sure he'd touched her womb.

But his own needs were becoming rampant and, as she bucked and jerked against him, he let his own feelings find release. He felt the drenching heat of her orgasm only moments before he shuddered in ecstasy, spilling his seed inside her in an agony of relief…

CHAPTER TWELVE

BLOODY hell!

Rafe opened his eyes to find himself slumped on top of Juliet's supine body. He was lying between her legs, which were spread confidingly. His semi-arousal was still buried deep inside her, only needing the slightest encouragement to harden into urgent life.

Which he mustn't allow to happen!

He stifled the oath that sprang to his lips and closed his eyes against the enormity of his transgression. Despite his determination not to do so, he'd made love to his cousin's fiancée. All the contempt he'd felt for Cary's behaviour was now heaped upon his own head.

He opened his mouth to say something, to attempt some pathetic effort at an apology, and then realised Juliet was fast asleep. With one leg curled around one of his, and a hand lying limply on his thigh, she was dead to the world. Obviously exhausted, he thought guiltily, and totally unaware of the possible consequences of what they'd done.

Well, for the moment, anyway, Rafe amended, realising that happy state wouldn't last long. As soon as she opened her eyes, as soon as she discovered how he'd taken advantage of her inexperience, she'd be horrified. She might never forgive him. She might never understand how much he hated himself right now.

How could he have done such a thing? All right. She was delicious: sexy, yet strangely innocent, and oh, so very sweet. Too good for Cary, he thought with an uncharacteristic surge of arrogance. Cary would never make her happy. He was much too selfish a man to care about anybody but himself.

But was he any better?

He didn't have an answer, the question a chilling reminder that he was the one who'd seduced her, not his cousin. He might have come up here with the best of intentions. He might have meant to apologise for the way he'd behaved earlier. But what he'd actually done was take her to bed, which was the most treacherous kind of betrayal.

He had to move. Apart from anything else, he was getting a cramp in his thigh. Lying here, hoping that she'd wake up and let him do it all again, was purely evil. If he had any sense he'd get out of there, before the old lady finished her game and started wondering what had happened to them. Somehow, he couldn't see Lady Elinor approving of his actions, when she'd been at pains to ensure that Juliet and Cary shouldn't share a room. Not that he felt much loyalty towards the old lady at the moment.

Although he got to his knees without too much effort and could have easily grabbed his clothes off the floor and dressed in the sitting room, ridiculously, he lingered. He hated the thought of leaving Juliet alone. That would give her entirely the wrong impression. However base his actions had been, he still had some self-respect left.

Not that he thought she'd regard his belated concern as any kind of comfort. Salving his conscience, maybe. What the hell was he hanging about for? Absolution? It wasn't going to happen. She'd never forgive him. He might just as well grab his clothes and crawl back under his stone.

'Where are you going?'

He had one leg in his boxer shorts when Juliet's drowsy words arrested him. Quickly shoving in his other leg, he hauled them up and turned around. 'Um—I think I ought to go and see what's going on,' he muttered, wishing he had a more satisfactory explanation. He should have anticipated what he was going to say before he started getting dressed.

'Does it matter?'

Juliet pushed herself up on her elbows, the coverlet, which he'd edged over her, falling away to reveal her full, perfect breasts. Dear God, he thought, this wasn't fair. He was only human. Didn't she realise what looking at her was doing to him? Oh, yes, she must. Those sleepy eyes had dropped to the tented bulge beneath his shorts.

'In—in the normal way, no,' he said now, finding the conversation almost esoteric. 'But it's possible that—' he had to say it '—that your fiancé might be looking for you.'

'And that matters?' She was so cool, he had the feeling he'd stepped into some alternative universe. 'Oh, I get it,' she went on contemptuously, dragging the offending coverlet back into place. 'It's OK to have sex with your cousin's fiancée, so long as you don't get found out, right? God help me, that I might get the wrong idea.'

Rafe closed his eyes for a moment, wishing he'd never started this. He should have gone when he'd had half a chance. Before he put his foot in his mouth and made her think he regretted what had happened. He did, of course, though not for the reasons she thought.

All the same, she was Cary's fiancée. That should mean something to her, shouldn't it? He might think the guy was a louse, but she'd got engaged to him. Where was this crazy conversation going? However attractive the idea, he couldn't believe she was prepared to ditch Cary just because she'd had sex with him.

But he had to find out before he blew his cover completely.

'What are you saying?' he asked now, reaching for his trousers. 'Are you telling me that what we just shared changes the way you feel about Cary? We've known each other for two days, Juliet. Do you expect me to believe you've fallen madly in love with me in that time and you want to have my baby? It sounds very flattering, but are you really going to break your engagement so we can be together?'

Juliet swallowed, the whole weight of her own deception descending on her shoulders. Of course, he was right. Anything else was pure fantasy on her part. Besides, it wasn't what he wanted; that was obvious. So it was just as well she didn't have a choice.

'I—I can't,' she mumbled at last, knowing what he'd think and taking comfort from it. Far better that he believe she was a gold-digger than some pathetic twenty-something with more imagination than sense.

There was a scornful expression on his face now. 'I didn't think so,' he mocked, and she found she had to say something in her own defence.

'No, you don't understand—' she began, but Rafe ignored her.

'Don't bet on it,' he said, and paradoxically, he sounded bitter. 'I understand very well what you want and it's not the old lady's *illegitimate* grandson!'

Rafe was working when someone knocked on the windows of his studio. He'd purposely drawn the blinds at the front of the building, pushing the rear service doors wide at the back to allow the pale sunlight to seep inside. He didn't want to see anyone, he certainly didn't want to talk to anyone, and he wondered who would have the gall to disturb him at barely eight o'clock on a Sunday morning.

The irritating tapping came again, but he tried to ignore it. It could be no one he wanted to admit. According to the old lady, her guests were leaving this morning, and they'd have no reason to make a detour to Polgellin Bay.

Unless Cary had found out...

'Rafe! Rafe! Dammit, I know you're in there. Have the decency to come and open this door and let me in.'

Not Cary, then. Rafe scowled. He should have realised there was only one person who would come here to exact an explanation for the way he'd behaved the night before. And it wasn't Lady Elinor.

Throwing down the knife he'd been using to scrape a layer
of paint from the canvas, he strode impatiently to the door.
Yanking it open with an aggressive hand, he glared coldly at the
woman who was waiting outside.

'What do you want?'

'Ooh, darling, so masterful!' Without waiting for an invitation, Liv Holderness squeezed delicately past him and into the
studio. She glanced about her. 'Are you alone?'

Rafe's mouth hardened as he reluctantly closed the door.
'What do you want, Liv? I don't believe we had an appointment
this morning.'

'We didn't.' But Liv wasn't perturbed by his ill humour. 'I just
thought you might want to tell me what last night was all about.'

Rafe aped a look of surprise. 'Last night?' he echoed carelessly. 'Didn't you enjoy it?'

'Not as much as you did, I'll bet,' Liv flashed back, with a
distinct note of resentment in her voice now. 'Why the hell
didn't you tell me that you were going to be there?'

Rafe grimaced. He'd been asked that question before by
someone he was trying hard not to think about, and he didn't appreciate Liv coming here and reminding him of the fact.

'I didn't know,' he said flatly. 'Believe it or not, I only
received my invitation after you'd gone home.'

'Yeah, right.'

'It's true.' Rafe was struggling to keep his temper. 'Now, if
that's all you've come to say—'

'It's not.' Liv drifted round the studio, picking up a photo-
graph here, a brush there, causing Rafe no small amount of aggravation. 'Why did Lady Elinor invite you? Do you know?'

Rafe sighed. 'In polite circles, it's usual to have an equal
number of men and women around the dinner table—'

'Don't patronise me, Marchese!'

'Then don't you pretend you give a damn why I was invited.
I was there. That's all there is to it. If your old man didn't like
what was said, take it up with Cary, not me.'

Liv seethed. 'As a matter of fact, Bobby enjoyed the evening. He and your grandmother get along very well.'

Rafe's lips twisted. 'Why wouldn't they? They've known one another for a lot of years.'

'You mean, they're nearer in age than Bobby and me.'

'I didn't say that.'

'No, but you meant it.' Liv huffed. 'Anyway, as you appear to know so much about me, why don't you tell me why I'm here?'

'Oh, no.' Rafe propped his jean-clad hips against a work-bench, crossing his arms over his paint-smeared T-shirt and regarding her with mocking eyes. 'I wouldn't presume to know how your mind works.'

'Jerk!'

'I've been called worse.'

And recently, he reflected, once again stung by how easily the memory of Juliet could knock him off balance, could cause an actual knot to form in his stomach.

Liv stopped in the middle of the floor and turned to face him, and for an uncomfortable moment he thought she'd guessed what was on his mind. But all she did was stare at him mutinously before saying, 'All right. So tell me why you left the party without even joining the rest of us for a final drink?'

Rafe's jaw compressed. 'I prefer not to drink when I'm driving. I don't have a chauffeur to take me home.'

'We could have taken you home,' pointed out Liv, as if the idea had just occurred to her. 'But as you know, we didn't get the chance to offer.'

'Sorry.' But he didn't sound it.

Liv frowned. 'So why did you walk out like that? I know Lady Elinor wasn't pleased.'

'Wasn't she?' Right then, Rafe hadn't cared what Lady Elinor had thought of his behaviour. 'I was tired, OK?' he muttered irritably. 'I've had a lot of work to do lately. Not a concept I imagine you'd know anything about.'

'Yeah, yeah.' Liv wasn't impressed with his excuses. 'So your departure had nothing to do with—what's her name—Juliet?'

Rafe managed to keep his expression blank with an effort. 'Juliet?' he echoed, as if the thought was new to him. 'No. Why would it?'

'Oh, come on.' Liv was incredulous. 'You spent most of the evening with her!'

'Excuse me!' Rafe was proud of the indignation in his voice. 'We spent—perhaps—half an hour together in the library, looking at the paintings.' He frowned, pretending to consider. 'Then I think she went up to her room, and I read for a while until you'd finished your game.'

'Really?'

'Yes, really,' he said, hoping God would forgive him for the lies he was telling. It wasn't good enough to assure himself he was only doing it to protect Juliet. The truth was, he was trying to save his own skin. 'Now, if you don't mind—'

Liv heaved a deep sigh. 'So what do you think Lady Elinor had in mind when she practically pushed the two of you together? I mean, I know Cary had some sucking-up to do, but making him play cards while his fiancée was alone with another man doesn't seem fair to me.'

'When you get to know the old lady better, you'll realise that fair play's no part in her vocabulary,' said Rafe drily. 'Now, do you mind getting out of here? I've wasted enough time as it is.'

Juliet and Cary got back to London in the late afternoon. Although she knew Cary would have preferred to hang around until later in the day, she reminded him of their bargain and with ill grace he'd been forced to give in.

He had gone to see his grandmother before they left, perhaps hoping that she would agree to prevail upon Juliet to stay longer. But Hitchins had apparently cut his visit short and the old lady hadn't seemed sorry to see him go.

'It's all that bastard Rafe's fault,' Cary muttered as they accelerated up the track to the main road. 'If he hadn't had so much to say for himself last night, the old girl might have begun to see the sense in what I was saying.'

Juliet shook her head. She had a headache, actually, and she wasn't in the mood for Cary's tantrums, but that particular accusation caught her on the raw. 'If Rafe hadn't interfered, as you put it, you'd have been in even deeper trouble,' she retorted tersely. 'You're not subtle, Cary. I think it was obvious to anyone who knew about that letter from the developer that you'd read it.'

'I don't think so.'

'Well, I do.' Juliet was impatient. 'Why do you think she asked you to make up a foursome for bridge and not Rafe? She wanted to punish you, that's all. You just want to hope she's forgotten all about it by the time you make your next visit.'

Cary snorted. 'Oh, yeah. My next visit. And when I turn up without you, what do you think she's going to say about that?'

Juliet sighed. She so didn't need this. 'Cary,' she said levelly, 'you knew this was a one-time occasion. And you must have realised that Lady Elinor would be disappointed when we—well, broke up, as she'll see it.'

Cary chewed on his lower lip, cursing when another driver blew his horn at him because he'd attempted to overtake without signalling. 'I don't suppose—that is, you wouldn't consider—?'

'Repeating the exercise?' Juliet gave him a disbelieving look. 'You can't be serious!'

'Why not?' Cary warmed to the idea. 'We've pulled it off this time, haven't we? No one suspects we're not a couple, do they?'

'No.' Juliet had to concede that. 'But there's no way I'd do anything like this again.' She turned to stare blindly out of the car's window. 'I hated doing it. I felt—dirty.'

'Oh, please.' Cary was angry and he wasn't in the mood to consider her feelings. 'You enjoyed it. Don't pretend you didn't. You ought to be grateful to me. People in your situation rarely get a second chance to make something of their lives.'

Juliet gasped. 'Do you really think pretending to be your fiancée is making something of my life?'

Cary was silent for a moment and she thought he'd seen the sense of what she was saying and decided to back off. But then he spoke again.

'It doesn't have to be pretence,' he ventured carefully, and Juliet's jaw dropped.

'What?'

'Hey, don't look so shocked.' Cary's scowl was dissolving into a smile of smug anticipation. 'I'm proposing here.' He laughed delightedly. 'Dammit, why didn't I think of it before? I need a wife and you need an occupation. How convenient is that?'

CHAPTER THIRTEEN

RAFE turned down the track towards Tregellin and drove resignedly towards the house. He hadn't visited the old lady since the disastrous evening of the dinner party over two weeks ago, and he wouldn't be here now if it weren't for Josie's frantic phone calls.

'You've got to come, Rafe,' she'd begged, just this morning. 'I'm getting really worried about her. That cold she had weeks ago has come back and she's not looking after herself the way she should.'

'So call Charteris,' said Rafe, as he'd advised before, still smarting from the shock of finding his and his mother's paintings lining the library walls, and his subsequent encounter with Juliet. The old lady had a lot to answer for and quite honestly he didn't feel any obligation to concern himself about her.

Yet here he was, just a couple of hours later, making a special trip out to Tregellin to see her. He could tell himself he was doing this for Josie until he was blue in the face, but the truth was, he did care what happened to the old lady. She was his grandmother, after all, however much they both might deplore the fact.

He parked in the usual place, and stood for a few minutes looking out at the estuary. It wasn't cold, but it was raining, a fine drizzle that soaked his hair and ran in cool rivulets over his forehead and down his cheeks. Swiping a hand across his face, he collected the things he'd brought from the back of the Land Cruiser and strode round to the rear of the house.

Josie was in the kitchen, as usual, and when Rafe opened the door Hitchins came to snuffle eagerly about his legs. 'Hey, small stuff,' he greeted the dog, depositing the bags he'd been carrying on the table and bending to pick up the Pekinese. 'What's happening?'

Josie turned from the sink, a relieved smile on her lined face. 'Thanks for coming, Rafe,' she said warmly, wiping her hands on a tea towel. She sniffed. 'We've missed you.'

'Yeah, right.' Rafe gave her an old-fashioned look before setting the little dog on the floor again. Then, ignoring Hitchins' protests, he nodded towards the bags on the table. 'I called at the supermarket on my way. I thought you might need one or two things.'

'You're too good to us!' exclaimed Josie, pulling one of the bags towards her and unloading its contents. 'Oh, smoked salmon! Perhaps I can persuade Elinor to eat a little of this.'

Rafe's brows drew together. 'She's not eating?'

'Hardly at all.' Josie exclaimed again when she found a leg of lamb and some fresh asparagus. 'She's not been right since she had that chest infection that she insisted was just a cold and I'm sure was probably flu. The cough has never properly gone away, though she won't admit it.'

Rafe felt a twinge of anxiety. 'So why haven't you called Charteris?'

'I did,' said Josie at once. 'He came, but she wouldn't see him. She told me to keep my nose out of her business. That if she needed a doctor, she'd call one for herself.'

'Crazy old woman!' Rafe blew out a weary breath. 'So that's why you've kept calling me.'

'Well, you're the only one she might listen to,' said Josie defensively. 'She thinks the world of you, Rafe; you know she does. She may not always show it, but she's very proud of you.'

Rafe scowled. 'And I suppose you knew all about those paintings,' he countered obliquely, and Josie coloured.

'I knew *of* them,' she agreed unwillingly. 'But I'd been told to say nothing to anyone, so—'

'So you kept them a secret.'

'It wasn't like that, Rafe.'

'What was it like, then? When was the old lady going to tell me about them? And why produce them that night without even a word of warning?'

'I don't know.' Clearly Josie was as perplexed as he was. 'Perhaps because you were coming to dinner.'

Rafe shook his head. 'So who put them up there? Don't tell me you were the one who moved the bookcases and hung the paintings because I won't believe you.' His eyes narrowed suspiciously. 'Was it Cary?'

'Heavens, no!' Josie was very definite about that. 'Cary knows nothing about them. I doubt he'd be very happy if he did.' She met his eyes squarely. 'She got Jem Helford to do it.' Jem and his family farmed Tregellin land further up the valley, Rafe recalled. 'He and his son came down on Saturday morning. It took them all of three hours to put everything in place.'

Rafe was stunned. 'But—why?'

'You'd have to ask Lady Elinor that.' Josie returned to unpacking the shopping. 'Oh, Rafe, we must pay you something for all this.'

'Forget it.' Rafe wasn't interested in being paid for his contribution to the household. 'Where is she? In the conservatory, as usual?'

'Actually, no, she's still in bed,' admitted Josie unhappily. 'She's taken to getting up later and later in the day. Some days, she doesn't get up at all.'

Rafe caught his breath. 'But isn't that hard on you? I mean, if you're having to run up and down stairs—'

'It does me good,' declared the housekeeper staunchly. 'And if I do go up and down the stairs, it's not for her I'm doing it. She asks for nothing. Not even her meals.'

'*Dios!*' Rafe swore. Things were so much worse than he'd expected and, as usual, he felt guilty for staying away.

With a rueful look in Josie's direction, he left the kitchen, striding swiftly across the hall before vaulting up the stairs, two at a time. If he gave any thought to the last time he'd climbed these stairs—and with what purpose—he didn't acknowledge it. That was just something else the old lady could blame him for and he'd had enough of being everyone's whipping boy.

Even so, when he reached Lady Elinor's bedroom door he paused for a moment to get his breath back. It wouldn't do for her to think he'd been worried about her. Then, after raking back his hair with an impatient hand, he tapped sharply on the panels.

There was silence for a few moments, and then a rather frail voice called, 'Come in, Raphael. If you must.'

Rafe stifled the resentment her words inspired and plastered a smile on his face. She'd evidently heard the car and she was just trying to get a rise out of him, but it wasn't going to happen. Pushing open the door, he sauntered into the room. 'Hello, old lady,' he greeted her, with similar irreverence. 'Do you know what time it is?'

He spoke carelessly, but the old lady's appearance shocked him. She looked so pale, her hair, which had always seemed more black than white, a loose grey curtain about her thin shoulders. Lying back against her white pillows, she looked every one of her almost eighty years and Rafe's stomach took a decided plunge.

'I believe it's after twelve o'clock,' she declared at last, and there was a reassuring trace of impatience in her voice. 'What's it to you, Raphael? You don't seem to care what happens to me these days.'

Rafe bit back the retort that first sprang to his lips and instead said mildly, 'That is not true, old lady. Anyway, it cuts both ways. Why didn't you let me know if you wanted to see me?'

'What? And have you tell me you didn't have time to waste coming here to see an old woman you both hate and despise?' Lady Elinor tilted her chin. 'I think not.'

Rafe sighed. 'I neither hate nor despise you,' he muttered

heavily. 'Whatever—or should I say whoever—gave you that idea?'

Lady Elinor turned her head aside to stare out of her window. 'What else was I supposed to think when you haven't said a word about the little exhibition I arranged for you? Indeed, it seems obvious to me that you were furious at my little deception and that's why you've stayed away. Not to mention the insulting way you walked out of here two weeks ago, without even acknowledging my kindness for inviting you.'

'Your kindness?' Despite the curb he'd put on his temper, Rafe found that was one word too far. 'There was nothing kind about confronting me with paintings I'd thought had been sold years ago. And how long have you had those paintings of my mother's? You let me think everything of hers had been either lost or destroyed when she died.'

'When she committed suicide, you mean?' Lady Elinor said flatly, stunning Rafe into silence. 'Oh, Raphael, you don't allow for anyone's vulnerabilities, do you?' Her voice shook a little now. 'How do you think I felt when I found out what had happened? Christina was my daughter. I loved her dearly. Yet she abandoned me to take up with some itinerant Italian labourer, who treated her so badly she was forced to run away.'

Rafe blinked. 'That's not true!'

'I'm afraid it is.'

'No. I mean…' He stared at her with tortured eyes. 'I know my father treated her badly sometimes. I remember the rows they used to have, the arguments that went on for hours. But my mother didn't commit suicide. She—she fell. From a hotel balcony.'

Lady Elinor turned to look at him again. 'That was the story I chose to tell everyone,' she said wearily. 'You were a sensitive child. I didn't know what kind of damage hearing your mother had killed herself might do to you. For years, I thought I might never tell you. But you're a man now, and I can't carry the burden alone any longer.'

Rafe shook his head. Then, dragging a chair from beneath the windows, he swung it round and straddled it to face her. 'So,' he said harshly. 'Tell me what really happened. Did she kill herself because of my father? Is that what you're trying to say?'

'No. No.' Lady Elinor sighed. 'Nothing so dramatic, Raphael. Christina had a little money of her own, so she took you and fled to Switzerland.' She paused. 'Regrettably, she started drinking. She did very little painting after she left Italy, and I'm fairly sure her money was getting short. Then, one night, she climbed up onto the rail surrounding the balcony of your hotel room. And, according to witnesses, she simply stepped off into space.'

Rafe's lips felt dry. 'So she did fall?'

'Yes, she fell.' The old lady sounded bleak, however. 'But there seems little doubt of what she'd had in mind. She'd written me a letter, you see. It arrived in England two days later. In it she asked if, in the event of her death, I would bring you back to England and give you a home.'

Rafe groaned, covering his head with one arm, burying his face against his sleeve. 'So that's why you never liked me.'

'Never liked you?' Lady Elinor sat up straight. 'I don't know what you're talking about, Raphael. I love you. I've always loved you, right from the first moment I saw you in that *kinderstube* in Interlaken.' She sniffed, reaching for her handkerchief, and Rafe was amazed to see that there were tears in her eyes now. 'They'd put you with the younger children, but I recognised you instantly. You were so tall; so handsome; so like Christina, I wanted to weep.' She sniffed again. 'I never even thought of trying to contact your father. As far as I was concerned, you were Christina's son, my grandson, and that was all that mattered.' She made a rocking movement of her hand. 'Later on, as I believe I told you, I made enquiries and discovered your father had been killed in a car accident soon after Christina left him. It has crossed my mind that that might have been what drove her to do what she did, but we'll never know for sure. The important thing, so far as I was concerned, was that she'd turned to me in her hour of need. You were here, at Tregellin, and whatever you think, I have never regretted it.'

Rafe didn't know what to think. When he'd driven here this morning, he'd had no idea the old lady was going to drop such a bombshell. Yet it made more sense; now that he was older, he could see that. His mother had been a passionate, emotional woman. It was fitting, somehow, that her death should be a passionate and emotional one, too.

'What are you thinking?'

Lady Elinor was regarding him anxiously now, and Rafe folded his arms across the back of the chair and rested his chin on his wrist. 'I'm thinking you've had it pretty tough yourself, old lady,' he admitted honestly. 'It can't have been easy losing both your children before their fortieth birthdays.'

Lady Elinor stifled what sounded suspiciously like a sob. 'Yes, Charles' death, too, was a devastating blow. For years I'd lived alone, and suddenly I had two young boys to care for.' She grimaced rather wryly. 'But, do you know, I do believe you and Cary kept me sane?'

Rafe frowned. 'OK. So why did you let me think that everything that belonged to my mother had been either lost or destroyed?'

The old lady sighed and sank back against her pillows. 'It was easier that way.'

'Easier?'

'Easier for me,' admitted Lady Elinor regretfully. 'I'm afraid it took me many years to forgive Christina for what she'd done. Having her child was one thing. Having her paintings around me—the thing that had driven her from me—was something else.'

'So?'

'So I had them all packed up and stored in the attic. Along with those early paintings of yours that I'd had a third party obtain for me.'

'The solicitor from Bodmin.'

'The solicitor from Bodmin,' she agreed, pressing her lips together for a moment. 'I knew you'd never forgive me, so I didn't tell you what I'd done.'

Rafe shook his head. 'But why did you do it?'

'Can't you guess?' Lady Elinor was succinct. 'I thought if I bought your paintings, they wouldn't be seen by other collectors. I'd already lost my daughter because of her love of art. I was so afraid I was going to lose you in the same way.'

Rafe stared at her for a long moment, and then, discarding the chair, he crossed the room to sit down on the bed beside her. 'You'll never lose me, old lady,' he said gruffly, gathering her frail body up into his arms and pressing her face into his shoulder. 'You may be a cantankerous old bird, but you're my old bird, and that's what matters to me.'

Lady Elinor yielded against him, but only for a few moments. Then, with a briskness that belied her age, she urged him away. 'I was right,' she said, though her voice was unaccountably thick, 'you're just like your mother. I can't do with all this emotion. I'm a plain woman. I say what I think.'

Rafe's smile was gentle. 'Treat 'em mean and keep 'em keen, yeah?'

'I don't know what you mean.' But her voice was definitely gaining in strength and there was a touch of colour in her cheeks. 'Anyway, let's talk about something else, shall we? Have you forgiven me for making you spend the evening with Juliet?'

Rafe got up then, pacing restlessly about the bedroom, not prepared to suffer the old lady's scrutiny at such close hand. 'What's to forgive?' he said at last, and he was proud of the indifference in his tone. 'I dare say it got up Cary's nose though.'

'Do you think so?' Lady Elinor was surprisingly restrained. 'Well, maybe because it was you, yes. But didn't you think Cary was amazingly cavalier about his fiancée?'

Rafe turned to frown at her. 'Cavalier?'

'Yes.' The old lady pleated the hem of the linen sheet. 'It made me wonder exactly what their engagement is all about.' She paused. 'Juliet left your mother's ring behind, you know?'

Rafe hadn't known. But then, how could he? This was his first visit to Tregellin since that fateful weekend.

'I expect Cary wants to buy her a ring,' he said offhandedly, not allowing himself to read anything into Juliet's gesture. 'Anyway, you'll be pleased to have it back.'

'Hmm.' Lady Elinor didn't sound particularly convinced. 'What did you think of her?'

'Juliet?' His stomach tightened convulsively.

'Who else?' There was a touch of asperity in her voice now. 'Josie's convinced the engagement won't last. She thinks Juliet has more in common with you.'

'You're joking!'

'No, I'm not joking.' Lady Elinor's mouth was tight. 'Josie's entitled to her opinion, isn't she?'

'Well, yes, but—'

'You mean, you've never thought of her in that way?' the old lady probed and Rafe blew out a frustrated breath.

'Of course I've thought of Juliet in that way,' he muttered, deciding there was no point in denying it. 'She's a beautiful woman. A man would have to be blind not to notice it.'

'And you're not blind, are you, Raphael?' Lady Elinor remarked drily. 'Not if half the stories I've heard about you are true.'

Rafe scowled. 'You shouldn't believe all you hear.'

'Oh, I don't.' The old lady nodded. 'But I have to say, on this occasion, I do agree with Josie. Juliet is far too good for Cary. Let's hope she realises it in time, hmm?'

CHAPTER FOURTEEN

THE letter was lying in her mailbox when she got home from work.

Juliet wasn't used to getting mail—unless it was a bill, of course—but the fine vellum of the envelope ensured it wasn't one of those. And it was her name that was printed in black typescript, her address correctly delineated, even down to the number of her apartment.

With a shrug, she put the letter into her bag and started up the stairs, wondering if it had anything to do with David. But her ex-husband never contacted her and he was unlikely to have come back to England. With a possible case for the fraudulent transfer of funds hanging over his head, she doubted—indeed, she hoped—that she'd never see him again.

Her apartment was on the second floor, and in the small entry she slipped off her jacket and kicked off her high heels. It would be July next week and the apartment was airless. Crossing to the windows, she released the security catch and pushed up the sash. Then, after taking a breath of cooler air, she turned back into the room.

She needed a shower, she thought, glancing down at her skirt with its ugly smear of tomato ketchup. Parents really shouldn't let children take hamburgers on the bus, she thought ruefully. Apologising when your six-year-old had dropped a burger into your neighbour's lap was not quite good enough.

She had a hard enough time of it as it was, keeping her clothes neat and clean without spending too much on them. But working in a small boutique required her to look reasonably smart at all times. Granted, the shortness of her hems and the amount of cleavage the management expected her to show weren't exactly high fashion. But the shop's clientele had certain expectations, and Juliet was so grateful to have a job, she hadn't been prepared to argue.

Not that she intended to remain at the boutique any longer than she had to. She was taking a course in computing and office management at evening class with a view to finding more interesting employment before the end of the year. She was optimistic of achieving her goal. Her tutor, a retired computer programmer, had said she had a real aptitude for the work.

It had been a struggle. Particularly as she'd refused to take the money Cary had offered her after their return from Cornwall. He'd thought she was a fool, but she'd felt bad enough as it was without taking what she suspected was Lady Elinor's money. By pawning her wrist-watch, she'd got by, and the reference she had accepted from him had been enough for Sandra Sparks, the boutique's manageress.

But now, she couldn't put off opening the letter any longer. Finding a knife in the alcove that served as both kitchen and dining area, she ran it under the flap and slit it across. Then, with what she recognised were delaying tactics, she put the knife back in the drawer before pulling out the single sheet of paper that was inside.

She saw at once that it was from a firm of solicitors in Bodmin. *Bodmin!* Her heart skipped a beat and the hand holding the sheet of paper trembled as she read on.

The letter advised her of the death—*the death!*—of Lady Elinor Margaret Daniels of Tregellin House, Tregellin, Cornwall, and invited her to the reading of Lady Elinor's will, which would take place on Monday, July 2nd, after the funeral service and internment at St Mawgan's Church in the village of Tregellin.

Juliet sank down onto the nearest chair. She was feeling sick and shaky, and she stared at the letter blindly, hardly able to believe what she'd just read. Lady Elinor—that bright, indomitable old lady—was dead. Dear lord, how must Rafe be feeling? He'd loved his grandmother. That had been evident. And now Cary would inherit Tregellin and the old house would be sold.

Curiously, she didn't feel much compassion for Cary. It had been obvious from the start where his sympathies lay. He wanted to sell Tregellin; to realise its potential for development. He'd probably already started planning what he was going to do once probate had been granted.

But Rafe was different. Although he'd never said as much, she'd sensed he loved Tregellin, too. Certainly he'd defended it when Cary had made his pitch for selling the land. But now that Lady Elinor was gone, there was nothing to stop Cary from doing as he liked.

Oh, Rafe...

Unable to sit still, Juliet got to her feet again and paced about the apartment. She'd tried so hard not to think about him since she'd got back to London, and she'd almost succeeded. Time was a great healer. She'd learned that both when her father died and when David had betrayed her. She'd hoped that in time she'd be able to think about Rafe without emotion, but she feared that situation was some way off yet.

Besides, it had probably been foolish to imagine she could dismiss what had happened without heartache, even if the memory of that whole weekend had assumed the aspect of a dream. It had been real enough, she acknowledged. It was she who'd made it illusory. Pretending to be Cary's fiancée; deceiving all of them, but most particularly Rafe.

She shook her head. And now Lady Elinor had died, possibly still believing she and Cary were engaged to be married. Why else would she have been invited to the reading of her will? Juliet felt so ashamed; so deceitful. She had no right to be involved in Lady Elinor's affairs.

She looked again at the letter. She should write back to this solicitor—Mr Peter Arnold—and explain that she and Cary were no longer seeing one another. No longer! Her lips twisted. They'd never been seeing one another. But that would take too much explanation, and she wasn't actually sure if what they'd done was entirely legal.

She bit her lip and frowned down at the sheet of paper. Whatever Cary had or hadn't said, this was a family occasion, and she had no part in it. She should simply write a polite little note to these solicitors, expressing her condolences to the family, and excuse herself on the grounds that she couldn't get the time off from her job. It was probably true, anyway. She hadn't been at the boutique long enough to qualify for special treatment.

Then, when the tears welled up in her eyes, she realised she didn't want to refuse the invitation. She'd liked Lady Elinor. She'd liked her a lot. She'd been kind to Juliet, offering her the ring and all. She was really sorry the old lady had died. And she would like to pay her last respects in person.

The knowledge that, if she did go to the funeral, she'd see Rafe again wasn't an issue, she told herself. Since she hadn't heard from him since she got back, it was obvious that what had happened had not meant as much to him as it had to her. Besides, he'd know her now for the liar she was. Cary couldn't have kept up his deception. Not without her participation.

She was still undecided what she was going to do when she went to bed that night. Whatever way she looked at it, her presence would be an intrusion into the family's grief. Poor Josie must be distraught, she thought. She and Lady Elinor had been together for so long. And when Tregellin was sold, she'd lose her home as well. Juliet didn't fool herself that Cary would give the old housekeeper's needs a thought.

After a restless night, she decided to ring the solicitor in Bodmin. She wanted to explain to him that she and Cary were no longer 'involved' and that, although she'd like to come to the funeral, she'd prefer not to attend the reading of the will.

She had to wait until her morning coffee break to ring the solicitor's office. And then she was put on hold for several minutes before a man came on the line. 'Ms Lawrence?' he asked, and she confirmed her identity. 'Oh—well, what can I do for you? I'm afraid my father's busy with another client, but I'm Stephen Arnold, his son.'

Juliet stifled a sigh and briefly explained why she was ringing. She didn't go into details, but she let it be known that she had no connection to the Daniels family any more. 'I'm hoping to attend the funeral,' she went on, 'but I'll return to London as soon as it's over. I'm afraid my being invited to attend the reading of the will was a mistake.'

'Oh, no.' Stephen Arnold was very definite about that. 'You are one of the beneficiaries, Ms Lawrence. Your inclusion was quite deliberate, I can assure you.'

Juliet's breath caught in her throat. 'No—that's not possible. I'm not a member of the family.'

'My father knows that, Ms Lawrence. But Lady Elinor was a very determined lady. When she made this clause in your favour, she told him you were a young lady she'd come to like and admire.'

'Admire!'

Juliet wanted to die of shame. If only she'd told the old lady the truth; if only she'd had the guts to refuse Cary's money before it was too late. As it was, the fraud they'd established had been perpetuated. And now that Lady Elinor was gone, there was no way she could make amends.

'So you will be present on Monday afternoon?' Stephen Arnold prompted pleasantly. 'I know my father is looking forward to meeting you.'

Really? Juliet didn't say the word out loud, but she must have made a suitable response, because a few moments later the phone went dead and she was forced to return it to its cradle.

'Problems?'

Juliet was still sitting staring at the phone when Sandra Sparks came into the office, where she'd been making the call.

The young manageress regarded her newest employee sympathetically, and Juliet gave a weary shake of her head.

'You could say that.' She paused. 'Is it all right if I take next Monday off? I've got to go to a funeral.'

Sandra frowned. 'A family member, is it?'

Juliet suddenly realised the difficulty. 'No.'

'Oh, dear.' Sandra sighed. 'Staff are only supposed to take time off to attend family funerals. Compassionate leave, so to speak. I'm really sorry, Juliet, but I can't allow you to go.'

Juliet stared at her. 'But I have to go!' she exclaimed. 'I've—promised. It's important to me, Sandra, or I wouldn't ask.'

Sandra sighed again. 'Where is this funeral? Perhaps I could allow you to slip out for a couple of hours. You'd have to keep it quiet, of course. If it gets around that I'm a soft touch, all the girls will use it as an excuse.'

Juliet bent her head. 'A couple of hours wouldn't do it, I'm afraid. The funeral's in Cornwall. At a place called Tregellin. Lady—Lady Elinor Daniels is—*was*—someone I've known for a long time.' Which was only a slight exaggeration of the truth.

'*Lady* Elinor Daniels?' Sandra was obviously impressed. 'So how do you know her? Was she your godmother or something?'

'It's a long story. She knew my father,' said Juliet flatly. 'Just recently—just recently, I stayed with her. It would mean a lot to me to be able to say goodbye.'

Sandra was weakening. Juliet could see it. 'And you would only need the one day?'

Juliet nodded. 'I'd go down on Sunday and come back Monday evening,' she said, hoping it would work out. 'I'm sure there must be trains. It's the holiday season, after all.'

So, they were still together.

Cary had said they were, but Rafe hadn't wanted to believe him. Certainly the last time Cary had visited their grandmother, Juliet hadn't been with him. He'd made some excuse about her having a cold and not wanting to infect Lady Elinor, but Rafe had been suspicious. Even if he hadn't had enough conviction to check up on her himself.

Which was just as well, in the circumstances, he thought grimly, his eyes flickering over the couple who stood at the opposite side of the grave. But that didn't stop him from feeling angry. So angry that he felt as if he was choking on it. And he didn't even want to explore why that should be so.

Perhaps he'd hoped that she wouldn't come, that some small shred of decency would prevent her from appearing at his grand-mother's graveside as if she had a right to be there. Had she no shame? She'd been engaged to Cary when he'd made love to her, and, despite that air of assumed innocence, she still was. How could she stand there, beside Cary, looking as if butter wouldn't melt in her mouth, when he knew damn well how hot she was?

His teeth ground together and Josie, who was hanging on to his arm, gave him a curious look. Her eyes were still swollen from the tears she'd cried since Lady Elinor passed away, but they were as sharp as ever and far too shrewd.

'What's wrong?'

Rafe shook his head. 'What could be wrong?' he demanded bitterly. 'The old lady's dead and Cary can't wait to get his hands on Tregellin. Everything's peachy.'

Josie sighed and patted his arm. 'You shouldn't jump to con-clusions, Rafe,' she said softly. 'Your grandmother might have been old, but she was nobody's fool. Give her a little credit, won't you? I'd have thought finding out about those paintings would have taught you that she had her secrets, too.'

'Too?' Rafe cast a wary glance in her direction. 'I've got no secrets. My life's an open book.'

'Is it?' Rafe wasn't sure, but he thought Josie cast a thought-ful look in Juliet's direction. 'Ah, well, we'll know soon enough. When Mr Arnold reads the will.'

Rafe scowled. He'd have just as soon not attended the reading of the old lady's will. There was so much hypocrisy in standing around, waiting to see how much his grandmother had left. Cary would be there, and Juliet, apparently. Scavengers, both of them, he thought savagely. They deserved each other.

Even so, he couldn't prevent images of the last time he'd seen Juliet from filling his mind. He might not want to remember how shamelessly beautiful she'd looked when she'd told him she had no intention of breaking her engagement, but he was powerless to stop it. And in the three months since she'd left Tregellin, he'd lived a celibate lifestyle. He'd never been precisely promiscuous, but he'd never felt such an aversion to having sex with another woman before.

Perhaps that was what was wrong with him, he reflected tensely. It wasn't just seeing Juliet and Cary together. It was the fact that it had been several months since he'd got laid. As soon as this pitiful charade was over he was going to drive into Bodmin, get a skinful of beer and find himself a woman. Any woman would do, he told himself. Just as long as she could drive all thoughts of Juliet out of his head.

Juliet, meanwhile, was not unaware of Rafe glowering at her from across the gravesite. If she'd ever had any doubts about his feelings, she could see now how foolish she'd been. He resented her being there. That was blatantly obvious. Their sexual encounter was something he'd sooner forget.

OK, she was guilty of not telling him the truth about her and Cary when he'd asked her about her engagement. But she'd been in a cleft stick, aware that anything she said would reflect on Cary in the most unfavourable way. Surely the fact that she and Cary had—as he would see it—broken up as soon as they'd got back to London should have told him something. If he'd wanted to hear it, of course, she appended. Which, judging by his present attitude, he evidently hadn't.

She sighed, and Cary glanced at her. 'It'll soon be over,' he said. 'Then we can get back to the house.'

For 'get back to the house' read 'hear what Lady Elinor's will has to say', Juliet thought bitterly. She doubted anyone around the gravesite had any illusions as to why Cary was really here.

The last words of the interment were said and Rafe bent to drop a handful of soil onto the brass-bound casket. 'Sleep well, old lady,' he said in an undertone, before turning and striding back to where the cars were waiting.

Juliet saw him go, but when she would have hurried after him Cary caught her arm. 'Where are you going?'

Juliet snatched her arm away. 'Is it any of your business?' Since she'd arrived at Tregellin that morning he'd adopted a very proprietary air towards her, almost as if he were responsible for her invitation. Which she knew, most definitely, was not the case. 'I'll see you back at the house.'

Cary scowled. 'You're hoping to talk to him, aren't you?' he demanded angrily. 'Well, forget it, love. I'm the one you should be seen with, not him.'

'Why?'

'Because—because they still think we're a couple,' muttered Cary, obviously with some reluctance. And at her look of horror, 'What was I supposed to say? Did you want the old girl to find out I'd been lying to her?'

Juliet couldn't believe her ears. 'So you think the only reason I've been invited here is because of you?'

'Looks that way.' Cary was smug now.

'I don't believe it. I don't believe you.' She gazed at him with contempt. 'Well, you'd better tell everyone that our "engagement" is over. And don't follow me, Cary. Not unless you want me to broadcast the fact that there never was an engagement in the first place.'

Rafe saw her coming. He was leaning against the bonnet of one of the funeral cars, waiting for Josie to pay her last respects and join him. He'd intended to drive his own car to the service, but Josie had begged him to accompany her in one of the limousines. 'People will expect it,' she said. And he knew by 'people', she meant Peter Arnold and his son.

He felt the muscles of his face tightening as Juliet stopped beside him. He wasn't going to speak first, he thought childishly.

As far as he was concerned, he wanted no empty sympathy from her. Despite the fact of what being this close to her again was doing to his equilibrium.

She looked so innocent, he acknowledged bitterly. Although Lady Elinor wouldn't have wanted anyone to wear mourning, Juliet's pale grey suit and salmon-pink top showed just the right amount of respect. High heels gave her the extra height so she only had to tilt her chin a little to look up at him, her silky hair a precarious knot on top of her head.

'Hi,' she said, when he didn't speak, and Rafe unfolded his arms and inclined his head politely. 'I just wanted to say how sorry I am that Lady Elinor has passed away. She—she seemed so strong, somehow. So vital. I was shocked when I got Mr Arnold's letter.'

That got his attention. 'Arnold wrote to you?'

'That's right.'

'Why?'

'I don't know why.' Juliet felt the same sense of uncertainty she'd experienced when she'd first opened the letter. 'I did phone him. I thought it must be a mistake.' She moistened her lips. 'He said—or rather his son said—it wasn't.'

Rafe's brows descended. 'You're telling me Cary didn't mention his grandmother's illness?' His lips twisted. 'Forgive me, but even for Cary that seems a little unlikely.'

'How could he?' Juliet twisted the strap of her handbag. This was harder than she'd thought. 'How could Cary tell me? I haven't seen him since we got back from Cornwall three months ago.'

Rafe couldn't hide his anger. 'Do you expect me to believe that?' he snarled. 'What kind of an engagement do you have? An open one, obviously. But pretending you haven't seen him—'

'I haven't!' Juliet looked up at him with frustrated eyes. 'Oh, what's the use? I knew you wouldn't believe me. Cary's filled your head with so many lies, anything I say is just so much hot air.'

'Hot, certainly,' said Rafe provokingly, and Juliet gave him an angry glare.

'Oh, believe what you like,' she said, turning away. 'You will anyway. If you must know, there never was an engagement. Cary persuaded me to act as his girlfriend, just for that one weekend. It was never intended to be an engagement. That was Cary's doing. I agreed because I needed the money. And he promised he'd give me a reference so I could get a proper job—'

Rafe stared at her incredulously. 'Cary paid you!'

'He was supposed to, but—in the end I wouldn't take his money.' She shook her head. 'After—after meeting Lady Elinor, I felt such a—such a—'

'Bitch?'

'—a fraud,' she amended huskily, feeling the hot sting of tears behind her eyes, but Rafe wasn't impressed.

'My God,' he said contemptuously, 'no wonder you were so anxious when I asked you if you were going to break your engagement. The old lady would have kicked both of you out if she'd known what a pair of liars you were.'

Juliet sighed. 'Do you think I don't know that?'

'So aren't you ashamed?'

'Oh, God, of course I'm ashamed!' Juliet caught her breath. 'But I couldn't let Cary down, could I? Can't you see that?'

'All I can see is a greedy, grasping female, with an eye to the main chance,' retorted Rafe coldly. 'But hey, this isn't the time to be breaking your engagement, lady. Not when Cary is just about to scoop the pool.'

Juliet felt chilled. 'I've told you, there was no engagement!'

'Then perhaps this is the time to start thinking about one,' he taunted, and she wondered how she could have ever thought that they might have a future together.

'Do you think I care about the money?' she asked bitterly, and Rafe lifted his shoulders in a careless gesture.

'You did.'

'No!' She was aware of the other mourners leaving the grave-side now, but she had to try and make him understand. 'I was practically destitute. I needed a few pounds, that's all. Just a few pounds to tide me over until I could find employment. But I've got a job now, so I don't need anybody's charity. And whatever you think, nothing—*nothing*—would persuade me to marry Cary Daniels. I don't even like him.' She swayed a little, but when he tried to help her she flinched away. 'As soon as this is over, I'm going home.'

CHAPTER FIFTEEN

THE train from Bodmin to Paddington rattled over the points and then resumed its steady rhythm. It wasn't full. Despite the season, the lateness of the hour had apparently put off all but the most determined travellers. Couples with children tended to prefer the earlier trains, although there were one or two toddlers sleeping on their parents' knees.

Juliet had been lucky enough to find a corner seat. Although there'd been a reserved ticket attached to it, no one had claimed the seat before the train left the station. In consequence, she wasn't obliged to make conversation with her neighbours. Tilting her head against the pane, she closed her eyes and tried to sleep.

But she'd known that would be impossible before she even tried it. Her mind was too full of the events and images of the day to find any escape in sleep. Even now, it was difficult to assimilate what had happened. Evidently Cary felt the same. Yet despite his disappointment, he had apparently decided to spend another night at the house.

Not that she cared what Cary did, one way or the other. Discovering he'd continued to deceive Rafe about their relationship had destroyed what little liking she'd had left. Her only consolation was that he hadn't deceived his grandmother. Lady Elinor had made it her business to learn everything there was to know about her grandson and his 'girlfriend'. According to Mr

Arnold, Cary's relationship with the stripper from the casino where he worked had not gone unremarked.

Cary had tried to deny it. He'd even had the nerve to appeal to Juliet to help him out of the pit he'd dug for himself. But Juliet wanted nothing more to do with him, and had said so. And then the surprise Mr Arnold had delivered to her had caused Cary to accuse her of ingratiating herself with his grandmother for her own ends.

It had all been rather unpleasant and Juliet hadn't been able to look in Rafe's direction. She was sure he must think the same as Cary. That she'd somehow hinted at her financial situation and Lady Elinor had decided to help her out. It wasn't true. She'd never discussed her finances with his grandmother. But who would believe her now?

Anyway, it appeared that Lady Elinor had left her the three rings she'd shown them from her jewellery box; the rings she'd offered Juliet to choose from that afternoon at Tregellin. There was the ruby ring, which had been Rafe's mother's, the emerald dress ring and the diamond solitaire. They were Juliet's now to wear or sell, as she pleased.

Juliet was both touched and embarrassed. The rings were heirlooms, all of them, and she felt she had no right to remove them from the estate. But Mr Arnold insisted that the codicil to the will and been added just weeks ago, at Lady Elinor's specific request, that she'd wanted her to have the rings with her blessing.

Josie, who was sitting beside her in the library, where the reading of the will was taking place, squeezed her hand. 'Elinor liked you,' she said in an undertone. 'She wanted you to have something of hers to keep.'

And Juliet knew that, whatever happened, she would keep the rings; two of them, at least. The ruby, which had been Rafe's mother's, she intended to return to him after she got back to London. That way, there'd be no chance of him throwing it back in her face.

Further bequests followed, to people Juliet hadn't heard of, and the doctor, whom she had. And Josie, of course. The housekeeper was given a lump sum of one hundred thousand pounds, which brought a gasp of disbelief from Cary, and the title to a small cottage in the grounds, where she could live when she retired.

Even Rafe looked surprised at Josie's good fortune, but unlike Cary he was the first to applaud the old lady's decision. 'You deserve it,' he said, his gaze skimming Juliet's flushed face before moving on to the housekeeper. 'Without your care and support, she'd never have been able to keep this place going.'

'And that's a reason to reward her?' Cary was scathing. He scowled. 'I knew the old girl wasn't as hard-up as she pretended to be. But giving away a hundred K! That's ridiculous!'

'It was her money, Mr Daniels, to do with as she wished.' The solicitor had regarded him with a reproving gaze. 'But now we come to the distribution of the bulk of Lady Elinor's estate. I suggest you allow me to proceed.'

That had silenced him, but Juliet shivered now as she recalled the events that had followed. No one had been prepared for the news Mr Arnold had to relate, but she supposed they should have had some intimation when he'd announced that Cary had been left two hundred thousand pounds in treasury bonds. The remainder of the estate—including the house, the farms surrounding it and the contents of a safety-deposit box lodged with her bank in Bodmin—had been left to Lady Elinor's eldest grandson.

'But that's me!' Cary exclaimed, confused by the distinction between his bequest and the latter designation. 'I'm the old girl's only legitimate grandson. Rafe...' He cast his cousin a scornful look. 'He's a bastard, in more ways than one.'

'I'm afraid not.' Before the solicitor spoke again, Juliet glimpsed the pain that briefly crossed Rafe's face. But then, Mr Arnold extracted another envelope from his briefcase and handed it to Rafe with a curious smile. 'This is yours, I believe. Your grandmother asked me to give it to you with her apologies.'

'What is it?' Cary demanded, his face red and angry, a mixture of fury and apprehension that things weren't as simple as he'd believed.

Rafe ignored him, drawing the document out amid the hushed silence that had fallen over the room. Then, his expression warned them all of the shock he'd just received. His skin had become so pale that Juliet half expected him to collapse. But Mr Arnold took it upon himself to explain that it was Rafe's parents' marriage certificate. A certificate that had been dated some thirty-two years ago, before Rafe was born.

Of course, Cary hadn't believed it. He'd been incensed, snatching the certificate out of Rafe's nerveless grasp and brandishing it in his face while he'd called him every offensive name he could think of. 'This is a fake,' he'd snarled. 'The old girl was off her rocker!' He'd swung round on Mr Arnold. 'Who did she get to forge this for her? No, don't bother to answer that. Marchese probably made it himself.'

'It's no fake,' the solicitor had informed him smoothly, taking the document out of his hand before any damage was done. Then he'd turned to the other man. 'I'm sorry, Rafe. I know she wanted to tell you before this, but she was afraid if she did she'd lose you. Tregellin's yours now. It's her gift to you. I think you'll find she's had this in mind all along.'

Juliet found her eyes were filled with tears now. Dear Lady Elinor, she thought. You knew which of your grandsons cared about Tregellin and which didn't. She supposed it was hard on Cary, bearing in mind that he'd expected to inherit the estate. But if he had, he'd have had no hesitation about selling it. And, although Rafe wasn't going to find it easy, she knew he'd do everything in his power to keep his legacy intact.

Juliet herself had slipped away while Mr Arnold was explaining the legalities to Rafe and Josie. She wasn't needed any longer and she had no intention of getting embroiled in Cary's vengeful schemes. She wouldn't put it past him to try and contest the will, if he could. But she had the feeling Mr Arnold was more than a match for him.

It was a couple of days later when she saw Cary again. She was coming out of the boutique at lunchtime when he accosted her. 'Hey,' he said, catching her arm and swinging her round to face him. 'Where did you get to the other afternoon? I thought you must be taking a last look at the property, but although I searched the place I couldn't find you.'

'Oh—I— It wasn't my place to be there,' said Juliet uncomfortably. And then, frowning, 'How did you know where to find me today?'

'Well, I went to the apartment,' said Cary at once. 'And some old lady told me you'd got a job at a boutique in town. She said she thought the place was called Close To You or something, and, as luck would have it, I remembered a place called Close-Up, and here you are.'

Juliet pulled a face. She guessed it must be Mrs Heaton who had given him the information. The old lady hadn't been well lately and, since Juliet had been going into town every day, she'd done a little shopping for her. Naturally, Mrs Heaton had asked where she was working and Juliet had seen no harm in telling her.

Now, though, she wished she'd been a little more vague about her employer. She couldn't imagine why Cary might want to seek her out, but her instincts told her it wasn't just to be polite. 'So what do you want?' she asked, aware that she didn't sound exactly friendly. 'I only get half an hour for lunch. I've got to be back at half-past one.'

Cary pulled a face. 'Hey, is that any way to greet your ex-fiancé?' he demanded.

'You're not my ex-fiancé,' said Juliet tersely. 'Come on, Cary, what do you want?'

Cary scowled. 'Let me buy you lunch. Then I'll tell you.' He lifted a hand as she started to protest. 'All right, just a sandwich. There's a coffee shop across the road.'

'I know that.' It was where Juliet occasionally spent her lunchtimes. If she'd brought her college books to work she sometimes spent half an hour studying for her course. Thankfully, today she hadn't brought the books with her. She didn't want Cary seeing them and ridiculing her efforts.

'OK, then.' Cary put a hand on her bare arm. 'Let's go.'

It was easier to go with him than to argue. Staff weren't encouraged to invite friends or relations to visit the shop. The last thing she needed was for Cary to kick up a fuss just outside the door and cause Sandra to come and see what was going on. But she yanked her arm out of his grasp before they crossed the street.

'You're not wearing one of the rings,' Cary observed, after she'd accepted a coffee. 'I don't know whether you realise it, but those rings were valued at over a quarter of a mill.'

Juliet's jaw dropped. 'You're not serious!'

'Sure am. I borrowed them one day when I was visiting Tregellin and took them into Bodmin. The jeweller there said he'd give me over a hundred thousand for the lot.'

Juliet stared at him. 'But you just said—'

'A valuation is for insurance purposes,' said Cary quickly. 'Selling the rings to a jeweller is something else. Anyway,' he hesitated a moment and then continued doggedly, 'I wondered if you'd be willing to lend them to me, as—as surety for a loan.'

Juliet swallowed. 'I can't.'

'What do you mean, you can't?' Cary had instantly gone from amicable to aggressive.

'I don't have all the rings,' she said. 'I sent the ruby back to Rafe yesterday. It was his mother's ring and—'

'You bloody fool!' Cary was furious. 'Didn't you realise the ruby was the most valuable of the lot? Oh, I know I didn't think so at first, but according to the jeweller it's a very fine Burmese ruby. Apparently, it's flawless and very rare.'

'Well, good.' Juliet was glad they were sitting in the coffee bar when she'd told him. She had the feeling Cary might not be responsible for his actions. 'I'm glad I sent it back to Rafe.' She paused. 'Anyway, if that's all you wanted, I think I'll get back to the shop.'

'But what about the other rings?'

'What about them?'

'Well, are you going to lend them to me, as I asked? You owe me, Juliet. Without that reference I gave you, you probably wouldn't have a job.'

Juliet caught her breath. 'Are you forgetting I fulfilled my part of that bargain? And it didn't cost you a penny, either. Use the money Lady Elinor left you. That must be enough to finance any deal you've devised.'

Cary scowled again. 'You must be kidding! That barely paid my debts.' Then, as she got to her feet, he grabbed her arm again. 'By the way, if you're hoping Marchese will thank you for returning his mother's ring, forget it. Good old Liv is already calculating the odds.'

Juliet didn't believe him, but later that evening, sitting over a ready-made pizza she'd cooked in the microwave, she couldn't help wondering what Rafe would do now. Inheriting Tregellin was a wonderful thing for him, but keeping the old place going was something else.

It was always possible he could do as Cary had suggested when their grandmother was alive and sell one of the farms to gain some capital. There was no doubt that the house needed some immediate renovation, and, although she could understand Lady Elinor's reluctance to face the upheaval, Rafe couldn't put it off indefinitely, not if he wanted the old place to survive.

Still, it was none of her business, she reminded herself. Her involvement had been transitory at best, and she still didn't feel she deserved the legacy Lady Elinor had left her. Her only consolation was that Cary had known about the rings and might have taken them. He'd have sold them without hesitation once his grandmother was dead. Possibly without Rafe knowing anything about it until it was done.

She was washing her dishes in the tiny sink when someone rang the bell downstairs. All the apartments were fitted with intercoms for security, and, although she dried her hands and went to pick up the handset, she was fully prepared for some stranger to have hit the wrong button.

'Hello?'

'Juliet?'

Her mouth dried instantly. 'Yes.'

'May I come up?'

Her hand trembled. She wanted to refuse him. After the way he'd spoken to her at the funeral, she owed him no favours. But the urge to see him again was even stronger. 'All right,' she said, depressing the switch. 'Push the door. It's open.'

In the few seconds it would take him to enter the building and climb the stairs, Juliet made a hasty dash to the bathroom. There was no time to wash her face or no time to change or put on some make-up, but she did run a comb through her hair. She'd worn it in a pony-tail for work and, as usual, she'd tugged off the elastic fastener as soon as she'd got home. Likewise, she'd shed her lacy smock and mini, replacing them with a well-washed pink T-shirt and grey shorts that had seen better days.

He knocked just a few moments later and she hurried back into the living room and closed her bedroom door. Then, barefoot, she padded into the lobby, taking a deep breath before releasing the deadbolt and opening the outer door.

'Hi.'

Rafe stood on the threshold, casually dressed in a black T-shirt and black jeans. Only on him, the clothes assumed a careless elegance, hinting at the taut muscles and lean power they concealed.

But it was the thick sheet of art paper he was holding like a shield in front of him that distracted her. It was a charcoal drawing of herself, half-reclining on a tumbled bed. It was a subtle drawing, innocent, yet sexy. A flattering interpretation of how she must have looked that evening after he'd made love to her.

Juliet swallowed, and Rafe took the opportunity to say, 'It's good to see you, Juliet. Are you going to invite me in?'

Juliet stiffened, trying not to be seduced by his lazy smile. It was obvious that he'd brought the drawing to disconcert her, and he'd succeeded. 'Is there any reason why I should?' she asked tightly. 'I'd have thought I was the last person you'd want to see.'

'Which just shows how wrong you can be,' remarked Rafe drily, his smile fading a little as she continued to block the door. 'Here.' He handed her the drawing. 'This is for you, if you want it. I've got at least a dozen others at home.'

Juliet gasped. 'Do you expect me to believe that?'

'I don't lie,' he said quietly. 'If you'd like to visit my studio again, I'll prove it.'

Juliet chewed on her lower lip for a moment. 'So what do you want?' she asked unhappily, pushing the drawing onto the coat stand just inside the door.

'To talk to you.' Rafe spoke simply. 'To apologise, I guess. I behaved like a jerk at the funeral. You seem to bring out the worst—and the best—in me.'

Juliet sighed. 'Well—OK,' she said, realising she was giving in again. She stepped back to allow him to pass her. 'Go ahead. The living room's through there.'

Rafe stepped inside and she was immediately assailed by the scent of his aftershave, the clean, heated smell of his body. He seemed to hesitate and she stiffened instinctively, but then he walked into the living room, looking about him with an intent dark gaze.

'Do you want a drink?' Politeness was second nature to her and it was a warm evening outside. Besides, it gave her something to do other than notice how much smaller the room seemed with him in it.

'A soft drink would be good,' he said, even though he wasn't driving. But he had the feeling alcohol would just add to his sense of inadequacy.

'Diet cola or orange juice?' she asked, pretending to study the contents of her small fridge. 'I've got both.'

'Orange sounds fine.' Then, noticing she was taking out a glass, Rafe came towards her. 'I'll drink it from the can.'

Juliet hesitated, but it was easier not to argue. Their fingers brushed and she felt tiny sparks of energy shoot up her arm. However, Rafe didn't seem to notice, flicking the tab on the can and drinking thirstily from it. Then he lowered it again and said, 'I needed that. Thanks.'

Juliet made a dismissing gesture. 'Why don't you sit down?' she suggested, the height difference between them pronounced by her bare feet.

He was still an intimidating figure, perched on the edge of the sofa, legs spread, his hands still holding the empty can hanging between. 'Why don't you join me?' He looked up at her enquiringly, but Juliet was reluctant to lose the small advantage she'd gained.

'I prefer to stand,' she said, pulling on the hem of the T-shirt that kept riding up over her bare midriff. 'So—was there something else?'

Rafe's lips twisted. 'Evidently you don't think so.'

'Well, you said you wanted to apologise, and you have. What else is there? Oh—' Juliet frowned as another thought occurred to her. She pushed her fingertips beneath her arms almost defensively. 'I'm glad your grandmother left Tregellin to you. I'm sure you deserve it much more than Cary.'

Rafe looked down at the can he was holding before placing it carefully on the low table near by. Then he leant against the cushions behind him, arms along the back of the sofa, one ankle resting on his knee. 'Was that why you ran away?' he asked mildly. 'Wasn't that a rather childish thing to do?'

'I didn't run away.' Juliet was indignant. 'I never wanted to attend the reading of the will in the first place, and you weren't interested in anything I had to say. I would have liked to say goodbye to Josie, but you and she were talking to the solicitor. I just walked into the village and called a taxi. I already had a ticket for the train back to London.'

Rafe's eyes smouldered a little. 'Did you travel with Cary?'

'No!' She gazed at him warily. 'Did he tell you that I had?'

Rafe shrugged. 'He might have said something,' he responded carelessly. 'I gather you've seen him. Despite your protestations, my cousin appears to play some part in your life still.'

'That's not true.' Juliet sighed. 'If you must know, he came to ask me to lend him the rings your grandmother left me.' And at his narrowing brows, 'I didn't do it. I couldn't. I was afraid that if I'd let him have them, I'd never see them again.'

'Ain't that the truth?' Rafe was sarcastic. 'My God, that man has no shame.'

Juliet considered a moment, and then she said, 'I think he doesn't believe I have any right to the rings. And, in all honesty, neither do I.'

'That's rubbish and you know it.' Rafe got to his feet again, looking down at her with a dark, disturbing intensity. 'The old lady wanted you to have them. All of them.' He put his hand into his back pocket and brought out the velvet box she recognised as being the one she'd sent to him. 'Including this.'

When he flicked the lid on the box, Juliet saw the Burmese ruby nestling on its white satin bed. It sparkled with a life of its own, its circlet of what she now realised must be real diamonds catching and reflecting the light.

'Beautiful, isn't it?' he said, with a peculiar huskiness in his voice. 'Here.' He held the box out. 'Take it.'

'No.' Juliet shook her head and deliberately thrust her hands behind her back. Rafe guessed she was unaware that in doing so, she'd proved to him she wasn't wearing a bra. 'It's yours,' she added, a little of the tension that had been between them in the cemetery sharpening her words. 'It was your mother's ring. No one has more right to it than you do. That's why I sent it back.'

Rafe tried to ignore the hardening in his groin and concentrate on what she'd said. 'So it wasn't just because it was my mother's ring?'

'No.' Nothing could be further from the truth.

He arched an enquiring brow. 'Then, perhaps you sent it back in the hope that I'd return it personally.'

'No.' She was indignant now. 'I wouldn't give you that satisfaction.' She paused. 'Besides, Cary told me that you and—Lady Holderness were—very close.'

'Oh, really?' Rafe was impatient. 'I might have expected something like that from him, but not from you.'

'Why not?' But she coloured in embarrassment just the same. 'You can't deny she knew her way round your apartment. And as for those pictures—'

'The sketches, you mean?' Rafe gave a weary shake of his head. 'I told you about them. She wanted me to paint her portrait for her husband's sixtieth birthday. It was intended to be a surprise. What was I supposed to do? Refuse the commission?'

Juliet caught her lower lip between her teeth. 'So did you do it? Paint her portrait, I mean?'

'Yes.' He shrugged. 'I finished it and she presented it to her husband. Apparently he was delighted, so it's not a secret any more.'

Juliet sighed. 'I'm sorry.'

'Yeah, so am I.'

'You can't deny she—well, she likes you.'

'And I like her. In small doses. Juliet, when I agreed to paint her portrait I hadn't even met you.'

'I know.' Juliet felt ashamed. She glanced towards the lobby. 'The drawing you brought—it's very good.'

'So you're not going to tear it up the minute I walk out the door.'

'No!' She was appalled.

'You sent back the ring.'

'And you know why.'

'Whatever Cary says?'

'Whatever Cary says,' she said fiercely. 'Cary's a liar. I know that now.'

'Oh, yeah.' Rafe closed the velvet box again and placed it on the table beside the empty can. 'But then, he wanted me to fund his overdraft by allowing him to sell the ring. As compensation, as he put it, for depriving him of his inheritance.'

Juliet shook her head. 'But you didn't. Deprive him, I mean.'

'I know. But, like you, I felt some guilt for the way the old lady had treated him.'

Juliet shrugged. 'Most people would consider two hundred thousand pounds more than generous.'

'Yes.' Rafe pulled a wry face. 'But all things are relative, I suppose, and nobody said Cary was cheap.'

Juliet twisted her hands together. 'So?'

'So I offered him the studio and the apartment above it. I said he could either use it as a holiday rental or sell it. I won't need it. I'm having the old coach-house studio where I used to work updated, and I'll be living at Tregellin from now on. Josie says she'll stay until I decide on her replacement. What with all the renovations and such, I couldn't do without her.'

Juliet hesitated. 'So how are you—?' She broke off abruptly. 'Forget I said that. It's nothing to do with me.'

'How am I financing the renovations?' guessed Rafe shrewdly, and Juliet coloured. 'Remember the safety-deposit box old Arnold mentioned?' And at her unwilling nod, 'It contained dozens of investment bonds that the old lady had had since my grandfather died. Arnold said I should cash them in and I did. There was tax to pay, of course, but even so there's more than enough money to restore Tregellin and finance its upkeep for a considerable number of years.'

Juliet's shoulders sagged. 'Well—good. I'm so glad everything's working out for you.'

'Are you?' She was totally unprepared for him to run a slightly unsteady hand over her hot cheek. 'Do you have any real idea of why I came here? Do you know how grateful I was when you returned the ring and I had an excuse to come and see you?'

Juliet quivered. 'Did you need an excuse?'

'After what happened on the day of the funeral? I think so.'

Juliet's nails dug into her palms. 'You were only saying what you thought of me—'

'No!' He shook his head. 'No, I wasn't.'

'Yes.' She licked her lips. 'And I don't blame you. What I did was unforgivable—'

'Juliet—'

'I'm sorry, OK? My only excuse is that at the time I was pretty desperate—'

'As I am now,' Rafe broke in harshly, capturing her startled face between his hands and gazing down at her with frustrated eyes. 'My darling, listen to me. I've regretted every word of what I said a hundred times over. Yes, I was angry with you; yes, I believed you and Cary were still together; and yes, I was blind with jealousy. But it had been a rough couple of months for me and seeing you with Cary just tore me up.'

'I understand.' Juliet gazed up at him. 'Your grandmother's death must have been a terrible shock for you.'

'Yeah, it was.' Rafe sighed. 'I really loved that old lady. But it wasn't just that. Before she died, she told me that my mother's death hadn't been an accident as I'd always thought. She said— she said my mother committed suicide. That when she fell from that balcony, it was a deliberate thing.'

Juliet gasped. 'But how could she know something like that? I thought they were estranged.'

'They were.' Rafe nodded. 'But she wrote to the old lady the day before she died, asking her if she'd look after me.'

'Oh, Rafe!'

'Yeah.' His lips twisted. 'I guess it's not what you expected to hear either.' He paused. 'Does it make a difference?'

Juliet swallowed. 'A difference to what?'

'What do you think?' He shook his head. 'You must know I care about you.' He expelled an unsteady breath. 'Dear God, Juliet, I'm in love with you.'

Juliet could hardly speak. But her hands came up to cover his. 'I don't know what to say.'

'You could say you feel the same,' he ventured softly. His eyes dipped to her mouth. 'Do you know how much I want to kiss you at this moment? Let me kiss you. You don't know it, but you have the most incredible mouth...'

This last was said against her lips, his breath filling her mouth with his taste, his scent. His hands cradled her head, holding her still while his tongue invaded and caressed, showing her how much he needed her with this simple act of love.

And Rafe was a past master at lovemaking. She knew that. But this time he touched her with love, with reverence, and when his finger sought the hem of her T-shirt she was eager to help him. Her insides turned to liquid as he stroked her, his tongue possessing first one swollen nipple and then the other. She was trembling in his arms. She'd longed so much for him to hold her again, and her husky whisper of, 'Of course I love you,' was almost inaudible against his throat.

But he heard her.

'You've no idea how desperate I've been since you left Tregellin,' he said, pulling her closer, letting her feel what her urgent confession had done to him. 'I really thought I'd blown it with you and you didn't even know about my mother. God, I haven't slept since you left me. Not to mention the fact I thought you and Cary were still together.'

'We were *never* together,' Juliet told him fiercely, twining her fingers in his dark hair. 'You do believe me, don't you? And I'm sorry about your mother, but grateful, too. If you'd still been living in Italy, we might never have met.'

'I believe you,' he assured her, his voice thickening as the blood rushed hotly into his groin. A moan vibrated in his chest and he gathered her against him. 'But, dear God, can we save any more explanations until later? I want you, I want to be inside you. Is that a concept you can recognise at all?'

Juliet's lips parted in a delicious smile. 'Oh, yes,' she said. 'I think so.' She paused a moment. 'Would you like to see where I sleep?'

'So long as you understand I don't have sleeping in mind,' said Rafe ruefully. Then he grinned. 'OK, show me. Perhaps I'll think of something else to show you.'

The windows were open in Juliet's bedroom and the muted sounds from the street outside drifted softly on the air. She would have closed the curtains, but Rafe wouldn't let her. 'If anyone wants to watch, let them,' he murmured huskily. 'I love you, Juliet. We've got nothing to hide.'

They undressed each other, slowly at first, but then with an increasing urgency. Juliet's T-shirt and shorts were easy, but it took her slightly longer to unfasten his belt and unzip his trousers.

'Juliet, let me,' he said, his hands shaking a little as he pushed the jeans down his thighs. 'I've had more experience than you,' he added, and she cast him a knowing look. 'Not as much as you think,' he assured her as she knelt on the bed in front of him. 'And I've never said I love a woman before. Except the old lady, of course. But she was something else.'

His mouth on hers was warm and urgent, his hands taking possession of her breasts, his thumbs rubbing sensuously over the hardened peaks. 'You are so beautiful,' he said, regarding her with such reverence that she was humbled. 'I can't believe I let you leave without telling you how I feel about you. My only excuse is, I didn't know you'd gone until afterwards.'

Juliet looped her arms about his neck. 'I couldn't wait to get away,' she confessed. 'I was so sure you must hate and despise me. I wouldn't have blamed you if you had. I hated and despised myself.'

Rafe gave a wry smile. 'And how did you feel about me?'

Her eyes widened. 'Need you ask?'

'I think so.' Rafe nodded. 'After the way I'd behaved.'

'Oh.' She drew back to rest her forehead against his, her smile gentle, her breath warm against his face. 'I think I've been in love with you since that first morning at Tregellin. You and Hitchins came to greet us and I thought you were the most attractive couple I'd ever seen.'

Rafe arched his dark brows. 'Are you sure about that? Hitchins wasn't exactly welcoming.'

Juliet giggled. 'No, he wasn't.' She frowned. 'Where is he, by the way? I'm sort of fond of that little dog.'

'He's at Tregellin. Where he belongs,' said Rafe, and circled her lips with his tongue. 'You'll see him soon enough. He's an amazingly good judge of character.'

But then he couldn't wait any longer. Bearing her back against the pillows, he buried his face between her breasts. 'I love you. So much,' he said, moving over her. 'Don't ever leave me again. I don't think I could bear it. I've filled the house with pictures of you, but they're not good enough. Nothing…' his voice sank to a sensual whisper '…nothing compares to the real thing…'

EPILOGUE

JULIET'S first Christmas at Tregellin was the happiest she'd ever known. She and Rafe had decorated the old house together, and branches of holly and mistletoe added their own particular aromas to the delicious scent of pine from the huge tree that stood in the hall.

They'd been married in October. The vicar had presided over the service at the small church in Tregellin village with just a dozen or so of their closest friends as witnesses. Then they'd spent a heavenly couple of weeks on an island in the Indian Ocean, before returning to the newly renovated Tregellin House and the life they would share together.

To begin with, Rafe had wanted her to give up her job and go back with him in the summer. But, although it had been a great temptation, she'd decided to complete her computer course. Besides, although he'd told her he loved her, she'd been half-afraid the emotional storm of Lady Elinor's passing had left him feeling vulnerable. She was so worried he'd regret being so impulsive when he'd had time to think.

Of course, she'd been completely wrong. Rafe had spent the subsequent three months travelling back and forth between Tregellin and London whenever his work permitted. He became such a frequent visitor at the apartment that old Mrs Heaton had asked if he'd moved in. 'Given half a chance,' Rafe had assured her humorously, and Juliet had found herself blushing furiously when he'd looked her way.

Since their return from honeymoon, Juliet had virtually taken over the running of the estate. Her newly acquired computer skills had enabled her to format all the accounts, and Rafe had been more than willing to leave the organisation to her.

His own career was going from strength to strength. Several commissions had followed on from his portrait of Lady Holderness, and his talent was being recognised by other galleries around the country. He had so much work that he'd had to cut back on the hours he'd spent teaching, but Juliet was always his first consideration.

As far as they knew, Cary was living in New York these days. He'd left England just after their wedding, leaving a stack of debts behind. Rafe had attended to most of them, despite his solicitor's disapproval. But afterwards, he'd confessed to Juliet that he'd done it for Lady Elinor, not himself.

Then, in January, two things happened that would have an impact on their lives.

The first was that Juliet discovered she was pregnant. She and Rafe had never discussed when they might start a family, and she was a little tentative when she broke the news to him. But Rafe was delighted, if a little anxious about her reaction. 'Do you mind?' he asked her honestly. 'I have to admit, I haven't always been as diligent about using protection as I should.'

'Oh, darling!' Juliet wound her arms around his neck and pressed the whole length of her warm body against him. 'I couldn't be more pleased. I can imagine nothing more satisfying than knowing I have your baby growing inside me. Can you?'

Of course, Rafe took pains to assure her he agreed and by the time they went downstairs again the afternoon was half over. It was snowing outside, the fluffy kind of snow they'd hoped to have for Christmas, and they spent some time watching the flakes falling over the estuary from the windows of the conservatory.

'Just think,' murmured Rafe, drawing his wife's still slim body back against him. 'Next winter, there'll be three of us.' He nuzzled her neck as his hands caressed the slight mound of her stomach. 'So I suppose I should make the most of having you to myself.'

The second thing that happened was totally different.

Towards the end of the month, when Juliet was beginning to suffer the effects of morning sickness, she got a letter from her father's solicitors. It informed her that her ex-husband, David Hammond, had died in George Town in Grand Cayman. He had apparently developed a virulent form of cancer six months ago, and he had made a will making her his only beneficiary.

To say Juliet was stunned would have been an understatement. The letter had arrived as she was making an early-morning cup of tea and she'd had to sit down for a few moments before she could go on. Although Josie still worked part-time at the house, her niece, Connie Boswell, had taken over much of the housework. However, both women were not due to arrive before nine o'clock, so Juliet usually enjoyed this time on her own.

Now, however, she set the cups and teapot on the tray and carried it upstairs to her husband. Despite the efficient heating system, it was still chilly, and she was glad when she could shed her robe and tumble back into bed.

'Mmm, you're freezing,' Rafe groaned as she curled her cold feet around his legs. 'Come here. Let me warm you.'

'Not yet.' Despite submitting to a sleepy kiss, Juliet insisted on wriggling up against the pillows. 'Listen to this,' she added when Rafe started to protest, and, resisting his efforts, she read the letter to him.

'Hell!' The contents of the letter were enough to put Rafe's drowsy appeals on hold. He frowned as he pushed himself up beside her. Studying her pale face, he said, 'Are you very upset?'

'Upset?' Juliet's brows drew together and Rafe thought how utterly delectable she looked, with her nightgown slipping off one shoulder and her hair a tumbled mass of honeyed silk about her head. 'I don't think I'm upset, exactly. Shocked, certainly. He was still so young.'

'Then how do you feel?' Rafe persisted gently, sliding one hand beneath her hair, massaging the back of her neck. 'You look awfully pale.'

'That's 'cos I've been sick again,' confessed Juliet philosophically. And when he started to protest that she should have woken him, she pulled a face.

'What could you do?' she asked, stroking his mouth with her finger. 'Besides, I don't mind, really. Dr Charteris says it won't last long.'

'All the same…' Rafe's mouth compressed for a moment, but when his wife arched her brows he gave in. 'All right,' he said. 'So what about David?' He grimaced. 'The guy must have had a conscience, after all.'

'Mmm.' Juliet was thoughtful. 'I suppose being handed what amounted to a death sentence really focuses the mind.' She sighed. 'I'm sorry, of course. No one deserves to die in those circumstances. But I never loved David.' She gave a tentative smile. 'I know that now.'

Rafe pulled her closer. 'I suppose you'll be a wealthy woman again,' he commented ruefully, but Juliet simply snuggled closer and shook her head.

'I don't want the money,' she said. 'However much or how little there might be.' She reached up to kiss him. 'Would you mind if I donated it to a charity?' And at his smile of approval, 'I've got everything I need right here.'

THE PREGNANCY
AFFAIR

CHAPTER ONE

THE sign informing passengers to *Fasten Seat Belts* flashed on above Olivia's head and she automatically reached to check that her belt was in place.

'We'll be landing at Newcastle International Airport in fifteen minutes,' the saccharine-sweet voice of the flight attendant announced smoothly. 'Please ensure that all your hand luggage is put away in the overhead lockers and that your tray tables are securely stowed.'

The aircraft dipped to begin its approach to the airport and Olivia's stomach lurched in protest. But it wasn't the amount of coffee she'd consumed that morning that was giving her such a sickly feeling. It was the knowledge that she was returning to Bridgeford after so many years that was tying her stomach in knots.

The landing was swift and uneventful. The airport was busy and the plane taxied efficiently to its unloading bay as passengers and crew alike began gathering their belongings together. There was little chit-chat. This was primarily a business flight, most of the passengers either on or returning from business trips, with only a handful of holiday-makers to make up the numbers.

Olivia's trip was neither business nor pleasure, she thought, and she wasn't at all sure she was doing the right thing by coming here. She doubted her father would want to see her, whatever reassurances her sister had given her, and there'd be no sympathetic shoulder for someone who'd messed up her life, not just once, but twice.

Still, it was too late to have second thoughts now. The plane had come to a complete standstill, the door was open, and her fellow passengers were all jostling to be first to alight. Eventually, of course, she had to get up and follow them. She should have worn flats, she thought as her ridiculously high heels caught in the metal of the stairway. But pride was a stubborn companion and Olivia was determined not to appear as desperate as she felt.

A short walk across the tarmac and she was in the terminal buildings, offering her passport for inspection and lining up to collect her suitcase from the carousel. She'd only brought one suitcase, leaving the rest of her belongings in storage in London. Because that was where she was going to find herself an apartment, she told herself firmly. This trip to Bridgeford was just to prove to herself—and her family—that she wasn't afraid to come back.

Her suitcase was one of the first to appear and Olivia pulled a wry face as she hauled it off the carousel. OK, she thought, it was time to face the music. Linda, her sister, had said she would come to meet her. Which was a relief. She was likely to be the least-judgemental of the family.

Beyond the doors, a crowd of people was waiting to greet the passengers, many of them carrying name boards to identify themselves. One thing, Olivia thought drily, there was no way she wouldn't recognise Linda. Whether Linda would recognise her was another thing altogether.

And then she stopped dead in her tracks, the suitcase she was towing behind her running on into the backs of her legs. But she hardly noticed the bump or the momentary discomfort it gave her. She was staring at the man who was standing at the back of the crowd of people, and, although she couldn't believe it, it seemed he was waiting for her.

She glanced quickly behind her, half convinced he wasn't looking at her at all but at some other person who'd followed her through the doors. But there was no one immediately behind her, no one else to coincide with his line of vision.

And then, to confirm her disbelief, he moved towards her, pushing his way through the waiting mob to fetch up by her side. 'Hi,' he said, taking the handle of the suitcase from her unresisting hand. 'D'you have a good journey?'

Olivia stared at him blankly. 'What are you doing here?' she asked, aware that it probably wasn't the politest thing to say in the circumstances, but she couldn't help it. If she'd been anxious on the plane, she was a hundred times more nervous now. Her heart was pounding, the blood rushing through her veins like wildfire. What the hell was Joel Armstrong doing here? She'd have expected him to avoid her like the plague. 'Wh-where's Linda?'

If he noticed the stammer, he gave no sign of it. 'At home,' he replied evenly, and because he started walking away from her, she was obliged to follow him. 'Your father's having a bad day,' he continued. 'She thought it would be wiser not to leave him alone.'

Olivia blinked. She could have said all her father ever had were bad days in her estimation, but she didn't. She was too busy trying to keep up with his long strides. Trying to ally herself, too, to the man who was walking beside her. Fifteen years ago, he'd been little more than a boy. Now he was a man.

And what a man, she thought, permitting herself a covert look in his direction. He'd always been tall, but now he'd filled out, the shoulders of the leather jacket he was wearing owing nothing to padding she was sure. A lean jawline showed just the trace of a five o'clock shadow, while his unruly dark hair was shorter than she remembered, exposing the handsome shape of his skull.

Not that handsome described him exactly. His youthful good looks had given way to a harsher profile altogether. Fans of lighter skin flared from the corners of his cool grey eyes, while deeper ridges framed the narrow-lipped beauty of his mouth.

God, he was attractive, Olivia thought, feeling a pang of awareness she'd never expected to feel again. It hardly seemed possible that they'd once been married. Had she really allowed a sense of pride to rule her reason? Would things have been different if she'd chosen to stay and fight?

She stumbled as they stepped out into the watery sunshine of an April day. It had been cool in London, but it was amazingly mild here. As Joel turned at her muffled exclamation, she regretted the urge she'd had to dress up for the journey. She'd wanted Linda to envy her her trim figure and designer clothes. She'd even chosen the shortest skirt in her wardrobe to show off the slender length of her legs. As for how much it had cost to have the ash-blonde highlights in her honey-brown hair renewed… She must have been crazy to think anyone would care.

'You OK?' Joel asked now and she nodded automatically.
'I'm fine,' she said quickly. 'Where are you parked?'

'Not far away,' he responded, slowing his pace a little.
'Be grateful it's not raining. It was earlier.'

Olivia pulled a face, but she refused to answer him.
Dammit, here they were, meeting one another after fifteen
years, and all he could talk about was the weather. Why
was she feeling so tongue-tied suddenly, when he was obviously quite at ease with her?

Whatever had happened to him in the last fifteen years
had definitely changed him. And for the better, she mused.
He'd left school at eighteen and, despite getting excellent
results, he'd gone to work for her father. He'd wanted to
marry her and they'd done so as soon as she was eighteen.
Everyone had expected it would last, even Joel. Or at least
she'd thought that was what he'd believed. Looking at him
now, she was beginning to wonder if that was just another
of her many mistakes.

'So—how are you?' she managed at last, relieved when
they turned between the aisles of parked cars. Surely it
wouldn't be much further. 'It's been a long time.'

'Hasn't it just?' he agreed, a faintly mocking twist to his
mouth as he looked at her and Olivia knew damn well he'd
never looked at her like that before. It was as if she amused
him. 'You seem OK,' he added. 'I guess living in the States
agrees with you.'

It didn't, actually, Olivia was tempted to respond, but
that had had more to do with the man she'd been living with
than with the country itself.

Joel stopped behind a huge four-wheel-drive and
juggled his keys out of his pocket. Flipping open the rear

door, he stowed Olivia's suitcase in the back and then went round and opened the passenger door.

Olivia was still admiring the vehicle, its mud-splattered wing in no way detracting from its sleek appearance. Was this Joel's or her father's? she wondered uncertainly. Whosoever it was, things at the farm must definitely be looking up.

'Nice car,' she said, and wished he wasn't watching her get in. The seat was high and her skirt rode up to her bottom as she levered herself onto it. And she was fairly sure Joel was suppressing another of those mocking smiles.

'I like it,' he said, without expression. He walked around the bonnet and climbed in beside her, the high seat offering no obstacle to his long legs. 'All set?'

'As I'll ever be,' said Olivia tartly, not seeing why he should have it all his own way. Then, as his hands gripped the wheel, she noticed the wedding ring on his third finger. Not the ring she'd given him, she realised, but a much more expensive band altogether. Her stomach tightened unpleasantly. 'Are you married?'

It was an impertinent question and she knew as soon as she'd voiced it that it was nothing to do with her. But dammit, he had been her husband first. Didn't she have a right to know if he'd replaced her?

'Do you care?' he countered now and, despite her determination not to let him see how she was feeling, Olivia felt the hot colour stain her cheeks.

'I—not particularly,' she muttered, turning her attention to a plane that was just coming in to land. 'This airport's busier than I remember.'

'Things change,' said Joel, reversing out of the space

and turning in the direction of the exit. 'And I'm divorced. For the second time,' he appended drily. 'I guess neither of us has had any luck in that direction.'

'What do you mean?'

Olivia's eyes were drawn to him now, and he gave her a sardonic look. 'Linda told me your second marriage broke up,' he said. 'Isn't that why you're back in England?'

Olivia expelled a resentful breath. Linda, she thought irritably. She might have known her sister wouldn't keep something like that to herself. 'I've come back to England because my work's here,' she retorted shortly. 'I don't know enough about the US housing market to get a comparable job in New York.'

'Ah.' Joel allowed the distinction, but Olivia still felt as if he didn't believe her. 'So you're going to do what? Join an agency in Newcastle?'

'London, probably,' she responded swiftly, hating the need she felt to justify herself in his eyes. Why did she care what he thought of her? If Linda hadn't seen fit to ask him to meet her, they might never have had this conversation.

Joel used the ticket he'd bought earlier to let them out of the car park, and then turned north towards Ponteland and Belsay. The sky had cleared and it was that shade of blue that seemed almost transparent. The trees were already greening with spring growth and here and there late daffodils bloomed along the hedgerows. Olivia had forgotten how beautiful the countryside could be. Living first in London and then New York, she'd become so much a city animal.

'Um—how is my father?' she asked at last, realising she was to blame for the uneasy silence that lay between them.

She tried to adopt a humorous tone. 'Still as irascible as ever, I suppose.'

'He has good days and bad days, as I'm sure Linda's told you,' answered Joel, permitting her a rueful grin. 'But since the stroke—'

'The stroke?' Olivia didn't let him finish. 'What stroke? Linda said nothing about a stroke.'

Joel blew out a breath. 'Didn't she?' His tone was flat. 'Well, maybe I shouldn't have either. I dare say the old man doesn't want it broadcasting to all and sundry.'

'Hey, I'm not "all and sundry"!' exclaimed Olivia, her efforts at conciliation forgotten at his words. 'I'm his daughter. Don't you think I have a right to know?'

Joel's thick dark brows arched indifferently. 'I suppose that depends on the kind of relationship you two have had over the years,' he remarked mildly. 'How long is it since you've seen him?'

Olivia huffed. 'You know exactly how long it is. I wasn't exactly encouraged to come back after—after we split up.'

Joel regarded her for a brief compelling moment. 'Is that supposed to be an excuse?'

'No.' Olivia felt herself colouring again. 'It's the reason why I haven't seen him. I have phoned, and written letters. I've never had a reply.'

Joel moved his shoulders in a rueful gesture. 'I didn't know that.'

'No?' Olivia wasn't sure whether she believed him. 'Well, why would you? I dare say you hoped you'd never set eyes on me again.'

Joel shook his head. 'You're wrong, Liv. I got over what you did years ago. I moved on. I got married. I had a son.

I realised we were too young when we got married. Neither of us knew what we really wanted out of life.'

Olivia had to force herself not to turn and stare at him now. He had a son! Of all the things he might have said, she realised that was the least expected. And the most painful, she acknowledged as the bile caused by too many cups of black coffee rose sickly in the back of her throat.

She had to say something, she thought, aware that she was taking too long to make a rejoinder. And, dammit, why should she care if he had a child? It wasn't as if she was the maternal type. But, all the same, it hurt. It hurt deep inside her. Like a wound that had been partially healed that was suddenly as raw and painful as the day she'd lost their son.

'Well—good,' she said at last, hoping he couldn't hear the thickness of her voice. 'But, even so, I wish Linda had warned me.'

'I imagine she was afraid that if you knew the truth you might change your mind about coming,' observed Joel shrewdly. 'Ben Foley isn't the best of patients. Without Dempsey's help, the farm would have gone down the drain long ago.'

Olivia was surprised. 'Martin?' she said curiously, speaking of her sister's husband. 'Does he work at the farm as well as at the garden centre?'

'They let the garden centre go,' replied Joel, accelerating past a tractor. 'They live at the farm now. It seemed the most sensible solution in the circumstances.'

Olivia was totally confused. When she'd gone away, Joel had virtually been running the farm for her father, and it had been understood that he'd take over when Ben Foley retired. That was one of the reasons why her father had been so angry with her when their marriage broke up. He'd depended on Joel. A lot. She caught her breath suddenly. Surely he hadn't punished Joel because she'd walked out?

They turned a bend in the road and suddenly it was possible to glimpse the sea in the distance. Redes Bay gleamed in the early-afternoon sun, shimmering like a mirage in the desert. Bridgeford was just a mile from the sea as the crow flies. A little further than that on the twisting roads that honeycombed the area.

'You must be hungry,' Joel said, glancing her way again, and Olivia managed a faint smile. But the truth was she felt too knotted up inside to care about an empty stomach. Though there was no doubt she'd probably feel better if the amount of coffee she'd consumed wasn't sloshing about inside her.

'I expect Linda will have a meal ready for you,' he continued. 'She still makes the best steak and kidney pie in the neighbourhood.'

'Does she?' Olivia felt even queasier at the thought of all those calories. In recent years she'd become accustomed to eating sparingly, always watching her weight for any fluctuation, living on tuna fish and what her sister would call rabbit-food. The idea of sitting down to a lunch of steak and kidney pie horrified her. Even empty, as she was, she knew she'd never get it down.

'It looks as if you could use a few extra pounds,' remarked Joel, slowing at yet another crossroads, and Olivia wondered at his perception. It was as if he'd known exactly what she was thinking.

'Oh, does it?' she said, her incredulity giving way to resentment. 'I suppose you prefer women with more flesh on their bones.'

Joel chuckled. He actually chuckled, and Olivia was furious. 'You could say that,' he agreed, and she badly wanted to slap him. She knew she was looking good—by New York standards, at least—and it was mortifying to have him *laugh* at her.

'And I suppose your second wife was everything I'm not,' she flung at him angrily, uncaring at that moment how peevish she sounded. 'Well, where I come from women care about their appearance. We don't all want to be milch cows!'

Joel sobered. 'No, I think you proved that when you got rid of our baby,' he retorted harshly, and she realised that for the first time she'd caught him on the raw. His jaw clamped shut for a few moments, as if suppressing another outburst, but when he spoke again he had himself in control. 'Forget it. I shouldn't have said anything.'

Olivia swallowed, remembering she'd promised herself she wouldn't say anything if she saw Joel either. But she couldn't stop herself. 'For the record,' she said unsteadily, 'I didn't *get rid* of our baby. At the risk of repeating myself, I had a miscarriage. Believe it or not, these things happen!'

Joel's tanned fingers tightened on the wheel and she saw his knuckles whiten at the pressure he was putting on them. 'Whatever,' he said flatly, but she knew he didn't believe her now any more than he'd believed her before. 'We'll be there in a few minutes. I'll drop you off and then I've got to get back to college.'

Olivia blinked. 'To college?' she echoed blankly.

'In Newcastle,' he agreed, without elaborating.

'You're at college?' she persisted, staring at him incredulously.

'I work at the university,' he corrected her drily. 'I gather Linda didn't tell you that either.'

Olivia's jaw dropped. 'No.'

In actual fact, Linda hadn't mentioned Joel at all. That was why she'd been so surprised to see him at the airport. She'd assumed she'd have to meet him sooner or later at the farm and that Linda was being tactful by putting off the evil day.

'Have I shocked you?'

Joel had relaxed again and Olivia knew she had to say something or run the risk of appearing envious. She'd never gone to university, although she had eventually taken an economics degree at evening classes.

Not that she'd ever needed it. By the time she'd graduated, she'd already been working in a large London estate agency. Her aptitude for the job, and the fact that she got on so well with the clients, had accelerated her climb up the corporate ladder. At age twenty-six, she'd already been earning a high five-figure salary, with added perks like her one-bedroom apartment in Bloomsbury.

Of course, she reflected, she'd given it all up when Bruce Garvey asked her to marry him. Despite her success at work, her life had seemed empty, and she'd found she missed her friends and family and the life she'd had in Bridgeford. She'd even missed Joel, though she'd been sure she'd never forgive him for walking out on her.

'I expect your parents were pleased when you left the farm,' she said at last, hoping she didn't sound as bitter as she felt. She moistened her lips. 'I'm sorry. I assumed you were still working there.'

Joel shook his head. 'I couldn't stay after—well, after what happened.'

Olivia's eyes went wide. 'You mean, my father asked you to leave?'

'Hell, no.' Joel gave her a satirical look. 'Not everything revolves around you, you know. I did what I should have done years ago. I took my qualifications and got myself a degree in IT at Leeds University.'

Olivia blinked. 'IT?'

'Information technology,' he said patiently. 'Computers, for want of a better word.'

Olivia pressed her shoulders back into the soft leather of the seat. 'I see.' She paused. 'I'm glad things have worked out so well for you.'

'Oh, yeah.' Joel was sardonic now. 'Two failed marriages and a child that might or might not have been aborted. Life's been peachy, Liv. So how has it been for you?'

CHAPTER TWO

FORTUNATELY, Olivia was saved the need of answering him. They'd reached Bridgeford and the Lexus splashed through the ford at the edge of the village before accelerating up the slope to the village green. She could pretend she hadn't heard him, pretend she hadn't been knocked off balance by the callousness of his words. Struggling with emotions she didn't even want to acknowledge, she looked instead at the Georgian homes and the handful of cottages that circled the village green. As a shiver of remembered agony slid down her spine, the beauty of her surroundings was a blessed panacea.

The village, at least, didn't seem to have changed much, she thought gratefully, although she could see the roofs of some new houses just visible beyond the trees in the churchyard. There were daffodils blooming here, too, and the almond blossom was just beginning to appear.

'Do your parents still live in the village?' she asked a little stiffly, feeling obliged to say something. The Armstrongs had never approved of Joel's relationship with her, and even after they were married Olivia had been left in no doubt that Mrs Armstrong didn't consider her good enough for her son.

'My father's retired now,' replied Joel amiably enough. Mr Armstrong was an accountant and had used to work for a firm in Chevingham, a small town some ten miles south of Bridgeford. 'They still own the house in Blades Lane,' he added, 'but they've recently bought a place in Spain. They spend a lot of time there in the winter months. They're in El Fuente at present, actually.'

Which explained a lot, thought Olivia cynically. She wondered if Joel would have been so willing to come and meet her if he'd had to explain himself to his parents first.

They passed the house Joel's parents owned on their way to the farm. Rose Cottage was set a few yards back from the road, screened by a tangle of wild roses that blossomed profusely in the season.

It reminded Olivia irresistibly of when she and Joel were teenagers. How many times had she come running down from the farm to find him waiting for her at his gate? They'd both attended the comprehensive school in Chevingham and the school bus used to pick them up at the end of Blades Lane.

Of course, Joel had been a year older, and once they'd got to school there'd been no opportunity to be together. Was that why their relationship had progressed so swiftly? she wondered. Had the excitement of forbidden fruit coloured that youthful infatuation?

'Does everything look the same?' Joel asked abruptly, and Olivia was grateful for the reprieve. She'd been in danger of remembering things that were best forgotten. As Joel said, they'd both moved on.

'Pretty much,' she said after a moment, forcing herself to take an interest in her surroundings. They were turning between white-painted gateposts now, crossing a cattle-grid that caused the vehicle's wheels to vibrate, and then accelerating up the drive to the farmhouse itself.

When the Lexus stopped, Olivia knew the journey was over. However, she felt—and she really wasn't feeling very good—she had to get out of the car and face whatever was to come. It would have been nice, she thought, if her father had invited her here. But it was Linda who'd suggested this visit. Linda, who'd told her so little of what to expect.

'You OK?'

She realised that Joel was looking at her now, probably wondering why she hadn't opened her door. And, dammit, she so didn't want to show him how she was feeling. Joel, with his new career and his precious son.

So, 'Why wouldn't I be?' she answered, with assumed lightness. She gathered her handbag into her arms and reached for the door handle. 'Thanks for the ride, Joel. It's been—illuminating.'

Now, why had she said that? she chided herself impatiently, as Joel's eyes narrowed on her face. 'Why do I get the feeling that you're mad at me?' he countered, but before Olivia could say anything else, Linda came out of the house.

At once, Olivia fumbled with the door catch, as eager to get away from Joel as she was to greet her sister. But she was all thumbs and, without asking her permission, Joel leant past her and thrust the door open for her, the hard strength of his forearm pressing briefly against her breasts.

She scrambled out then, dropping down from the high seat, almost ricking her ankle in her haste to get away from him. Steadying herself against the wing, she mentally squared her shoulders before starting a little uncertainly across the forecourt.

'Hi, Linda,' she said, in what she hoped was a confident tone. 'It's good to see you.'

Her sister shook her head and Olivia was surprised to see tears in her eyes. 'Oh, Livvy, it's good to see you, too,' she exclaimed eagerly and, opening her arms, she gathered the other girl into a welcoming hug.

Olivia was shocked. She hadn't expected such a warm greeting. Linda had never been a touchy-feely kind of person and when they were younger any contact between them had always been initiated by Olivia herself.

But evidently the years had mellowed her, and when she drew back she regarded Olivia with what appeared to be genuine affection. 'I'm so pleased you decided to come,' she said. 'This is still your home, you know.'

Olivia was trying to absorb this when Linda's eyes moved beyond her to where Joel was standing beside the Lexus. 'Thanks, Joel,' she added. 'We owe you, big time.' She paused. 'You'll come in and see Dad, won't you?'

'Not right now,' said Joel, opening the back of the car and hauling out Olivia's suitcase. 'I've got a tutorial at four o'clock, I'm afraid.'

A tutorial!

So he was a lecturer, no less. If Olivia was surprised, Linda clearly wasn't, going to take charge of Olivia's luggage without further argument. 'Well, come back soon,' she said, as he climbed back into the vehicle. 'Just because Livvy's here, you don't have to be a stranger.'

'Yeah, right.'

If Joel's response was less enthusiastic, Linda didn't

seem to notice it, and, with an inclination of his head towards Olivia, he reversed the car across the yard. Still cringing from the childish name her sister had always called her, Olivia was motionless, and it wasn't until he'd driven away that she realised she hadn't even waved goodbye.

Pulling herself together, she went to rescue her suitcase from her sister. 'I can take that,' she said, but Linda wouldn't let it go.

'In those heels?' she asked, with just a trace of the animosity that had blighted Olivia's childhood after their mother died. 'No, I can manage. Come along. I've warned Dad to expect you.'

'You didn't warn me that he'd had a stroke,' ventured Olivia as she climbed the shallow steps after her, and Linda's back stiffened in what might have been resentment.

'I thought it was wiser,' she said as they entered the square hall of the farmhouse. She set the suitcase down at the foot of the stairs and then went on, 'You know how sensitive he's always been about his health. And if he'd thought you were only coming here because he was ill...'

'I suppose.' Olivia shrugged, half understanding her reasoning. 'So how is he? Joel said very little.'

'Oh, he's improving every day,' Linda assured her. 'But you'll soon see for yourself.' She paused. 'You, on the other hand, look half-starved. I suppose you're on one of those fancy diets.'

Olivia caught her breath. 'I'm fine,' she said, wishing she dared say that obviously Linda didn't worry about her weight.

'Oh, well, you know best, I dare say,' remarked Linda carelessly. 'Come on. We'll go and see Dad before I show you your room. His bed's in the old morning room. It saves him having to climb the stairs. I hope you don't mind, but I've given you Mum's old sewing room. Jayne and Andrew have our old rooms and Martin and I are sleeping in the main bedroom at present.'

Olivia nodded. She didn't much care where she slept. She had the feeling she wouldn't be staying very long. But she had forgotten about her niece and nephew, who'd been little more than babies when she'd left Bridgeford. Jayne must be eighteen now, with Andrew a year younger. Jayne was the same age as she'd been when she'd married Joel, she reflected incredulously.

'So are the children in school?' she asked as Linda led the way across the hall, and her sister turned to give her an old-fashioned look.

'You've got to be kidding!' she exclaimed. 'Jayne works at a dress shop in Chevingham. She's doing really well, actually. And Andy's probably gone into Alnwick with his father. Martin said he needed to pick up a new rotor arm for the tractor.'

Olivia couldn't hide her surprise. 'I see.'

'I suppose you think we should have encouraged them to continue their education as you did,' went on Linda, a note of aggression in her voice now. 'Well, it didn't do you much good, did it? For all Dad scraped and saved to let you stay on at school, you just upped and married Joel Armstrong as soon as you were eighteen.'

Olivia was taken aback. She hadn't known her father had had to scrape and save to let her stay on to take her A levels.

All the same...

'In any case, we don't have a lot of money to throw around, Livvy,' Linda continued. 'What with losing the cattle to foot-and-mouth, it's been a struggle, I can tell you. We got some compensation from the government, but it's never enough. That's why Martin's trying to persuade Dad to diversify—'

She broke off abruptly at that point and Olivia couldn't decide whether Linda thought she'd said too much or because they were nearing her father's door and she didn't want him to hear what she was saying. Whatever, she lifted a finger to her lips before she turned the handle, putting her head around the door before advancing cheerfully into the room.

'Dad,' Olivia heard her say in a sing-song voice as she followed her in. 'You're awake. That's good.' She glanced behind her. 'Livvy's here.'

Her father made some kind of gruff response, but Olivia could barely hear it. However, when she managed to circle her sister's bulk to see the man who was lying in an armchair by the windows, a rug covering his bony knees, she thought she could understand why. The stroke had evidently left one side of Ben Foley's face paralysed and his hair was completely grey. When he spoke he did so with apparent difficulty.

'Hi, Dad,' she said, very conscious of Linda's eyes watching her. She struggled to hide the shock she felt as she went closer and bent down to kiss his lined cheek. Then she forced a smile. 'It's been a long time.'

Ben Foley grunted. 'Whose fault is that?' he got out thickly, and she was relieved that she could understand him.

'Mine, I guess,' she said, although she doubted he would have welcomed her back any sooner. When she'd lost the baby her father, like Joel, hadn't believed her explanation. And, when he'd heard she and Joel were splitting up, he'd told her to find somewhere else to live.

She wondered now if he'd have felt the same if he'd known Joel was going to leave the farm. They'd been sharing the house with her father and, although it wasn't the best arrangement, it had been all they could afford at that time. Joel had already moved out of the house, but she guessed her father had hoped he'd come back after her departure. Perhaps he had, but not for long. It must have been a bitter pill for Ben Foley to swallow.

Trying to put the past behind her, she went on, 'Well, I'm here now, Dad. So how are you feeling?'

'How do I look?' demanded her father, with a little of his old irascibility, and Linda bustled forward to lay a conciliatory hand on his shoulder.

'Livvy's only showing concern for your welfare,' she said soothingly, but Olivia couldn't help wishing she'd leave them alone. 'Now, do you want some tea? I'll make us all a cup while Livvy settles in.'

Ben Foley scowled. 'I thought she'd come to see me,' he muttered, giving his younger daughter a look from beneath a drooping eyelid.

'I have,' began Olivia, but once again Linda intervened.

'You'll have plenty of time to talk to Livvy later,' she said firmly, tucking the rug more securely about him. 'Come along,' she added to her sister. 'I'll show you where you're going to sleep.'

Joel slept badly and was up before seven the next morning, making himself a pot of coffee in the sleek modern kitchen of his house.

The house was large, but graceful, situated in a village just half a dozen miles from Bridgeford, where his ex-wife still lived. He'd bought it, ironically enough, after he and Louise had broken up. With four bedrooms and three bathrooms, it was really too big for his needs, but it meant Sean could come and stay whenever he liked.

He came fairly often, for weekends and holidays. Joel and Louise had had a fairly amicable divorce, both admitting they'd made a mistake in rushing into marriage. Louise had married again, and, although Joel wasn't overly fond of her new partner, he had been forced to concede that Sean should make his permanent home with them.

Still wearing nothing but the cotton boxers he'd slept in, Joel moved to the kitchen window, staring out over the large garden that happily he employed a gardener to keep in order. An expanse of lawn, where he and Sean played football, stretched away to a hedge of conifers, and beyond the hedge there were fields where sheep and their newborn lambs grazed.

It was all very peaceful, but Joel felt anything but untroubled at the present time. The smooth tenor of his life had been disturbed, and no matter how often he told himself that Olivia's return meant nothing to him, he couldn't quite make himself believe it.

Seeing her again had definitely unsettled him. When he'd agreed to go and meet her, he'd anticipated coming away with a certain smug satisfaction that he'd done the right thing all those years ago. What he'd expected, he realised, was that the image he'd kept of her all this time would have been flawed by age and experience. But it wasn't true. Instead, she was just as lovely, just as sexy, as he remembered.

Which annoyed the hell out of him. Dammit, just

because she'd taken care of her appearance didn't change the woman she was inside. The most beautiful creatures in the world could be deadly. Even so…

He scowled, rubbing his free hand over his jaw that was already rough with stubble. Then, swallowing a mouthful of his coffee, he turned away from the window and started towards the door. He needed a shave and a shower, not necessarily in that order. He'd probably feel better if he could look at himself without immediately noticing the bags beneath his eyes.

He'd made it as far as the stairs when the doorbell rang. He glanced at his wrist, realised he wasn't wearing his watch, and cursed under his breath. What the hell time was it? Not later than seven-thirty, surely. It had to be the mail, but he wasn't expecting any parcels as far as he knew.

He set his cup down on the second stair and trudged back to the door. The wooden floor was cold beneath his bare feet and he wished he'd stopped to put on a robe. But who knew he was going to have to face a visitor? he thought irritably. Particularly this morning, when he was feeling so bloody grumpy to begin with.

The door was solid oak so he couldn't see who it was until he'd released the deadlock and swung it open. Then his eyes widened and he stared disbelievingly at the child who was standing outside.

'Sean!' he exclaimed blankly. But then, noticing that the boy was shivering, Joel hurriedly stepped back and invited him in. He closed the door as Sean moved inside, dropping a backpack he'd been carrying on the floor. His brows drew together. 'How the hell did you get here?'

Sean shrugged. He was tall for his age, lean and wiry,

with Joel's dark hair and colouring and his mother's blue eyes. He was approaching his eleventh birthday, and in recent months Joel had noticed he'd developed an increasingly stubborn attitude.

'I caught the bus,' he said at last, moving into the kitchen. 'Got any cola?'

Joel paused in the doorway, watching as his son took a can of cola out of the fridge and flipped the tab. 'There are no buses this early in the day,' he said, as Sean swallowed thirstily. 'Does your mother know you're here?'

'She will soon,' said Sean, removing the can from his lips and glancing about him. 'Can I have something to eat?'

Joel sucked in a breath. 'What does that mean, exactly? *She will soon.*' He repeated what his son had said. 'Come on, you might as well tell me.'

Sean shrugged. 'I've left home,' he said, opening the fridge door again and pulling out a pack of bacon. 'Can I make myself a sandwich? I'm really hungry.'

Joel stared at him. 'Hold it,' he said. 'Before we go any further, I want you to explain how you got here and why your mother doesn't know yet. Then I'll ring her and put her mind at rest.'

'I shouldn't bother.'

Sean was fiddling with the plastic wrapper of the bacon but before he could go any further his father stepped forward and snatched it out of his hands. 'Answers, Sean,' he said. 'Then we can talk about breakfast. Why are you shivering? For God's sake, have you been out all night?'

'No.' Sean was indignant, but Joel didn't believe him.

'So where have you been?' he demanded.

'I can walk, you know.' Sean hunched his shoulders. And

then, seeing his father's expression, 'All right, I spent the night in the barn up the road.' He grimaced as Joel showed his horror. 'It wasn't so bad. There was some straw in the loft and a horse blanket. It smelled a bit, but it wasn't bad.'

Joel stared at him. 'So how come your mother doesn't know yet?'

'How'd you think? She and the hulk went out last night and they don't usually check on me when they come in.'

'Don't call Stewart "the hulk",' said Joel, though he had to admit Louise's second husband did have a beer belly. 'And what are you saying? That they went out and left you in the house on your own?'

'Hey, I'm old enough,' protested Sean, eyeing the bacon enviously. 'Look, couldn't we just have something to eat before you phone Mum?'

Joel hesitated, then he tossed the bacon back to him. 'I'll ring your mother,' he said resignedly. 'Don't set the place on fire.'

'Thanks, Dad.' Sean grinned now. 'D'you want some, too?'

His father shook his head. 'I'm going to take a shower after I've made that call. If you're cold, just adjust the thermostat on the Aga. You know how, don't you?'

Receiving his son's assurance that he did indeed know how to adjust the stove which heated the entire house, Joel went across the hall to the stairs again and rescued his coffee. As expected, it was cool now, but he intended to ring Louise before doing anything else. And from his bedroom. He had no intention of allowing Sean to listen in.

His ex-wife answered the phone with a note of irritation in her voice. 'Yes?' she said, and Joel guessed she'd probably had a late night. For the first time, he resented the fact that she and Stewart had custody of Sean. What kind of role models was he being faced with every day?

'It's me,' he said abruptly. 'Do you know where Sean is?'

'Still in bed, I expect.' Louise didn't sound worried. 'I've banged on his door and told him he won't have time for any breakfast, but does he listen? No way. Anyway, if you want to speak to him, Joel, you'll have to wait until tonight.'

The temptation to say 'OK' and ring off was appealing, but the last thing Joel needed was for Stewart Barlow to accuse him of kidnapping his son. 'He's not in bed, he's here,' he said, without preamble. 'As you'd know, Louise, if you'd bothered to check on him last night.'

Louise was briefly silenced. She wasn't used to Joel criticising her and he guessed she was wondering how to respond. 'Are you saying he's been with you since yesterday evening?' she demanded, after a moment. 'Don't you think you should have taken the trouble to let me know before this?'

'How do you know I didn't ring last night?' asked Joel flatly.

Another silence. Then, 'So he has been with you all night? Oh, Joel—'

'No.' Joel interrupted her. 'I was only making the point that you weren't there, even if I had phoned.' He sighed. 'I thought children had to be at least thirteen before being left alone.'

Louise sighed. 'We weren't out for long—'

'Even so…'

'What's he been telling you?' She sounded suspicious now. 'He can be a little monkey, you know.'

'I know.' Joel was reluctant, but he had to be honest. 'As a matter of fact, he only arrived on my doorstep a few minutes ago.'

'So where did he spend the night?' She sounded worried now.

'He says in a neighbour's barn.'

'My God!' Louise was horrified. Then she hesitated. 'So why didn't he come to you last night?'

'I'm afraid I was out, too,' said Joel unwillingly. 'I had a meeting at the college. I didn't get back until late.'

'So you weren't part of the welcome-home committee for Olivia Foley?' teased Louise, not without a touch of jealousy. 'I expect you've heard she's come back to see her father.'

Joel quelled his impatience. He had no desire to discuss Olivia's return with his ex-wife. 'If I'd known Sean was likely to turn up, I'd have been here,' he retorted shortly. 'And I don't think you should have left him alone in the house.'

'I don't, usually.' Louise was defensive. 'But Stewart wanted to go out and I didn't think there was any harm in it. We were only down the road, for goodness' sake! If he'd needed anything, he had the pub's number.'

'Whatever.' Joel wasn't prepared to discuss it over the phone. 'Look, I haven't had time to talk to him yet. I need to find out why he decided to do a bunk. Give me the rest of the day, can you? I'll give you a ring tonight.'

'But what about school?'

'He can take a day off, can't he? It wouldn't be the first time, I'm sure.'

'What do you mean?'

'Nothing.' Joel backed off. 'Come on, Louise. Give the kid a break.'

Louise was obviously not happy about the situation, but she decided not to be awkward. Perhaps she was afraid Joel might report her to the authorities. The custody order could be changed in his favour if he chose to complain.

'Well, OK,' she said at last. 'But I think you should bring him home tonight.'

'We'll see.'

Joel didn't argue, but he didn't promise anything either. He still had to find out why Sean had chosen to run away.

Fortunately, he only had one tutorial this morning and he could take his son to the university with him. Sean could play on the computer in his office while he was in the lecture hall.

His coffee was cold now, and, putting it aside, he studied his reflection in the mirror above the bathroom basin. He didn't look good, he thought ruefully. He looked as if it were him, and not Louise, who'd had a heavy night.

He wondered now why he'd married her in the first place. It wasn't on the rebound. Well, not precisely, anyway. After Olivia left, he'd wasted no time before applying for a place at university, and the next four years had passed with the minimum amount of pain.

It wasn't until he'd returned to Bridgeford that the whole sorry mess of his marriage to Olivia had come back to haunt him. Had he thought that marrying someone else and having a child would make him happy? It hadn't, although the son they'd had meant everything to him. And he was determined to ensure that Sean didn't suffer because of his mistakes.

CHAPTER THREE

OLIVIA was in her room, sorting through the clothes she'd brought with her and wondering whether a trip to the nearest town for reinforcements was needed, when Jayne knocked at the door.

Since her arrival a few days ago, her niece had become a frequent visitor, always making some excuse for disturbing her, finding reasons to stop and chat. Olivia guessed the girl found the fact that her aunt had lived in New York for several years fascinating, and her obvious admiration was reassuring in the face of her brother-in-law's hostility.

Not that Olivia had seen that much of Martin Dempsey, thank goodness! Apart from the evening meal, which they all shared, he spent much of his time outdoors.

'Hi,' Jayne said now, coming into the room at her aunt's summons and casting an envious eye over the clothes spread out on the bed. The girl was tall and slim, much like Olivia herself, but her hair was russet-coloured, like her father's, and her features were almost completely his. 'Oh, my, what are you doing?' She fingered the ruched sleeve of an ivory tulle shirt. 'You have such beautiful clothes.'

'Thanks. I think.' Olivia pulled a wry face. 'I was just

wondering if I ought to buy myself some jeans and a couple of T-shirts. I didn't bring a lot of clothes with me and those I have brought don't seem appropriate somehow.'

'Who says?'

Jayne spoke indignantly, but Olivia could tell she wasn't really interested. And Olivia knew better than to say the girl's father resented her being here. Martin apparently didn't like women who showed any independence, and her clothes seemed to be an added source of aggravation.

Jayne perched herself on the end of the bed and regarded her aunt consideringly. 'Can I ask you something?'

'You can ask.' Olivia was half amused.

'Well, were you really married to Joel Armstrong?' she ventured, and Olivia was taken aback.

'Yes,' she said at last, warily. 'Why do you want to know?'

'Oh...' Jayne looked a little embarrassed now. 'I just wondered. I mean, Mum said you were and I believed her. But since I've got to know you, you don't seem the type to—well, play around.'

'Play around?' Olivia caught her breath. Was that what they'd told her?

'Yeah, you know. There was another man, wasn't there? Or so Mum says.'

'There was no other man.' Olivia spoke tersely. 'We were just—not compatible. It didn't work out. That's all.'

'Really?' Jayne stared at her. 'Cos, like, he's really hot, don't you think? Or no, I suppose you don't. But he drives that really powerful SUV, and I think he's, like, totally the man!'

Olivia was stunned. Did Linda know her daughter thought of Joel in this way? Obviously she didn't share her confidences, and the last thing Olivia needed was one of his groupies on her own doorstep.

'I think I ought to finish sorting these things,' she said at length, not wanting to offend the girl, but not wanting to continue this conversation either. For heaven's sake, Joel was old enough to be Jayne's father.

'Oh—yes.' The girl got up from the bed now and pressed her fingers to her mouth. 'I've just remembered. Grandad wants to see you.' She pulled a face. 'He said to say he'd like you to come down.'

Olivia didn't know whether to be glad of the invitation or sorry. She'd been looking forward to finishing this task and then taking a bath. She'd discovered it wasn't wise to expect to have the bathroom to herself in the mornings. Someone was always hammering on the door, asking how long she was going to be.

'OK,' she said now, and, seeing Jayne admiring a silk camisole, she picked it up and tossed it across the bed. Perhaps it would take her mind off other things, she thought hopefully. 'It's yours,' she told her when Jayne looked up at her with disbelieving eyes. 'If you'd like it.'

'Would I?' Jayne was evidently delighted, cradling the scrap of lace to her chest. 'Thanks so much, Aunt Livvy,' she added gratefully. 'I've never worn anything as sexy as this.'

Olivia managed a faint smile at her pleasure, and, passing the girl, she opened the door and allowed her to precede her from the room. But she hoped it wouldn't prove another black mark against her. With a bit of luck, Martin Dempsey might never find out.

Downstairs, she bypassed the dining room, where Linda and Martin were still sitting. She could hear their voices, though not what they were saying, and instead she made her way along the hall to her father's room. She'd visited him several times in the last few days, but this was the first time she'd been on her own. Usually, either Linda or Jayne was with her, ostensibly to ensure that the old man didn't upset her.

Tonight, however, Jayne had scurried off to her room. Probably to try on the new camisole. Which meant Olivia entered her father's room without an escort, feeling almost conspiratorial in consequence.

He wasn't in his chair tonight, he was in the bed across the room, and, closing the door behind her, Olivia crossed the floor. 'Hello,' she said, when she saw his eyes were open. 'How are you tonight?'

'Better for seeing you,' he muttered, and, although his words were slurred, they were perfectly audible. 'I see you managed to shake off your watchdog.' He lifted his good arm and gestured for her to take the chair nearest to him. 'Come and sit down where I can see you.'

Olivia didn't know if he was joking about her having a watchdog, but she acknowledged that Linda and Martin did want to know where she was every minute of the day. 'Thanks,' she said, deciding not to take him up on it. 'I must admit, I've wondered how you felt about me coming back.'

Her father frowned. 'Because of what happened with young Armstrong?' he demanded.

'Well, yes.'

He nodded. 'That was all a long time ago.'

'You never answered any of my letters,' she reminded him painfully. 'According to Linda, you rarely mentioned my name.'

'Yes, well, we all make mistakes, Liv. Mine was in not seeing you were too headstrong to take any advice from me.'

Olivia sighed. 'If it's any consolation, I haven't exactly made a success of my life.'

'No?' Her father's lids twitched in surprise. 'I heard you were doing well in London. Of course, then you upped and went off to America with that man, Garvey. I gather that marriage wasn't happy either.'

Olivia bent her head. For a moment she'd been tempted to say that her marriage to Joel Armstrong *had* been happy. Until she'd discovered she was pregnant, that was, and panic had set in.

She could remember well how she'd felt at that time. It wasn't how she'd have felt now, but that was irrelevant. Then, all she could think was that they were both too young to have a baby, that they couldn't afford another mouth to feed. She'd wanted Joel's baby, of course she had. She'd spent hours—*days*—trying to find a way out of their dilemma that wouldn't entail her losing the child. Like any other would-be mother, she'd fantasised about what it would look like, whether it would take after him. But the problems had seemed insurmountable at first. After all, they could barely support themselves.

But her father wouldn't want to hear that. He and Joel had been on the same side and she had no intention of trying to change his mind now. So instead, she said, 'I should never have married Bruce. I made the mistake of thinking that because he said he loved me, I'd have everything I'd ever wanted.'

'Was he wealthy?'

Olivia shrugged. 'I suppose so.'

'Was that really why you married him?'

'No.' Olivia shook her head. 'Believe it or not, I was lonely. I needed someone who'd care about me. He was smart and good-looking and it seemed like a good idea at the time.'

'You were lonely?' Her father picked up on that. 'So why didn't you come home?'

'I didn't think I'd be welcome,' she confessed honestly. 'And—well, I assumed Joel would still be here.'

'He left. A couple of weeks after you went to London.'

'Yes, I know that now. But not then.'

'Linda kept in touch with you, didn't she?'

'Yes.' But her reports were decidedly selective, Olivia thought, though she didn't say so. 'Anyway, it's all in the past, as you say.'

'So tell me about this man you married. Bruce Garvey. What went wrong? Did he treat you badly?'

'No.' Olivia sighed. 'It's a long story, Dad.'

Her father made an impatient gesture. 'Well, I'm not going anywhere, as you can see.'

'Why not?' Olivia used his words to try and change the subject. 'Don't you have a wheelchair? Don't you ever go outside?'

'I don't want a wheelchair,' retorted the old man grumpily. 'Bloody things. They're for invalids. I'm not an invalid. I'm just—stuck here, that's all.'

'In other words, you are an invalid,' said Olivia, without trying to be tactful. She knew her father of old. He could be totally stubborn, even at the risk of cutting off his nose to spite his face.

'And d'you think I want everyone to know that?' he snapped shortly. 'It's all right for you, coming here and telling me what to do. I don't want anyone to see I can hardly stand, let alone walk!'

'I should think everyone knows that already,' replied Olivia practically. 'This is a small village, Dad. People know you. People care what happens to you.'

'Yes, well, I don't need their pity,' said her father, mopping at the trail of saliva that trickled from the paralysed side of his mouth. 'Nor yours, either,' he muttered. 'If that's all you've got to say to me, you can go.'

Olivia sighed. 'All right, all right. We won't talk about it.' She smoothed her palms over the knees of her trousers. 'I didn't come here to upset you.' She paused. 'Actually Jayne said you wanted to see me.'

'Hmmph.' The old man relaxed again. 'Well, why wouldn't I want to see my daughter? You're a sight for sore eyes, and that's a fact.'

Olivia smiled. 'Thank you.'

'Don't thank me. You were always the beauty of the family. And the brains, more's the pity!'

'Dad!'

'Well, you must know Linda and Martin are running the show around here while I'm—while I can't.' Olivia nodded, and he went on, 'So what do you think of their bright idea?'

Olivia frowned, not at all sure she ought to ask it, but doing so anyway. 'What bright idea?'

The door opening behind them and Linda bursting into the room drowned out any reply the old man might have made. 'Dad!' she exclaimed crossly. 'And Olivia. I thought you were in your room.' She turned back to her father. 'You know you're supposed to be resting. Anything you have to say to Olivia can wait until tomorrow, I'm sure.'

* * *

Olivia was up early the next morning. She'd had enough of being confined to the farm and she intended to catch the bus into Newcastle and spend the day doing some shopping. She also intended to find an agency and hire a car, though she kept that part of her plans to herself.

'Couldn't you get what you want in Chevingham?' Linda exclaimed, when she heard what her sister intended to do. 'Andy could give you a lift in the Land Rover. That would save you having to take the bus.'

'Thanks, but I prefer to go into Newcastle,' said Olivia politely, still feeling some resentment towards Linda for the way she'd behaved the night before. She'd acted as if Olivia had had no right to go and sit with her father. Not without clearing it with her first.

And, of course, any chance of further private conversation with him had been over. Although he'd protested, Linda had been adamant that he'd had enough visitors for one day. Olivia had only had time to squeeze his hand and tell him she'd see him later, before her sister had bustled her out of the room.

It was strange being back in the city after so many years had passed. It seemed so different, so modern, the alterations that had only been in the planning stage when she left now making the centre of town a vibrant, exciting place to visit.

She found a café and, after ordering an Americano, she took a seat in the window overlooking a shopping mall. It was a relief to be away from the farm and drinking a decent cup of coffee again. The instant brand Linda favoured was so bitter in comparison.

Revitalised, she left the café and spent some time exploring the shops. There were certainly plenty to choose from and, despite what Jayne had said, Olivia bought jeans and a couple of T-shirts, as well as a pair of combat boots to wear around the farm. The boots looked incongruous with the suede jacket and matching fringed skirt she'd worn to come to town, and she was laughing with the assistant when she looked through the shop window—straight into Joel Armstrong's eyes.

She couldn't help it. Her eyes widened and her breath caught somewhere in the back of her throat, so that when the assistant spoke again she found it very hard to answer her.

'Um—yes. Yes, I'll take them,' she said, knowing the girl was looking at her strangely. 'Thanks,' she added, quickly slipping her feet into the high-heeled pumps she'd taken off to try the boots on.

She was at the counter, paying for the boots with her credit card, when she became aware that Joel had entered the shop. It wasn't that he'd spoken to her or done anything to announce his presence; it was just a premonition she had that it was him.

It was madness but she could feel him near her, sensed the pressure of the air had changed since he came in. She wanted to turn and look at him, to ensure herself that she wasn't mistaken. God, she was going to be so disappointed if she was wrong.

But she wasn't wrong. When her purchase was completed and she could justifiably collect the bag containing her boots and turn around, he was there waiting for her. 'Hi,' he said as she crossed the shop towards him, and once again her stomach started its crazy plunge.

He looked so good, she thought helplessly. Even in a worn corded jacket with leather patches at the elbows, he looked big and dark and disturbingly familiar. His jeans hugged his legs, worn in places she knew she shouldn't be looking. And, goodness, she shouldn't be so glad to see him.

'Hi,' she answered in return, uncertain what to do next. 'Are you looking for shoes, too?'

'Do I look as if I need to?' he countered humorously as they stepped outside, drawing her eyes to the scuffed deck shoes he was wearing. 'No. You know I'm not.' His eyes skimmed her face. 'Are you on your own?'

Olivia nodded. 'Are you?'

'Until half-past two, when I've got to see one of my students,' he agreed, his warm breath fanning her cheek. 'Have you had lunch?'

Olivia swallowed. 'No.'

'So—d'you want to get a sandwich with me?'

There was nothing Olivia would have liked more, but she knew getting involved with Joel again was dangerous. She'd been sure she was so over him. Now she had goose-bumps just because he'd invited her to lunch.

'Well—I was going to see about renting a car,' she said lamely, and knew immediately from his expression that he wasn't fooled by her excuse.

'In other words, you'd rather not,' he said, lifting one shoulder dismissively. 'OK.' He paused. 'Some other time, perhaps.'

'No, wait!' As he would have turned away, she caught his sleeve and stopped him. 'I—I can see about renting a car after lunch. And I've got to eat. So—why not with you? If the offer's still good.'

Joel regarded her consideringly, wondering if he wouldn't be wiser to just call it a day. He still wasn't sure why he'd asked her, why he wanted to prolong what could only be an awkward interlude in his day.

'I get the feeling you're just humouring me,' he said, and her hand dropped quickly from his arm.

'I'm not.' Olivia's tongue circled her dry lips. 'I just didn't think it through, that's all.' She paused, and then added huskily, 'I didn't want you to feel—obliged to ask me.'

'Why would I feel that?'

He wasn't making it easy for her, and Olivia wondered now if he had had second thoughts. 'You know what I mean,' she said defensively.

Joel shook his head. 'I assume you mean because of what we once had.' His eyes darkened. He wouldn't let her humble him. 'Liv, I've told you already, I'm long past caring what you did or didn't do.'

Olivia wanted to scream. It wasn't fair, she thought. She'd done nothing wrong. Did he think she had no feelings at all?

But Joel wasn't finished. 'If you can't see I was only being civil,' he declared tersely, 'then perhaps we should just go our separate ways.'

Well, that was certainly telling her, he thought, refusing to back down. But, seeing the flush of colour that swept into her cheeks at his words, he couldn't help wondering why he felt this need to punish her. She'd inadvertently saved him from himself, hadn't she? He'd never have been satisfied with working at the farm permanently. And how could he have been able to afford four years at college if he'd had a wife and child to support?

'If that's what you want,' she said now, and in spite of himself, Joel couldn't let her go.

'It's not what I want,' he said between clenched teeth.

'For God's sake, I asked you, didn't I? I just never thought such a simple request would result in this inquisition.'

Olivia sighed. 'I'm sorry.'

So was Joel. But not for the same reason.

'So—where would you like to go?' she asked, and Joel jammed his balled fists into his pockets. *Bed*, he thought savagely, an insane image of Olivia spread-eagled on his sheets, her silky hair draped across his pillow, suddenly front and centre in his mind. 'It's very busy,' she went on. 'Do you think you'll have time?'

Another opportunity, but Joel didn't take it. 'How about buying a sandwich and eating it outdoors?' he suggested. 'Lots of people do that.'

'OK.'

She was annoyingly cooperative and as they walked to the nearby sandwich bar Joel reminded himself that he'd engineered this meeting, not her. He'd be far more convincing if he behaved pleasantly. Allowing her to bug him, to make him angry, would only convince her he wasn't as indifferent to her as he claimed.

CHAPTER FOUR

However, the nearby park was buzzing with young people. As well as there being nowhere to sit, Joel realised he had no desire to share the space with his own students.

He should have thought of that, he told himself irritably, turning his back on the open area with a feeling of frustration. Where now? he asked himself. And could only come up with one solution.

'Look, how do you feel about coming back to my office?' he suggested, and saw the way her eyes widened at his words.

'Your office?'

'My room at the university,' he explained abruptly. 'It's just a short walk from here.'

'All right.'

After a moment's pause, Olivia agreed, keeping any doubts she might have had about the advisability of doing such a thing to herself. After all, Joel couldn't have made his feelings any plainer. If she was suffering any pangs of memory they were hers alone.

The City University was one of the smaller places of learning. Concentrating mainly on computer technology, it attracted students from all over the country as well as some from further afield. It had an unparalleled reputation and Joel never stopped feeling amazed that he'd been accepted onto its faculty. There was even a certain amount of satisfaction in taking Olivia there, even if he'd never intended to do so.

His room was on the second floor, overlooking the central courtyard. Below his windows, a quadrangle of grass was surrounded by a cloistered walkway where both lecturers and students could walk even on the wettest days.

Predictably, Olivia walked straight across to the windows, looking out with such concentration that Joel wondered if she was estimating her chances should she have to make her escape that way.

'Nice,' she said at last, turning and resting her hips on the broad sill, and he didn't know whether she was referring to the view or to the generous proportions of his room.

'I'm glad you like it.' Joel unloaded the carrier containing the sandwiches and two bottles of mineral water onto his desk. 'I have to admit, it took some getting used to.'

'What?' She left the window and came over to the desk. 'This room—or your appointment?'

'Both, I guess,' he said, with a wry smile. 'I was lucky.'

'Oh, I doubt that.' Deciding she might as well try and relax, Olivia flopped down into the leather chair behind his desk and swung it round in a full circle as a child might do. 'I'm sure you're very good at your job.'

'Gee, thanks.' Joel was sardonic. 'Your approval means a lot to me.'

Olivia pursed her lips. 'Don't be sarcastic!' she retorted,

and then, sensing he was laughing at her, she pulled a face. 'Anyway, what do you do?'

'Try to instil my love of technology into my students,' he replied, tearing open the sandwich wrappers.

'Is that all?'

Joel's brow ascended. 'Isn't it enough?' And when she continued to look at him, he said, 'Actually, I'm studying for a doctorate myself.'

'So you write, too?'

'Some.' Joel pushed the sandwiches towards her. 'Help yourself.'

Olivia reached for a bottle of water instead, unscrewing the cap and raising it to her lips. She was thirsty, she realised, or perhaps it was just being alone here with Joel that was making her mouth feel so dry.

'Tell me what you've written,' she said, watching as he pulled a sandwich out of its container and took a bite. She was trying to divert herself from noticing how strong and white his teeth looked against the undoubtedly sensual curve of his mouth. 'Could I have seen it?'

'Not unless you're into artificial intelligence,' responded Joel, swallowing rapidly. He studied his sandwich for a moment before continuing, 'I have had a couple of articles published in *Nerds Monthly*.'

Olivia stared at him 'You're making that up!' she exclaimed. 'I'm sure there's no such magazine.'

'Isn't there?'

He was evidently enjoying her confusion and she pulled a face. 'Joel—'

'OK, OK.' He finished his sandwich and reached for his own bottle of water. Then, before taking a drink, he added, 'They were in *Hot Key*, actually,' mentioning the name of an international computer publication that even Olivia had heard of.

'Fantastic,' she said applaudingly. 'Do you have copies?'

'I guess so.'

Joel was telling himself not to be seduced by her obvious admiration, but he couldn't help feeling impatient at his deliberate choice of verb. Dammit, they were talking, that was all. So why was he enjoying the sight of her sitting in his chair so damn much?

'Here?' she asked, looking about her.

'No, not here,' he replied flatly. 'At home.'

'Your home?' Olivia cradled her water bottle between her palms and regarded him curiously. 'Where do you live? In town?'

'Now, why would you want to know that?' Joel asked the question and then wished he hadn't. He was making too much of it. Before she could respond, he went on swiftly, 'I have a house in Millford. I bought it after Louise and I were divorced.'

'Louise?' Olivia said the name slowly. 'That would be your second wife?'

'Well, I haven't had a third. Yet.'

'Yet?' She picked up on that, as he'd known she would. 'Do you have someone in mind?'

'And if I had, do you think I'd tell you?' he countered smoothly. 'Eat your sandwich. It's getting warm.'

Olivia ignored his instruction, her tongue appearing briefly at the corner of her mouth. 'So—did you meet Louise at university?'

Joel sighed, wishing he'd never mentioned his ex-wife.

'I met her again when I went back to Bridgeford,' he said resignedly. 'After I'd got my degree.'

Olivia's jaw dropped. 'You don't mean to tell me you married Louise—*Webster*!'

'Why not?' Joel was defensive now. 'We always liked one another.'

'She liked you,' said Olivia with sudden vehemence. 'My God! Louise Webster. You used to say she was boring as hell!'

'I used to say a lot of things,' retorted Joel, pushing his other sandwich aside with a feeling of revulsion. 'And perhaps *boring* was what I wanted. I hadn't had a lot of success with anything else.'

Olivia glared at him for a few moments, her lips pursed mutinously, and then she pushed herself up from his chair and started towards the door. 'I knew I shouldn't have come here,' she said, and now Joel could hear a faint tremor in her voice. 'Thanks for the water. I find I'm not very hungry, after all.'

'Liv!' Despite the warning voice inside him that was telling him to let her go, Joel found himself taking the couple of strides necessary to put himself between her and the door. He leaned back against it. 'I'm sorry. I shouldn't have said that.'

'No, you shouldn't.'

Olivia halted uncertainly, her heart tripping over itself in its efforts to keep up with her hammering pulse. It wasn't just what he'd said that was making her heart race and causing the blood to rush madly through her veins. It was the painful realisation that she was jealous: jealous of his ex-wife, jealous of the child they'd had together, jealous of the success he'd made of his life once she was out of it.

'Look, why don't you go and sit down again and eat your sandwich?' he suggested gently, and something inside Olivia snapped.

'I'm not one of your bloody students,' she exploded, charging towards him with every intention of forcing him out of her way. 'You go and sit down. I'm leaving.'

Joel didn't move, however. He just lounged there against the door, lean and indolent, one ankle crossed over the other, apparently indifferent to her futile display. And, unless she wanted to grab his arm and try to drag him bodily away from the door, she had to stand there, feeling like an idiot, waiting for him to make the next move.

'What do you want me to say, Liv?' he asked suddenly, his voice lower, deeper, disturbingly sensual. He put out his hand, his lips twisting when she flinched, and plucked a silvery hair from the shoulder of her jacket. 'You and I know one another too well to indulge in this kind of lunacy. Does the fact that Louise and I got together annoy you? Is that why you're behaving like a spoiled brat?'

'You wish!'

But Olivia was panicking now. When he'd reached out, she'd been half afraid he was going to touch her cheek. And, conversely, now that he hadn't, she felt cheated. She'd wanted him to touch her, she wanted to feel those strong fingers stroking her heated flesh.

Oh, God!

'Just get out of my way, Joel,' she said, controlling the quiver in her voice with an effort.

'What if I don't want to?' he countered, and the breath she was taking caught somewhere in the back of her throat.

'Now who's being childish?' she panted. 'Be careful,

Joel, I'll begin to think you're the one who's got a problem. Why should I care who you chose to marry? I just hope you made her happier than you made me.'

Joel moved then. His hand grabbed her wrist, twisted it viciously behind her, forced her towards him whether she wanted it or not. 'Take that back,' he snarled, but Olivia was too stunned to do anything but gaze up at him with wide, startled eyes. 'Go on,' he persisted. 'Do it, or I'll break your bloody arm.'

Olivia blinked, and just like that the realisation that it was Joel who was holding her, Joel who was crushing her breasts against the rough lapels of his jacket, took all her fear away.

'You wouldn't do that, Joel,' she said, with amazing confidence in the circumstances. And although there was a heart-stopping moment when she thought she was wrong, finally, with a muffled oath, he thrust her away from him.

'No, I wouldn't,' he said hoarsely, stepping away from the door. 'I have more self-respect than that. Now—get out of here!'

Olivia hesitated. She knew that was what she should do. But she also knew that in some strange way the tables had been turned. Seeing the grim look on Joel's face as he waited for her to open the door, she sensed that, for all his harsh words, he wanted her out of there now just as much as she'd wanted to go a few minutes earlier.

But why?

It was an intriguing puzzle.

Was it only because he was angry with her for questioning his masculinity? Or had touching her disturbed him as much as it had disturbed her?

'What are you waiting for?'

He would have reached past her and jerked the door open then, but now Olivia put herself in his way. 'Joel,' she said huskily, moving towards him and grasping his forearms. 'We can't leave it like this.'

'Why not?'

He would have shaken himself free of her, but she was insistent, holding on to his arms, feeling the muscles bunch hard beneath her fingers. 'I thought we were friends, Joel,' she murmured, her thumb caressing the sleeve of his jacket. 'I'm not your enemy, you know.'

'This isn't going to work, Liv,' he warned, but she just gazed up at him with innocent green eyes.

'What isn't going to work?' she queried softly, and he growled deep in his throat.

'This,' he said savagely, gripping the back of her neck, pushing the silky shoulder-length hair aside, his fingers digging into her flesh. 'I should have known I couldn't trust you.'

Olivia opened her mouth to deny his claim, but the words were never spoken. With a muffled oath, Joel fastened his lips to hers, silencing anything but the moan of pleasure she couldn't quite restrain.

The kiss was deep and erotic, the sexual thrust of his tongue igniting all the raw, primitive emotions she'd suppressed for so long. She wanted him with an urgency that defied rhyme or reason, sinking into him completely, hazed by desire.

Without her hardly being aware of it, her arms were around his neck and he was moving her back against the door behind her, leaning into her sensually, his hands burning her hips. She only realised he'd rucked her skirt above her knees and parted her legs with his thigh when she felt the cool air upon her skin.

His mouth ate at hers, bruised the soft flesh, left her weak and trembling beneath the weight of his body as he leant against her. She could feel every part of him, feel every bone and angle. And every unguarded muscle, so that when the pressure against her stomach became unmistakable, she put down a hand and caressed his length through the taut fabric of his jeans.

She heard him say an oath thickly, and then he was tipping her jacket off her shoulders, tearing open her blouse so he could press open-mouthed kisses between her breasts. His palms pressed against the taut nipples swelling against her half-bra, his fingers rough against her soft skin.

He groaned and she felt an answering pain deep in her belly. There was a pulse throbbing between her legs and she knew she was already wet. When his hand dropped lower, cradled her thigh, before moving round to probe beneath the thin silk of her thong, she let out a moan of protest. But she didn't try to stop him. She honestly didn't think she had the strength.

'Dear God, Joel,' she whispered unsteadily, wondering if he intended to take her there against the door of his office. It was possible. She was certainly making it easy for him. Like some cheap tart, an inner voice taunted, and suddenly she felt sick. Had she really sunk that low?

Thankfully, it wasn't a question she had to answer. Whether Joel would have unzipped his jeans and pushed himself into her hot, wet heat became a moot point when someone knocked at the door.

They both froze, and Joel at least was reminded of a

similar occasion when they were both still at school. Then, they'd arranged to meet in her father's loft and, like now, things had rapidly got out of hand. Until Ben Foley had come into the barn...

Predictably, it wasn't something he wanted to remember at this moment. Dammit, he thought, he'd sworn Olivia would never get under his skin again. And now here he was, caught like some guilty schoolboy, the only difference being he was still wearing his trousers.

Olivia was the first to recover. Scrambling out from under him, she scooped her jacket off the floor and put it on. Dragging the two sides together over her unbuttoned blouse, she reached for her bag.

'Aren't you going to answer it?' she hissed, checking that her skirt didn't look too creased. It did, of course, and she was sure anyone with half an eye would know what they'd been doing. But there was nothing she could do about it. She was fairly sure she hadn't a scrap of make-up left on her face.

Joel extended his arms and pushed himself away from the door with an effort. He'd sagged against the panels when she'd moved, reluctant to display the treacherous evidence of his need. God, he realised, feeling dazed, it was half-past two already. It would be Cheryl Brooks, ready and eager to discuss the finer points of binary calculus.

He was so screwed, he thought dully, or rather he wasn't. He flexed his shoulders and straightened, turning to regard Olivia through narrowed eyes. He should be grateful for the interruption, so why was he feeling so frustrated? But heaven help him, he could feel Olivia's essence on his fingers, was still breathing the potent scent of her arousal into his lungs.

She was getting agitated. He could see it. She arched her

brows, nodding pointedly towards the door, showing him in every way she could without speaking again that he should see who it was. Joel felt his lips twitch in spite of himself. Would she still be as eager when she saw Cheryl was his visitor?

'OK, OK,' he mouthed, running slightly unsteady fingers through his hair, checking there were no tell-tale signs to betray him. Then, turning, he reached for the handle. Without further ado, he opened the door.

Olivia tensed. She couldn't help it. Whoever it was, she had no desire to stay and be introduced. She wanted out of there, immediately. Her senses had cooled now and she was appalled at the way she'd behaved.

The girl waiting outside only looked to be about eighteen, but she was probably older. It hadn't occurred to Olivia before now that Joel would have female students as well as male and the knowledge disturbed her. The girl had long blonde hair, worn over one shoulder, her tight jeans and cropped top accentuating her youthful appearance.

'Hi, Joel,' she said, proving their relationship was fairly familiar. Then she saw Olivia and the smile she'd been wearing faded.

'Cheryl,' Joel said feebly, aware that he wasn't quite up to this. He glanced at his watch. 'You're early.'

'Just five minutes,' Cheryl protested, and Olivia could tell she wasn't suited either. She'd probably been looking forward to a cosy tête-à-tête with her professor, and now Olivia had spoiled the mood.

'Yeah, right.' Joel glanced briefly at Olivia and then back at his visitor. 'Well, why don't you come in? Um— Mrs Garvey was just leaving.'

CHAPTER FIVE

THE next couple of days passed without incident and, waking up one morning, Olivia realised it was almost a week since she'd arrived at Blades Farm. How long was she going to stay? she wondered. She had planned for this to be just a flying visit. But somehow now she was in no hurry to get back to London and Linda hadn't mentioned anything about when she was going to leave.

There had been a little animosity when she'd arrived back from Newcastle driving a small Renault from the rental agency. But it had soon blown over and Olivia was finding the sense of freedom having her own transport gave her well worth any unpleasantness from her brother-in-law. Besides, it enabled her to get out and see something of the area she'd grown up in, and she had every intention of persuading her father to join her. Eventually.

The car had even helped to put her encounter with Joel to the back of her mind. She hadn't forgotten what had happened. How could she? And sometimes, particularly at night, she'd wake up and find her breasts tingling and a moist place between her legs.

But she'd get over it. The pangs of frustration she was

feeling were just her body reminding her that she was still a young woman with a young woman's sexual needs. During her marriage to Bruce she'd had to stifle those needs, and it was unfortunate that it had been Joel who'd aroused them again.

But any attractive man would have done, she assured herself fiercely, flinging back the duvet and swinging her legs over the side of the bed. It was her misfortune that she'd let Joel get close enough to stir emotions she'd kept in check for the better part of six years.

And remembering how their encounter had ended, she felt again the surge of resentment that had filled her when he'd dismissed her. OK, she'd been planning to leave—desperate to get out of there, actually—but had he had to make her feel as if she'd been just another drain on his precious time?

She breathed deeply, refusing to let thoughts of Joel ruin her day. She'd seen him, they'd talked, and now she didn't care if she didn't see him again. Let him make eyes at his adoring students. The female ones, of course.

For once the bathroom was empty, and, aware that there were no guarantees that that state of affairs would continue, Olivia quickly washed and cleaned her teeth. Promising herself a more thorough inspection later, she returned to her room and dressed in jeans and a T-shirt, her only concession to style the scarlet chiffon scarf she knotted about her neck.

Downstairs, she found her sister in the kitchen, loading the dishwasher, the crumbs and dirty dishes from breakfast still littering the table.

'Let me do that,' said Olivia at once, but Linda merely shook her head.

'Don't be silly,' she said, her glance saying that, even in the stone-washed jeans and cotton T-shirt, Olivia looked over-dressed. 'There's coffee on the stove. Help yourself.'

'Has Dad had his breakfast?' asked Olivia, doing as Linda had suggested. She took a sip of the coffee and stifled a grimace. 'I'll go and see how he is, shall I?'

'He's resting,' said Linda, as she said every morning. So far, Olivia had been unable to repeat the occasion when she and her father had had a chance to talk alone together. 'D'you want some toast?'

'I'll get it.'

Olivia refused to let her sister wait on her, and, taking the cut loaf out of the stone barrel, she extracted a slice and popped it in the toaster. Then, tucking the tips of her fingers into the back pockets of her jeans, she added, 'Haven't you ever thought of getting Dad a wheelchair?'

It was the first time she'd mentioned it to Linda, hoping against hope that she'd have another chance to speak to her father about it. But beggars couldn't be choosers and she was determined to get him out of the house.

Linda stared at her now. 'A wheelchair!' she echoed disparagingly. 'You can't think Dad would ever use a wheelchair!'

'Why not?'

'You know why not.' Linda returned to her task. 'He's far too independent.'

'He's not very independent, stuck in that room all the time,' retorted Olivia steadily. 'It would do him good to get some fresh air.'

Linda shook her head. 'I suppose that's why you insisted on hiring that car, is it?'

'No—'

'You didn't think we might have tried to get him out in the Land Rover or his old Saab?'

Olivia could feel herself weakening, but she stood her ground. 'And have you?'

Now it was Linda's turn to look defensive. 'What would be the point? I've told you, Dad will go out when he can do so under his own steam and not before.'

'And when will that be?'

'Who knows?' Linda's voice had sharpened. 'Nurse Franklin comes in every week to help him with his physical therapy. Perhaps you ought to ask her. Though I have to tell you, you're wasting your time.'

Olivia heard the bread pop out of the toaster and was grateful for the opportunity to have something else to do. Buttering the slice with a knife she found on the table, she helped herself to a smear of marmalade before taking a bite.

'Anyway, I wanted to talk to you,' said Linda with a distinct change of tone. She closed the dishwasher and switched it on. 'Martin's gone into Chevingham, but he'll be back about half-past ten. Maybe we could all have coffee together?'

Olivia kept her eyes fixed on the slice of toast she was holding, wondering what had brought this on. In the week since her arrival, she and Martin had barely said more than a dozen words to one another. She couldn't imagine him wanting to sit down and share morning coffee with someone he evidently despised.

Unless…

She recalled suddenly the silk camisole she'd given to Jayne. Had they found out about that? And if so was she to bear the brunt of their joint displeasure? Had Linda decided she needed her husband's support on this occasion?

'Um—well, I was thinking of going out,' she murmured awkwardly, even though what she'd really been hoping to do was spend a little more time with her father. With or without Linda's chaperonage.

'I see.' Linda stood at the other side of the scrubbed pine table, regarding her coldly. 'Oh, well, don't let us stop you. Not if you'd prefer to go out.'

Olivia sighed. Perversely now, she felt ashamed. They were trying to be friendly, and she was throwing their kindness back in their faces.

'No,' she declared firmly. 'I can go out any time. What do you want to talk about, anyway? I hope I haven't done anything wrong.'

'Heavens, no.' Linda was all smiles now. 'It's just— well, you've been here a week now and you've got some idea of the way the farm works. Martin and I have come up with an idea that we'd like to put to you. But I'd rather wait until he's here to explain it to you himself.'

In spite of her misgivings, Olivia was intrigued. Was this anything to do with what her father had started to tell her when Linda had burst in on them the other evening? He had definitely mentioned some idea his daughter and son-in-law had had. Was she to find out what it was from an entirely unexpected source?

The time between her agreeing to listen to what they had to say and Martin's return dragged. Having checked that her father was indeed sleeping and therefore unable to be disturbed, Olivia decided to go for a walk. She had over an hour before the half-past-ten deadline, and it was a pleasant morning. Collecting her boots and a jacket from upstairs, she let herself out of the front door and walked briskly away from the house.

She had no particular direction in mind. Just a need to escape Linda's overpowering presence. Despite being a pushover where her husband was concerned, Linda certainly liked to throw her weight around with the other members of the household.

Avoiding the immediate environs of the house for fear Linda would see her, Olivia skirted the trees that screened the paddock and made her way across the stockyard to the barn. There were chickens running loose here and even a couple of geese that hissed alarmingly. But Olivia wasn't troubled. It was amazing how the memories of childhood came flooding back.

She could see her nephew in the distance. Andy was up on a ladder, apparently painting one of the cottages that housed the families of the men who worked on the farm. Which was odd, she reflected, frowning. The tenants usually looked after the cottages themselves.

Perhaps he wasn't painting, she thought, dodging into the barn so he wouldn't think she was spying on him. He could just be repairing the guttering. Or cleaning the windows—but that wasn't likely either.

The barn was familiar. Although she would have preferred not to think about it, this was where she and Joel had used to meet after school. There'd been a loft, fragrant with the heat of the sun on the hay her father had stored there. It had been their own private hideaway—though she guessed now that her father had known exactly what was going on.

The ladder leading up into the loft was still there and,

after assuring herself that she was alone, Olivia couldn't resist climbing it. For old times' sake, she told herself firmly. To see if anything had changed.

However, as she started up, she heard a rustle in the straw and she stiffened instinctively. Rats? she wondered uneasily. Or just a bird that had taken up residence in the roof. She sighed. Was she really going to let anything, bird or animal, frighten her away? Whatever it was, it would be far more frightened of her.

She continued up, listening hard for any other sound, but she heard nothing. All the same, when she stuck her head above the hatch, she knew a moment's apprehension. She'd seen enough horror films to be able to imagine the worst.

But all appeared to be as it should be and she started down again. Only to come to an abrupt halt when she heard something scrape across the floor above her head. That was no bird, she thought. No rat, either. Her fingers tightened on the rungs of the ladder. She ought to go and report what she'd heard to Andy or one of the other men.

But, come to think of it, she hadn't seen any other men about the farm. Of course, she hadn't spent much time on the farm since she'd come back, so perhaps that wasn't so surprising. And calling Andy seemed like such a feeble thing to do. Who could be up there? Wouldn't they have tackled her sooner if they'd intended her any harm?

It was nerve-racking but, steeling herself, she started up again. 'Hello there,' she called, giving whoever it was plenty of warning if they wanted to escape. She seemed to remember there was a gantry at the other side of the loft where the hay had been loaded. It was at least an eight-foot jump to the ground, but if the intruder was desperate…

Once again she reached the hatch, but this time she climbed up into the loft. It had occurred to her that it might be kids. What an ideal place to bunk off school.

Olivia looked about her. 'I know there's somebody here,' she said, trying to see beyond the tumbled bales of hay into the shadowy corners of the loft. 'If you don't come out, I'll—I'll—' she had a spurt of inspiration '—I'll go and fetch one of the geese to find you.'

Not that that was remotely likely, she acknowledged. Although she wasn't afraid to cross the yard, she doubted she'd have the guts to pick up one of the geese. But, hopefully, a kid might not know that. Particularly one who wasn't familiar with birds or animals.

There was no movement, however, and Olivia sighed. 'OK,' she said. 'If that's what you want.' She pretended to take hold of the ladder. 'I'll be back—'

'No, wait!'

The voice was definitely that of a child's, she thought with some relief. It had occurred to her that some vagrant might have spent the night in the barn. But, as she watched, a boy detached himself from the pile of sacks where he'd been hiding. A tall boy, but not much more than eleven years old, she thought.

He stood beside the sacks for a moment, his face in shadow, only his eyes reflecting the light. Blue eyes, Olivia saw; resigned yet mutinous. As if he'd been expecting someone to come looking for him, but that didn't mean he had to like it.

'Hi,' said Olivia after a moment. 'You do realise you're trespassing, don't you?'

'How do you know?' he demanded, and she realised she

didn't. Could he possibly belong to one of the families who lived on the farm?

'What's your name?' she asked, but this time he didn't answer her. 'You don't live on the farm, do you? You might as well tell me. I'm going to find out anyhow.'

The boy's chin jutted. 'No, I don't live on the farm,' he admitted at last. 'I wish I did. Anything would be better than living with my mum and the hulk!'

Olivia gasped. 'Don't call your father the hulk!'

'He's not my father,' retorted the boy at once, and Olivia felt a glimmer of understanding. Obviously his parents were separated, and he wasn't happy with the arrangement.

'All the same,' she said, trying to think of something positive to say, 'I expect they'll be worried about you. Shouldn't you be in school?'

The boy shrugged, which she assumed was a yes, and leaned down to grab the handle of a backpack lying on the floor. As he did so, a ray of sunlight streaming through a crack in the wall illuminated his thin features, and Olivia felt her heart turn over.

'What's your name?' she asked again, though she was fairly sure she knew his surname. Goodness! She moistened her dry lips. He had to be Joel's son. And it all fit, she realised. Him, living with his mother; his parents separated—*divorced*! The only thing Joel hadn't told her was that Louise had married again.

'Sean,' the boy muttered now, completing his identity. 'What's yours?'

'Olivia. Olivia—Foley.' She used the name deliberately, guessing he would know who owned the farm.

He regarded her defiantly. 'Are you going to tell Mum where I am?'

Olivia sighed. 'I've got to. I can't leave you here. How long have you been up here anyway? What time did you leave for school?'

'I didn't,' said Sean, low-voiced, and Olivia stared at him in disbelief.

'Oh, no!' she exclaimed. 'Don't tell me you've been up here all night?'

Once again, Sean didn't answer her, and she was left to fill the gaps herself. His mother must be desperate by this time. Losing a child was every parent's nightmare.

'I must tell your mother you're safe,' she said gently. 'What's her name?' Not Armstrong, obviously. 'Where do you live?'

'I'd rather you told Dad,' said Sean miserably, and once again Olivia's heart flipped a beat.

'Why?' she ventured, aware that it wasn't really anything to do with her, but assuring herself she was only trying to make sense of his answer.

'Cos he didn't believe me last time,' the boy declared obliquely. 'I told him I didn't want to live with Mum and—and Stewart.'

'Stewart?' Olivia was fishing, and Sean took the bait.

'Stewart Barlow,' he said without thinking, instantly supplying the one name she didn't have.

Olivia absorbed this without saying anything, aware that Sean was regarding her with hopeful eyes. 'Will you speak to my dad?' he asked, twisting the strap of his backpack round his thin wrist. 'Honestly, he won't be mad at you if you don't tell Mum first.'

Olivia tucked her thumbs into the back pockets of her jeans. 'So what's your dad's name?' she asked, realising she wasn't supposed to know who he was.

'It's Armstrong,' said Sean much more cheerfully. 'Joel Armstrong. He's a teacher,' he added, as if that carried more weight.

A quiver of apprehension ran down Olivia's spine and she shivered. She could hardly believe she was standing here, talking to Joel's son, trying to decide what was best for the boy. She was fairly sure Joel wouldn't like the idea of her being involved in his private affairs. But, in spite of that, she couldn't deny a tremor of excitement at the power Sean had inadvertently given her.

'Where do you live, Sean?' she asked again, and the boy's eyes narrowed.

'You're not going to tell my mum, are you?' he blurted. 'Oh, please, I don't want to live with them any more.'

'Why not?' Olivia frowned. 'They don't—well, they don't hurt you, do they?'

'No.' Sean was sulky. 'I just don't like my stepfather, that's all.'

Olivia considered. Bearing in mind her own feelings about Martin Dempsey, she could sympathise. But Sean was too young to make that kind of decision for himself. 'Why don't you live with your father, then?' she asked. 'You like him, don't you?'

'Oh, yes!' Sean's face lit up. Then he hunched his shoulders as reality kicked in. 'But he works at the university in Newcastle. Besides, Mum said I needed two parents, not just one.'

'I see.' Olivia was beginning to understand the situation.

'But Stewart's not my parent!' exclaimed Sean, his expression darkening with frustration. He broke off and looked at her, waiting for her to say something. 'Please, don't tell my mum.'

'Tell me where you live and I'll think about it,' replied Olivia cautiously, and Sean expelled a heavy sigh.

'Twenty-six Church Close,' he muttered unwillingly. 'But she won't be there. She'll be at work.'

Olivia doubted Louise would be at work if she knew her son was missing. In the same situation, Olivia knew she'd have been doing everything in her power to find out where he'd gone. 'Church Close?' she said. 'Is that in Bridgeford?'

Sean nodded. 'It's one of the new houses behind the church.'

'Ah.'

'It's a horrible place. I don't like it,' he added vehemently. 'My dad's house is much nicer. And it's bigger, too.'

'Is it?' Olivia accepted his assessment, but she couldn't help thinking it was the people who occupied the houses, not the houses themselves, that were determining his opinion. 'OK,' she said at last, deciding she owed Louise no favours. 'I'll ring your father.' But when his face cleared, she went on warningly, 'Be prepared. He probably knows all about the fact that you're missing by now.'

CHAPTER SIX

JOEL was in the library at the university, doing some research for a paper he was writing, when his mobile phone trilled.

Immediately, half the eyes in the room turned in his direction and he made an open-handed gesture of apology as he reached to turn the phone off. Whoever it was would have to wait until he finished what he was doing, he thought impatiently. Certainly none of his colleagues would think of disturbing him here.

But he couldn't help noticing the number being displayed as he flipped the mobile open. It was unfamiliar to him and conversely that troubled him. He was remembering what had happened a few days ago, and, although he had no reason to suspect this call had anything to do with his son, he gritted his teeth and pressed the button to connect the call.

'Yeah,' he muttered, barely audibly, though the pained looks he was receiving proved he wasn't fooling anybody. Stifling an oath, he gathered his papers together and thrust them one-handed into his case, quitting the room with ill grace.

'Joel?'

Bloody hell, it was Olivia. Joel thought he'd have recognised her voice even in his sleep, but that didn't make him feel any the less aggressive at having to take her call.

'What do you want, Liv?' he demanded, and even to his own ears he sounded belligerent. He half expected her to make some biting comment and ring off.

But she didn't. With creditable coolness, she said, 'There's someone here who wants to speak to you, Joel,' and a moment later a timid voice said,

'It's me, Dad,' and he knew he hadn't been wrong in anticipating trouble.

'Sean!' he exclaimed. 'Hell's bells, why aren't you in school?'

'Because I'm not,' said Sean defensively. 'Can I come and see you?'

Joel sagged back against the wall outside the library, dropping his book bag at his feet, raking impatient fingers through his hair. 'Sean, I'm at the university. I've got a lecture in—' he consulted his watch '—in exactly forty-five minutes. I don't have time to see you now.'

Sean made no response to this but Joel heard a muffled exchange going on in the background. And as he listened, he realised something that he should have questioned right away. Sean was talking to *Olivia*! How had *that* happened?

'Sean,' he said sharply, resenting the fact that he couldn't hear what they were saying. 'Sean, where are you?'

There was another pause, while frustration welled up inside him, and then Olivia spoke again. 'I'd have thought you'd have had the grace to abandon your lectures while your son was missing,' she said accusingly, and Joel felt as if the ground had just opened up beneath his feet.

'What did you say?' he asked harshly, but he already knew what she meant.

'Sean didn't go home last night,' said Olivia flatly. 'Don't pretend you don't know.'

'I don't. Or rather I didn't!' exclaimed Joel, trying desperately to get a handle on the situation. 'What do you mean, he didn't go home? How do you know? Did Louise tell you?'

'Louise, no.' Olivia sounded impatient. 'I haven't spoken to Louise. Sean told me. And he insisted on me calling you first.'

'Damn!' Joel pushed himself away from the wall, unable to control his agitation. 'So how long has he been with you?'

'Well, not all night, obviously,' retorted Olivia crisply. She paused. 'I—found him in the barn about an hour ago.'

'The barn?'

'Yes, the barn. In the loft, actually. I suppose that was why no one knew he was there.'

Joel groaned. Unwillingly the memory of their meetings, their lovemaking, in the loft came back to haunt him again. But evidently Olivia had no such sensibilities.

'He apparently spent the night there,' she continued evenly. 'What I can't understand is how you didn't know he was missing.'

Joel could have told her. It was obvious that when—*if*— Louise had discovered her son's disappearance, she'd immediately assumed that once again he'd sought refuge with his father. But he hadn't, and Joel's blood ran cold at the thought of what could have happened to the boy.

'Did he tell you this is the second time he's run away in less than a week?' he asked, though it was hardly an explanation.

'No.' There was another brief silence while Olivia absorbed this. Then, 'Are you saying he came to the university to find you?' and Joel blew out a weary breath.

'To my house in Millford, actually,' he said tersely. 'Now do you see why I might not have been told what was going on?'

'I'm beginning to,' she answered. And then, in an entirely different tone, 'What do you want me to do? Take him home?'

Joel heard Sean's vehement protests that she'd promised he could see his father and made an immediate decision. 'Do you think you could bring him to Millford?' he asked, aware he was going to have to get someone to cover his lecture. 'I know it's an imposition, but I could meet you there in—say, forty minutes?'

Another pause, shorter this time, before Olivia said, 'I could do that.' She took a breath. 'OK. Sean can give me directions. We'll see you in about three-quarters of an hour.'

Although she knew Linda wouldn't be very pleased that her plans were being disrupted, Olivia didn't tell her what was going on. She guessed if Linda found out that Joel's son had spent the night in the barn, she would insist on informing his mother. And while that was possibly the most sensible thing to do, if Louise was worried about her son, why hadn't she been going from door to door, asking if anyone had seen him?

Fortunately, Martin hadn't come back yet so Olivia was able to collect her keys and unlock the rental car without incident. All the same, after reversing up to the barn and telling Sean to jump in the back and keep his head down, she felt absurdly guilty. This wasn't her problem and she was all kinds of a fool for getting involved.

It was still too early when they arrived at Joel's house, but Olivia was happy to be away from Bridgeford. She knew no one in Millford; hoped no one would recognise her. And, besides, it gave her a little more time to talk to Sean.

Joel's house overlooked the village green; an elegant Georgian structure, it had windows on either side of an oak door, with a distinctive fanlight above. What had once been a coach-house now served as a garage, Sean told her. He obviously liked being her guide and proudly showed her round to the back.

There was a football lying on the lawn and Sean immediately dropped his backpack onto the patio and started kicking the ball around. 'Can you play football?' he asked, seeing her watching him, and Olivia shook her head.

'You've got to be kidding,' she said, laughing. 'I've got two left feet.'

'What does that mean? Two left feet?' Sean looked puzzled.

'It means I'm no good at sports,' explained Olivia wryly. 'I go running instead. That doesn't need any skill at all.'

Sean started heading the ball. 'Where do you run? Around the farm?'

'No.' Olivia realised she hadn't had any exercise since she'd arrived in Bridgeford. 'I used to live in New York. I did all my running there.'

Sean stopped what he was doing and stared at her. 'New York,' he echoed. 'That's in America, isn't it?'

'Yes. Have you been there?'

'Not to New York,' said Sean seriously. 'But Dad took me to Disneyworld last year. That's in Florida,' he added, in case she didn't understand, and Olivia made an admiring face.

'Cool,' she said. 'And did you enjoy it?'

'Oh, yeah.' Sean picked up the ball, cradling it in his arms. 'It was great.' He grimaced. 'Stewart doesn't like holidays. Not unless he can play golf all the time.'

Olivia bit her lip, not wanting to get into family politics. 'Do you play golf?' she asked instead, hoping to divert him. 'My—my ex-husband was very keen.'

'You were married?' Sean gazed at her. 'Was that when you lived in America?'

'I—Yes.' She glanced about her. 'Do you come here a lot?'

It was the wrong thing to say. She knew that as soon as Sean's lips turned down. 'Hardly at all,' he muttered gloomily. 'Just some weekends, that's all.'

'That sounds like quite a lot to me,' said Olivia cheerfully. 'So what do you and your dad do? Go to football matches, that sort of thing?'

'Sometimes,' admitted Sean, still looking dejected. 'Do you think he'll be long?'

Realising Joel's arrival was playing on the boy's mind, too, Olivia endeavoured to distract him. 'Tell me about when you went to Florida. Did you see any alligators?'

Sean brightened at once. 'Oh, yeah,' he said. 'When we stayed in Miami, we went on a trip into the Everglades. We went on one of those hover-boats. It was really exciting.'

'You mean an airboat,' said Olivia, nodding. 'Mmm, I've been on one of those, too. They go really fast, don't they?'

'They're awesome,' said Sean, with boyish enthusiasm. 'Dad says we can go back some time and do it again.'

'Hey, well, that's something to look forward to,' said Olivia, hoping to sustain the mood, but Sean hunched his shoulders now.

'Holidays aren't very long,' he muttered. 'I want to live with my dad. Not just see him now and then.'

Olivia sighed. 'I'm sure you love your mother, too,' she said. 'How would she feel if you lived with your father?'

'She wouldn't care,' said Sean sulkily. 'So long as she's got Stewart and—and—'

'And who?'

'Nobody.' Sean scowled. 'Do you think I should go and look for Dad's car?'

Olivia frowned, but she couldn't think of any reason why not, and, nodding, she let him go. But she sensed he had something on his mind, something more than just his eagerness to be with his father. Could his stepfather have anything to do with it? She didn't want to think so, but there was something he wasn't telling her. Perhaps he'd tell his father. After all, she told herself again, it wasn't her problem.

Following Sean round to the front of the property, she was just in time to see Joel's Lexus pull to a halt at the gate. He thrust open his door and got out and, despite everything, her heart quickened and her mouth went dry.

He was so attractive, she though painfully. Even now, in khaki cargo pants and a cream chambray shirt, the neck open to reveal the brown column of his throat, he looked dark and disturbingly male. Despite the worried expression marring his deeply tanned features, he was strikingly familiar. Big and strong, coiled strength and brooding grey eyes. Heavens, no wonder she'd behaved so outrageously in his office at the university. Just looking at him now, she felt her palms dampen and her body begin to heat.

Sean hesitated a moment and then ran back around the

house and Olivia wondered if he thought his father's grim expression was solely directed at him. She didn't kid herself. Her involvement hadn't gone unnoticed. Joel might be grateful to her for bringing the boy here, but he was probably resenting every moment of it.

If Joel wondered why his son should have run away, he didn't show it, and Olivia shifted a little nervously as he slammed the car door and strode through the wrought-iron gate that footed the garden path. But she refused to scurry away like a scared rabbit. She found she cared too much about Sean to do that.

Joel's eyes found hers and she steeled herself to face his censure. But all he said was, 'Thanks for bringing him here, Liv. God knows what he might have done if you hadn't found him when you did.'

Olivia managed a careless shrug. 'What do you think he'd have done?' she asked, stepping out of his way.

'Found his way here. I hope,' said Joel fervently. 'As he did a few days ago.' He shook his head, looking along the path his son had taken. 'Crazy kid! What the hell am I going to do about him?'

Olivia took an unsteady breath. 'He wants to be with you,' she said, aware as she did so that she knew exactly how Sean felt. Being with Joel again was reminding her of how it had been when they were together. Despite what he'd done to her, she still had feelings for this man.

'And how am I supposed to handle that?' Joel pushed agitated fingers through his hair. 'Dammit, I agreed that he should live with Louise and Stewart. I thought their situation was a more normal one for an impressionable child.'

'Stewart's not his father,' said Olivia, unable to ignore

his anxiety. She paused. 'How old was Sean when you—well, when you and your wife split up?'

'Six,' said Joel tersely. 'But the marriage hadn't worked for ages. Louise and I were already living separate lives.'

'Stewart,' said Olivia, understanding, and when Joel nodded in assent she badly wanted to put her arms around him and comfort him.

But that was too much, even for her. Swallowing, she pushed a hand into the front pocket of her jeans and pulled out her keys. 'Well, I'll leave you to it,' she said, with enforced lightness. 'Don't be too hard on him. He's a good kid.'

'I'm glad you think so.' Disturbingly, Joel's voice had thickened and she found she couldn't look away from his searching gaze. 'He should have been our son, Liv,' he muttered fiercely. 'Yours—and mine.'

Olivia felt a quiver of awareness sweep over her. The intimacy of the moment, his nearness and the bone-deep remembrance of all they'd shared—and lost—was turning her legs to jelly. For a moment she couldn't move, frozen by the force of words that tore her composure to shreds. The desire to reach out to him was almost overwhelming, but then, as if regretting his own weakness—or had she only imagined it?—Joel inclined his head.

'Thanks again for looking after him,' he said stiffly. 'I appreciate it.'

'You're not going!'

Unnoticed, Sean had ventured back along the path, probably wondering what was taking so long, Olivia reflected tensely. He had the football in his arms again, clutched to his thin chest like a talisman, his blue eyes round and filled with concern.

'Mrs Garvey's got to get back,' said Joel at once, going towards him. As he passed her, Olivia's nostrils were assailed by the mingled scents of soap and man, but her response was arrested by the indignant expression on Sean's face.

'You said your name was Olivia Foley!' he exclaimed, proving he hadn't forgotten their conversation. 'You said you lived at the farm.'

Olivia didn't remember saying that, but she understood his confusion. 'My name is Foley,' she told him. 'It used to be Garvey, but I changed back to my old name last year.'

'When you got a divorce,' said Sean, turning triumphantly to his father. 'You see. I knew I was right.'

'Well, it's good to be right about something,' remarked Joel drily, still angry with himself for confronting Olivia. 'So—let's go indoors and you can tell me why you ran away. Again.'

'Can she come, too?'

Evidently Sean had decided he needed some support, but all Olivia wanted to do was get away. 'I can't, Sean,' she said, hating having to disappoint him. 'You talk to your father; I'm sure he'll understand how you feel.'

She was forced to look at Joel then, willing him to re-inforce what she was saying, but conversely, Joel didn't im-mediately respond. He could see Sean had taken a liking to Olivia and, while that ought not to please him, the temp-tation to have a woman's angle had to outweigh his own feelings towards her.

'You can stay if you like,' he said offhandedly, half hoping she'd turn him down. At least, if she did, Sean couldn't blame him for her decision. God, he thought incredulously, was he really pandering to the boy after the way he'd behaved?

'Oh, well, I—'

'Please!' Sean came forward now and touched her sleeve. 'I want to show you my room.'

Olivia shook her head, but it wasn't an indication of what she was thinking. 'I'm sure your father would rather have you to himself,' she said, glancing at Joel's taut face for a moment. 'Wouldn't you?'

Joel's jaw tightened. 'Stay and have coffee at least,' he said carelessly, but Olivia knew he was deliberately forcing her to make the decision.

'O—K,' she said, unable to resist smiling into Sean's relieved face. 'Now, you're not going to take that football into the house, are you?'

CHAPTER SEVEN

JOEL had no real idea how he felt as he fished his keys out of his pocket and opened the door to his home.

Despite the fact that he hadn't lived like a monk in the years since his second divorce, he'd never brought a woman to his house before. And the fact that it was Olivia made it all the more unsettling. He didn't want her here; didn't want the certain knowledge that after she'd gone, he'd still feel her presence. But it was too late now.

Beyond the heavy door, a square entrance hall gave access to the main rooms of the house. A polished parquet floor was spread with a couple of colourful rugs he'd picked up on a trip to India, and a carved oak chest sat at the foot of a curved staircase.

Joel closed the door and Olivia concentrated on her surroundings. That way, she hoped, she wouldn't reflect on the fact that apart from Sean they were alone here.

And it was easy to admire the high-ceilinged rooms she glimpsed as Joel led the way to the kitchen. Without the obvious financial restrictions they'd had when they were married, he'd proved he had excellent taste. The mix of ancient and modern, of different textures and subtle colours, was exactly what the old house had needed.

'I'm hungry,' said Sean at once, opening the fridge with the familiarity of long use and looking inside. 'Can I have some cheese, Dad?'

'I suppose so.' Joel had gone immediately to fill the filter with coffee, but now he glanced over his shoulder with a resigned expression. 'Don't they feed you at Church Close?'

Sean's face darkened. 'Yes,' he muttered sulkily. 'But I haven't had any breakfast.'

'And whose fault is that?' retorted his father at once and Olivia closed her eyes for a moment, knowing that was exactly the wrong attitude to take with his son.

'Mine, I suppose,' blurted Sean, and she was sure there were tears in his eyes when he dropped the unopened cheese onto the counter and charged out of the room. They heard his footsteps thundering up the stairs and then the distinctive thud of a slamming door.

Joel hunched his shoulders and turned from what he was doing to rest his hips against the fitted unit. Then, looking absurdly like his son, he exclaimed, 'Now what did I say?'

'You know what you said,' Olivia told him evenly. 'Be a bit more understanding, can't you? He's very —fragile right now.'

Joel snorted. 'And you'd know this, how? Or have you a growing family I know nothing about?'

Olivia propped her shoulder against the door frame, but she didn't say anything in response to this provocation, and after a moment Joel muttered an apology.

'I just don't know what's wrong with him,' he sighed wearily. 'I mean, he's never been exactly happy living with

Louise and Stewart, but until recently he didn't have a lot of complaints. God knows, it's not what I want for him either, but I don't have an alternative.'

Olivia frowned. 'Why couldn't you and Louise share custody, at least until Sean's old enough to make an informed decision? Surely there's someone who could look after him when you're not here? Your mother, for instance.'

'Yeah, right.' Joel was sardonic. 'Like she's going to give up her freedom to look after a precocious ten-year-old.' He shook his head. 'And why should she? It's not her problem.'

'Sean's no one's problem,' said Olivia firmly. 'He's just a growing boy who wants to spend more time with his father. And—well, I think it might be a good idea to give him a break, if you can arrange it. If he's run away twice in one week, you have to see it as a cry for help.'

Joel's gaze sharpened. 'Has he told you something I should know?'

'No.' Olivia wrapped defensive arms about her midriff. 'It's just a feeling I have, that's all.' She paused. 'Couldn't he stay for a few days? Given enough time, he might tell you what's troubling him.'

Joel scowled. 'So you do think something's troubling him?'

Olivia sighed. 'At the risk of sounding like his social worker, I think he has—issues.'

'What issues?' Joel was perplexed.

'If I knew that, we wouldn't be having this conversation.' Olivia frowned. 'You know what it's like. When you're a child, problems assume a lot more importance than when you're older.' She paused. 'Can't you remember what you were like at his age?'

Joel looked up at her through lashes that were long and thick and dark as pitch. 'My memory doesn't kick in until the day you started at the comprehensive,' he told her roughly. 'You were waiting for the school bus when I got there and I thought—'

But he broke off at the point, pushing himself up and away from the unit, turning back to switch on the coffee machine. 'This won't take long,' he said, despising his sudden weakness. 'Then I'd better go and make my peace with Sean.'

'Would you like me to speak to him?' Olivia didn't know why she was prolonging this, but she knew it wasn't wholly for Sean's sake.

Joel shrugged, glancing at her over his shoulder. 'If you think you can talk some sense into him,' he said tersely, aware that Olivia gave him an impatient look before walking out of the room.

They were down again in a little over ten minutes. Sean still looked uneasy, but at least he wasn't sulking. 'Sorry, Dad,' he mumbled as they entered the kitchen, and then, with a quick look at Olivia, he came and gave Joel a hug.

Joel met Olivia's eyes over the boy's head, but he couldn't read anything from her expression. And, after returning the hug with interest, he turned his attention to the boy. 'That's OK, son,' he said, nodding towards the table. 'Sit down. I've made you a toasted cheese sandwich.'

'Cool,' said Sean at once, pulling out a chair and giving Olivia a grateful grin. It was obvious he was seeking her approval, and Joel wondered why it didn't annoy him that she seemed to have such a good rapport with his son.

'Coffee,' he offered, holding out a mug of the steaming beverage. Olivia took the cup and tasted it approvingly.

'Um, that's good,' she said, smiling at him now. 'You always made—that is, *I* always enjoy a good cup of coffee.'

She'd almost betrayed their previous relationship, she realised, wondering if Joel was aware of it. It wasn't that she wanted to hide it from Sean, but right now she felt he had enough to contend with.

'Let's go into the sitting room,' Joel said now. He smiled at his son. 'Finish your sandwich first, right?'

'OK, Dad.'

Sean seemed quite content to do as he was told for the moment, but Joel guessed that as soon as his stomach was full he'd begin to have second thoughts.

Which was why he wanted to have a quick word with Olivia before his son joined them. But to his surprise, she apologised as soon as they were out of earshot of Sean. 'I'm sorry,' she said. 'I mean, I don't mind if you tell him.' She paused. 'But perhaps he doesn't need to hear it right this minute.'

Joel's brows drew together. 'Am I missing something here? What doesn't he need to hear right this minute?'

'That we were married,' she said awkwardly, aware that their time alone was limited. Then, when he continued to regard her uncomprehendingly, 'Well, obviously you didn't notice the slip I almost made. I'm sorry I mentioned it.'

She subsided huffily onto a soft leather sofa, one of two that flanked an open grate set in a delicate marble surround. Taking another sip of coffee, she cradled the mug between her palms, feeling frustrated. Was she the only one who was aware of the anomalies here? He was asking his first wife for advice about the child he'd had with his second, and she was worrying because she'd almost said the wrong thing. Unbelievable!

To her surprise—and a certain amount of apprehension—Joel came and sat beside her. The powerful muscles of his thigh depressed the cushion nearest to her. And, when he leaned forward to set his coffee mug on a glass-topped occasional table in front of the sofa, the hem of his shirt separated from his trousers.

Dear lord!

She sat back abruptly, directing her eyes anywhere but at that tantalising wedge of brown skin. Yet, she couldn't deny, there was something incredibly vulnerable about it. It proved how agitated he'd been when he'd got into his car at the university. He hadn't even stopped to grab a jacket before making the twelve-mile drive to Millford.

Her eyes darted irresistibly in his direction again. Evidently, he still tanned as easily as he had used to when they were together. An image of them skinny-dipping in Redes Bay when they were teenagers was as vivid now as it was unwelcome.

But he ensured she couldn't ignore him for long, whatever her feelings. Turning towards her, he unsettled her still more by laying one arm along the back of the sofa behind her. 'Now, tell me what you mean,' he said as her eyes fastened on the cluster of hairs just visible in the open V of his shirt. 'Don't you want Sean to know about us?'

'There is no "us",' she told him stiffly, in no state to have this conversation.

'I know that.' His voice rasped. 'But there used to be.'

Now, why had he said that? Joel asked himself irritably.

Just because he was sitting so close to her, because he could smell the indefinable perfume of her skin, he'd spoken recklessly. But it wouldn't do. Dammit, she'd always been able to drive him crazy when he was near her. Right now, all his heat-hazed brain could think about was that scene in his office and how much he wanted to touch her again.

But it wasn't going to happen!

Then she spoke, her voice low and a little unsteady, and the intimacy of their situation swept over him again. 'It's up to you—whether you want to tell him or not. I just didn't want to say the wrong thing.'

'As opposed to doing the wrong thing,' he muttered, unable to pull his eyes away from the rounded swell of her breasts. She was wearing a black T-shirt today and tight jeans that emphasised the slender curves below her waist. And a scarlet chiffon scarf, like a flag of defiance. He would have liked to wind that scarf around his hand and use it to drag her provocative body into his arms. 'Yeah, I see what you mean.'

'Are you saying I've done the wrong thing by coming here?' she asked, her words distracting him, and Joel closed his eyes for a moment against the pull of an attraction he'd been sure he'd conquered long ago.

'No, I have,' he said at last, opening his eyes again and scowling at her. 'By inviting you into my house.'

Her lips parted. 'Well, I'm sorry—' she began indignantly, but he didn't let her finish. Before he could control the impulse, he'd reached out and brushed his knuckles over the visible peaks of her breasts. He was almost sure she wasn't wearing a bra, and the notion drove all sane thoughts out of his head.

'Joel!'

She scrambled backwards, but he was too quick for her, his hand reaching for the arm of the sofa, keeping her in her seat. 'Now do you see what I mean?' he demanded, gazing down at her with oddly possessive eyes. He used his free hand to trace a tantalising path from her breast to the button at her waist. 'I'm wondering if we had sex together if it might help me to get you out of my skull. What do you think?'

'In your dreams!' Olivia sucked in a trembling breath, horrified by her own reaction to his outrageous suggestion. Oh, yeah, her libido applauded. Go for it, girl! Let's get it on. But what she forced herself to say was, 'Let me get up, Joel. I'll get out of here and solve your problem.'

Joel shook his head. 'You think it's that easy?'

Olivia didn't think it was easy at all. Her heart was pounding, her pulse was erratic, and her body felt as if it was on fire. If she wasn't careful, he was going to realise her dilemma, and that made her edgy. 'I have no desire to have sex with you, Joel,' she insisted, and then recoiled with a gasp when his nail scraped down her zip.

For a breath-stealing moment she thought he'd opened it, and she knew her panties were already wet. Heavens, she thought with relief, discovering she'd been mistaken, if he'd slipped his hand inside her jeans he'd have soon found out what a liar she was.

But he wasn't finished with her. 'Sure?' he asked, lowering himself until his chest was just touching hers. The clean male smell she'd noticed earlier rose from his opened shirt, and she could tell from the stubble on his jawline that he hadn't shaved since the night before.

She couldn't deny the moan that rose into her throat as he deliberately pressed closer. His chin scraped her cheek and he used both hands to pull her T-shirt out of her jeans. Then warm palms spread against her midriff, his thumbs brushing the undersides of her breasts with wilful intent.

'In my dreams, hmm?' he taunted her softly, and this time she wasn't mistaken about the invasion of his hand. 'Oh, baby,' he muttered thickly as his fingers found her secret, and then his mouth sought hers and the room began to spin dizzily about her.

The sound of footsteps crossing the parquet floor was instantly sobering. 'Damn,' muttered Joel savagely, hauling himself away from her, and by the time the boy appeared in the doorway his father was standing by the window, apparently watching the lambs in the distant field.

Olivia didn't want to get up. Her legs felt like jelly and every nerve in her body felt as raw as an open wound. But she had to prove—to herself as well as Joel—that she was no pushover. Pushing her T-shirt down and herself up, she turned to smile at the boy.

'Feeling better?' she asked with assumed brightness and Sean made a face.

'That depends,' he muttered, his eyes moving to his father. 'What have you two been talking about?'

'Not that it's any business of yours,' said Joel irritably, and Sean hung his head.

But the truth was, Joel was feeling both thwarted and guilty. Dammit, his son was more important than the unwanted hunger Olivia inspired in him. Yet he only had to look at her to feel again the mindless need of total fascination.

How many more times was he going to let her make a fool of him? OK, she hadn't exactly invited him to make love to her, but she hadn't tried very hard to stop him either. Aching with frustration, he struggled to remember what was important here.

'I'll—talk to your mother,' he told the boy flatly, and then wished he hadn't made it sound like a done deal when Sean flung himself into his arms.

'Thanks, Dad!' he exclaimed fervently. 'I knew Olivia would help you see it my way.'

'Olivia?'

Joel scowled, and Olivia hastily tried to put him straight. 'I just said I was sure you'd put things right with his mother,' she mumbled awkwardly, and Joel gave her a suspicious look.

But when he spoke to his son, he didn't question it. 'I'm not promising anything, Sean,' he said, peeling the boy's arms from around him and holding him by his shoulders. 'But I've got to tell her where you are, anyway, and I'm sure she'll agree to let you spend the night here at least.'

She'd better, Joel added silently, meeting Olivia's eyes again, letting her see his frustration. When would Louise have asked him about their son's whereabouts? he wondered angrily. Did she even care?

Then, realising Olivia would interpret his expression differently, he continued, 'You approve?'

Olivia lifted her shoulders but, before she could make any response, Sean intervened. 'Just tonight?' he asked plaintively, and she realised he did tend to push his luck with his father.

'Look, I've got to be going,' she said, hoping to prevent another confrontation. 'Nice to meet you, Sean.'

Sean's face dropped, and he swung away from Joel to stare at her. 'But we'll see you again, won't we?' he protested. And then, to his father, 'Olivia's staying with her father, too,' almost as if their situations were comparable.

'I know.' Joel nodded. 'Say goodbye, Sean. And thank Mrs—'

'Olivia,' put in his son at once. 'She said I could call her Olivia.'

'OK.' Joel forced a tight smile. 'Thank—her for taking the trouble to bring you here.' Then, gritting his teeth, 'We both appreciate it.'

'Do you?'

Olivia's lips twisted and Joel's stomach tightened in spite of all his efforts to ignore what had happened. Dammit, was having an affair with her the only way he was going to get her out of his mind?

'You better believe it,' he responded now, but even to his own ears he sounded rattled. 'Sean?'

'Oh, yeah. Thanks, Olivia.' His son had no such hang-ups. 'But I can come and see you at the farm, can't I?'

'Sean!'

'Of course you can,' she responded, her eyes challenging Joel to contradict her. 'See you—both—later.'

CHAPTER EIGHT

OLIVIA drove back to Bridgeford, her head buzzing. What had happened to all her brave predictions of not getting involved with her ex-husband? Here she was, befriending his son, letting Joel back into her life and her emotions.

And why?

In Sean's case, it was easy. She liked him, she liked him a lot. All her thwarted maternal instincts came to the fore when she saw how unhappy he was.

With Joel, however, it was anything but easy to understand. Hadn't he hurt her enough? Was she so desperate for a man that she was prepared to go to any lengths to satisfy her sexual needs? If so, she was pathetic!

But that wasn't the whole story. In truth, she'd forgotten how vulnerable she'd always been where Joel was concerned. Hadn't that day at his office taught her anything? She should have remembered that in the old days he'd only had to look at her in a certain way and she'd be begging him to make love to her.

She'd only been fourteen when she'd become aware that Joel was interested in her. Oh, she'd noticed how attractive he was. All her friends had thought he was totally hot! Ironic, really, that Jayne had used the same adjective. But it had been such a thrill when he'd first asked her out.

Naturally, her sister had warned her against getting involved with a boy who was older than she was. At fourteen, sixteen had seemed like a great age. But she hadn't been willing to listen to anyone's advice. She'd assured Linda she knew what she was doing. The physical attraction that had initially brought them together had deepened into love, and she'd believed that nothing and no one would ever split her and Joel up.

Until she'd succeeded in doing it herself...

Martin's car was in the yard when she got back to the farm, and she took a guilty glance at her watch. It was a quarter-past eleven, three-quarters of an hour later than she'd intended. But surely, when she explained the circumstances, they'd understand.

However, when she entered the kitchen, only Linda was sitting at the table, glancing through some coloured brochures spread out in front of her.

'Hi,' said Olivia awkwardly. 'Sorry I'm late.'

Linda looked up. 'Where have you been?'

'To Millford.' Olivia realised some further explanation was needed, and added, 'Joel's son needed a lift.'

'Joel's son?' Linda frowned. 'You mean Sean?'

'Mmm.' Olivia moved to the stove to help herself to some coffee, not wanting Linda to study her too closely. 'Where's Martin?'

'He's gone to help Andy clear out one of the cottages.' Linda got up from her chair. 'How did you meet Sean Armstrong? I didn't know you knew him. Shouldn't he have been in school?'

'I expect so.' Olivia looked down into her cup of coffee, refusing to meet her sister's accusing gaze. She told herself she wouldn't be intimidated into revealing things that were really none of Linda's business. 'What did you want to talk to me about?'

Linda was taken aback. 'Oh, well, Martin's not here at the moment—'

'I'm sure you don't need Martin to hold your hand,' said Olivia, her taste buds protesting at the bitter taste of the coffee. 'Come on, Linda. Do you want me to leave?'

'Heavens, no!' Linda sounded horrified. 'You're welcome to stay here as long as you like.'

'So?'

Linda sighed, and then she bent and picked up one of the brochures she'd been looking at when Olivia came in and handed it over. 'What do you think of that?'

Olivia put down her coffee and looked at the glossy publication. It had been issued by the local tourist board and contained a list of holiday accommodation in the area. It dealt primarily with farms offering bed and breakfast and others that had cottages to rent.

'Well?' There was a trace of excitement in Linda's voice now. 'Could Martin and I handle something like that?'

Olivia blinked. 'Offer bed and breakfast, you mean?'

'No!' Linda clicked her tongue. 'We don't have enough room here to offer bed and breakfast. No, I meant the cottages. We want to modernise the ones we have and offer them as holiday rentals. What do you think?'

Olivia looked at the brochure again, trying to concentrate. 'But aren't the cottages occupied?'

'Not any more,' said Linda at once. 'I told you about the

sheep and cattle being destroyed. There was no point in paying men we didn't need and couldn't afford.'

'You asked them to leave?'

Linda was dismissive. 'Some of them left of their own accord. They got jobs elsewhere.'

'And the rest?'

'I believe they were offered council accommodation.' She sighed. 'It wasn't our problem. Livvy. We all have to do what's necessary to make a living.'

Olivia shook her head. She doubted she could have been so ruthless. Or her father either. Had this had anything to do with his illness? It must have been a blow when he lost everything.

Now she said, 'If you think renovating the cottages is viable, go for it.' She hesitated. 'What does Dad say?'

'Oh, you know Dad.' Linda was impatient. 'In any case, he's not running the farm now, Martin is. And once Dad sees how successful we are, he'll come round. It's not as if he's ever going to be able to run the place himself again.'

Olivia shrugged. 'Well, it's really nothing to do with me, is it? I mean, I don't live here.'

Linda bit her lip. 'No,' she conceded. 'But—well, we do need your help.'

'My help?'

'Yes.' Linda hesitated. 'Look, I won't beat about the bush, we need—financial assistance. We can't go to the bank because they won't lend Martin any money while the farm still belongs to Dad. And you know what he's like about going into debt.'

Olivia stared at her. 'So Dad's opposed to this venture, then?'

'Need you ask? He's never forgiven us for giving the men notice. He's not practical, Livvy. Whatever he thinks, we can't live on fresh air.'

Olivia nodded. Actually, she sympathised with their predicament. She might not like Martin, but she'd never accuse him of being lazy. And the leisure industry was booming.

'It sounds—feasible,' she said at last. 'I'm sure you'll have no trouble attracting visitors to this area. But—' She pulled a face. 'I can't help you, Linda. I wish I could, but I don't have any money. Just enough for a deposit on an apartment, if I'm lucky.'

Linda looked stunned. 'You're not serious.'

'I'm afraid I am.'

'But you told Dad that Bruce was a wealthy man.'

'He was.' And then before Linda could interrupt her again, she went on, 'I left Bruce, Linda. He didn't want me to and consequently there was no generous settlement when we divorced. Besides, I didn't want any of his money. I wanted a clean break. That's partly why I came back to England.'

'But what about your own money? You'd been earning a good salary. What happened to that?'

Olivia was tempted to say it was none of her sister's business, but she didn't want to fall out with her, so she answered truthfully, 'Lawyers' fees are expensive, Linda. And although I earned a healthy salary when I was in London, I'm afraid I never saw the need to save in those days.'

'So why did you leave Bruce? Was there someone else?'

'Not as far as I was concerned, no.'

'But if you're saying he was the guilty party,' Linda said, 'you were entitled to half his assets, weren't you?'

Olivia didn't want to get into the reasons for the break-up or relate how impossible it would have been for her to prove that Bruce was seeing someone else. 'I just wanted out of the relationship,' she said quietly. 'I'm sorry, Linda. I wish I could help you, but I can't.'

'Yes, well, being sorry isn't going to pay for the renovations. Those cottages have needed updating for years.'

Olivia sat down in the chair opposite. 'If there was anything I could do—'

'There is.' As if the idea had just occurred to her, Linda stared at her through narrowed eyes. 'You could talk to Dad, persuade him that this is the only way to keep the farm.'

'Oh, I don't know…'

'Why not? You said you wanted to help, and he'll listen to you. You're the prodigal daughter. If you say you're in favour, he might be prepared to consider getting a loan.'

As luck would have it, Andy came in at that moment and Olivia was able to make her escape without answering her. She knew it was only a temporary release, that sooner or later she would have to come to a decision. But for now, she was grateful for the chance to be on her own.

But, in the days that followed, it seemed that Martin had persuaded his wife to give her sister some breathing space. The plan wasn't mentioned again and Olivia was able to pretend she didn't have the sword of Damocles hanging over her head. Instead she pursued her efforts to get her father to use a wheelchair, seducing him with promises of taking him out in her car, away from the prying eyes of Bridgeford.

Nurse Franklin agreed with her and, whether she thought that leaving them alone together would achieve her own ends or not, Linda put her considerable weight behind it, too. So much so that Ben Foley said he was heartily weary of being put upon. But then he delighted them all by agreeing to give the wheelchair a chance.

Consequently, a week later, Olivia and Linda helped the old man out of the wheelchair and into the front seat of the Renault. It had been arranged that Olivia would drive him down to the coast and Linda had prepared a flask of coffee for them to take with them. She was evidently doing her best to sweeten the atmosphere and Olivia had been so pleased with her father's progress that she hadn't thought of leaving for days.

Olivia drove to Redes Bay, driving down the precarious cliff road and parking on the dunes above the beach. The place seemed deserted; the children were all in school and it was too early in the season for holidaymakers to brave the cool north-east wind that was blowing off the sea. Across the road from the beach, the small pub was doing better business, but no one was taking advantage of the outdoor tables today.

However, inside the car it was snug and cosy. And the view was magnificent: a stretch of almost deserted sand with the white-capped waves stretching as far as the eye could see. Ben Foley heaved a sigh and then turned his head to look at his daughter. 'Thanks for this,' he said sheepishly. 'I've been an old fool, haven't I?'

'Just stubborn,' said Olivia gently. 'No change there, then. Now, do you want a cup of Linda's coffee? Or would you rather have a beer?'

Her father gaped. 'A beer,' he said fervently. 'It's six months since I had a beer.'

'You're probably not supposed to have alcohol,' said

Olivia doubtfully, half wishing she hadn't mentioned it. 'But one beer won't do any harm, will it?'

Her father agreed, and, leaving him sitting in the car, she walked across the road to the pub. She was wearing jeans and a warm woollen jersey but she was still cold. She really would have to toughen up, she thought, if she was going to make her home in this area.

Now, where had that come from?

She'd been thinking about it for some time, she realised. Having got to know her father again, she was loath to go back to London and only get the chance to see him a couple of times a year. If she got a job with an estate agency in Newcastle, she could buy herself an apartment there. That way, she'd be able to visit the farm as often as she could.

There was a big four-wheel-drive vehicle parked in front of the pub. It looked like Joel's Lexus, she thought uneasily, but when she stepped into the bar there was no sign of him. And, after all, she told herself as she ordered her father a beer and herself a diet cola, there must be other cars like his in the area. When the weather was bad, a four-wheel-drive vehicle was invaluable.

After paying for the drinks she stepped outside again, shivering as a gust of wind blew her hair across her face. Scooping it back, she hurried across the road to where she'd left the Renault, and then stopped short when she saw the man beside her car.

It was Joel.

So what's new? she thought irritably. Although it was over a week since she'd seen him, she couldn't deny she'd thought about him. A lot. And Sean, she defended herself, noticing that her father didn't seem to have any objections to the visitor. His door was open and Joel was standing with one arm draped across the roof of the vehicle and one foot propped on the sill.

Joel straightened at her approach, though she observed the smile he'd been giving her father was distinctly thinner when it was directed at her. In tight jeans and a black T-shirt, a leather jacket left open, he didn't seem to feel the cold. 'Liv,' he said, and she didn't know whether to get into the car or stand and face him. 'Linda said I'd find you here.'

Olivia frowned. 'You went to the farm?'

'No.' Joel spoke levelly. 'I tried your mobile—'

'How did you know my number?'

Olivia spoke impulsively, but Joel merely said, 'My phone records all calls.' He paused. 'Anyway, as you probably know, I could only get voicemail. That was when I called the farm.'

'Oh.' Olivia remembered rather guiltily that she'd turned her phone off. But she'd reasoned that no one was likely to call her here. 'So you spoke to Linda?'

'Right.' Joel was patient. 'She said you'd taken your father to the coast, so I guessed you'd come here.'

'Did you?' Olivia's lips twisted.

'Yes.' His grey eyes were penetrating. 'I knew it was a favourite haunt of yours.'

'Of yours, too, if I remember correctly,' she replied tartly. Then, as his eyes darkened, 'Why did you want to speak to me?'

Joel sighed. 'I've got a problem.'

'What kind of a problem?'

'Why don't the two of you go for a walk along the beach and he can tell you?' suggested her father, mopping his mouth. 'I'll just sit here and enjoy my beer in peace.' He held out his good hand. 'Joel, will you just unscrew the cap for me?'

Olivia was forced to hand the bottle to Joel and she watched somewhat resentfully as he opened it and put it into Ben Foley's hand. There was a gentleness about him as he dealt with her father that she hated to acknowledge. But it was there just the same: an understanding of the old man's dignity that she couldn't ignore.

'I don't have a coat,' she said now, wrapping her arms about herself.

'Here, you wear this,' said Joel, taking off his leather jacket. 'I've got a duffel in the boot.'

'No, it's all right,' she began, but he'd already shed the coat and wrapped its folds around her.

'Just give me a second,' he said, and sprinted off across the road to where the Lexus was parked.

'I didn't say the wrong thing, did I?' her father asked anxiously and Olivia was obliged to reassure him.

'No—'

'I mean, he picked you up from the airport, didn't he? And Linda tells me you gave his son a lift to Millford the other day.'

'It's OK, Dad.' Olivia forced a smile. 'Now, are you sure you'll be all right on your own?'

'I'm not a baby, Liv,' he said, the unparalysed side of his face twisting in resignation. 'Besides, it'll be good for the two of you to catch up.'

To catch up!

Olivia gritted her teeth and thrust her arms into the sleeves of the soft leather jacket. As if she and Joel needed to catch up. It would be truer to say they knew too much about one another as it was.

Even so, she couldn't deny the jacket protected her from the wind. It was redolent with his distinctive maleness, still warm from the heat of his body, and she wrapped it closely about her. And refused to accept that her rising temperature was caused by anything more than the quality of the leather.

Joel came loping back wearing a hooded duffel. Once again the coat was unfastened, but his hands in the pockets kept the two sides together. 'All set?' he asked, with a quick smile for her father.

'As I'll ever be,' said Olivia ungraciously, but he had to understand this was at his instigation not hers. She'd half expected him to avoid the farm so long as she was around.

They left the car and walked down the path that led through the dunes and onto the beach. The wind was considerably stronger here, and Olivia sucked in a breath as it tried to drag the jacket sides away. 'Let me,' said Joel, and, brushing her hands away, he swiftly attached the zip and pulled it up to her chin. 'Now put your hands in the pockets,' he instructed. 'That should work.'

Olivia did as he said because her fingers were already tingling with the cold. And it was true, now that the jacket was fastened, it had no chance to billow in the wind.

'Thanks,' she said offhandedly, and Joel cast her an ironic look.

'Yeah, right,' he said, and then cursed as the soft sand spilled into his loafers. Emptying them out, he walked barefoot onto the firmer sand.

Admiring his fortitude, Olivia hurried after him, grateful

that her own boots prevented the sand from invading her feet. Not that Joel appeared to notice that the firmer sand was damp and chilly. With his gaze fixed on the horizon, he seemed indifferent to his surroundings. And to her.

'You wanted to talk to me?' she prompted, not happy at being ignored when he'd come here expressly to find her. She glanced up at his unsmiling face. 'How's Sean?'

Joel's jaw compressed. 'Do you care?'

Olivia caught her breath. 'You know I do.'

'Do I?'

Olivia sighed. 'Is this going to be another pointless argument? Of course I care about Sean.' She paused, her eyes widening. 'Don't tell me he's run away again.'

'No.' Joel blew out a breath. 'As a matter of fact, Louise and I have come to an agreement. She's letting Sean stay with me for the next two weeks.'

'That's great!'

Olivia was genuinely pleased for him, but Joel's expression didn't change. 'It's not great as it goes,' he told her flatly. 'I told her I'd be available, but now I won't.'

Olivia frowned. 'Why not?'

'Because the tutor who was going to cover my absence has broken his hip.' Joel grimaced. 'Hell, I feel sorry for the guy, but it couldn't have happened at a worse time as far as I'm concerned.'

Olivia's brows ascended. 'So—what now?'

Joel bent his head, aware that when she'd left his house in Millford a week ago he'd determined that, whatever Sean said, they weren't going to be seeing Olivia again. Yet here he was, telling her his troubles, hoping, he acknowledged ruefully, that she'd be able to help him out. Again.

'When are you leaving?' he asked suddenly, and Olivia pulled a hand out of the pocket of the jacket and pressed it to her throat.

'Well, that's pointed enough,' she remarked, despising herself for feeling hurt by it. 'What's it to you? You're not going to tell me you'll miss me. That would be totally out of character.'

'Can't you stop trying to score points, Liv?' Joel sounded weary. 'I only asked when you were leaving because I was hoping you might be agreeable to working for me for a couple of weeks.'

'Working for you?' Olivia stared at him. Then comprehension dawned. 'You want me to look after Sean?'

'Yeah.' Joel bent and picked up a pebble and sent it skittering across the waves. 'I know it's presumptuous and you're probably going to blow me out, but I do think you're the only person I could ask.'

Olivia shook her head. 'And what would I have to do?'

'Not a lot.' Joel looked at her. 'Just take him to school in the mornings and pick him up again at half-past three. Then stay with him until I get home. He can wait and have his supper with me. I can't give you my actual schedule. It can change from day to day. But unless I have any evening tutorials, most days I'm home about six.'

Olivia's breathing quickened. 'And while Sean's at school?'

'Your time's your own, of course.'

'I'd sleep at the farm.'

Joel looked away. 'Of course.'

Olivia considered. 'Well—OK. I'll do it.' She paused. 'But I don't need any payment. I'll do it for Sean.'

Joel exhaled heavily. 'I don't need charity, Liv.'

'Nor do I,' Olivia retorted shortly. She glanced back along the beach to where she'd left the car. 'If that's settled, I presume we can go back.'

CHAPTER NINE

ON MONDAY morning Olivia was up at half-past six.

Hurrying into the bathroom, she washed her face and cleaned her teeth, and then, because it felt chilly, she dressed in warm woollen trousers and a purple sweater. She didn't bother with much make-up, just a trace of eyeliner, mascara and a smear of lip gloss. Then, with her leather coat over her arm, she went downstairs.

Linda wasn't about, but someone—Martin, possibly—had made a pot of tea and left toast crumbs all over the drainer. Olivia wasn't hungry, but she poured herself a cup of lukewarm tea and drank it on the move.

She still had to tell the rest of the family what she was doing, and as she swept the crumbs away and washed both her cup and Martin's she hoped they would approve.

Her father knew, naturally. She hadn't been able to hide what Joel had wanted from him, and he'd looked at her a little oddly when he heard that she and Joel were planning to share responsibility for the boy.

'Are you sure about this, Liv?' he'd asked as they drove back to the farm. 'I mean, giving the kid a lift is one thing. Committing yourself to two weeks of driving back and forth to Millford, just so Sean can spend a few days with his father, does seem quite a chore.'

'You can't say two weeks on the one hand and then imply it's only for a few days on the other,' Olivia had pointed out evenly. And then, because she'd known her father was only thinking of her, 'Well—I couldn't refuse, could I?'

'Why not?' Ben Foley had been indignant. 'OK, you and Joel have got history. No one can deny that. But he got over you soon enough and married the Webster girl. What does she think about you looking after her son?'

'I doubt if she knows.' Olivia had been terse, stung by her father's assessment of Joel's behaviour. Was that what he'd done? she'd wondered. It had been galling to think that that was what everyone in Bridgeford thought.

Thankfully, the old man hadn't questioned how well she knew Sean. He'd probably assumed the boy had accompanied Joel when he'd picked her up at the airport. But Linda had still to be told and she could only hope it wouldn't become a bone of contention, before she told her what she was doing.

Joel had said Sean had to leave for school at a quarter-past eight, but Olivia realised it was only a quarter-to when she reached Millford. She was far too early and, not wanting to look too eager, she parked some distance from the house and got out of the car.

Millford was smaller than Bridgeford, but just as picturesque. Pulling her coat out of the back of the car, she put it on and strolled across to the church.

Evidently there'd been an early-morning service and the vicar was standing at the door, saying goodbye to the few stalwarts who'd braved the uncertain weather. Olivia halted by the lych-gate, feeling an odd sense of familiarity when she looked at the man. But that was silly, she thought impatiently. She'd never been to this church before.

She was about to turn away when he hailed her. 'Liv! Olivia,' he called, striding towards her. 'My goodness, it is you. What are you doing in Millford?'

Olivia watched the man as he approached, realising why he'd seemed so familiar. Despite the fact that his angular frame was disguised by the flapping folds of his surplice and he'd lost most of his hair, she recognised him at once.

'Brian!' she exclaimed. 'My Go—I mean, Brian Webster!' She paused. 'You're a vicar!'

'For my sins,' he said drily. 'And Olivia Foley.' He said her name again. 'I heard you were in the States.'

'I was.' Olivia shook her head. 'And I thought you were in the army.'

'For almost eight years.' He nodded. 'I thought it was what I wanted to do, but after Kosovo—' He blew out a harsh breath. 'I knew I had to get out.'

'But a vicar!' Olivia could see that he was still emotionally disturbed by his memories and tried to lighten the mood. 'Who'd have thought it? Brian Webster! Mrs Sawyer's personal nemesis. I don't think she ever got over you putting that frog in her desk.'

Brian laughed. 'Innocent times,' he said ruefully. 'Today it would probably be a tarantula or something equally terrifying.'

Olivia smiled. 'So how long have you been—living here?'

'How long have I been a vicar, do you mean?' He turned briefly to acknowledge one of his parishioners. 'About five years, give or take. How about you? Are you staying with your dad?'

'At present,' said Olivia, remembering that time was passing and she really ought to go. But with that thought came another: Brian Webster was Louise's cousin. If Joel hadn't informed his ex-wife of the arrangements he'd made, she was soon going to find out.

'So what are you doing in Millford?' Brian frowned, detecting she was uncomfortable with that question. 'Don't tell me you're looking for Joel Armstrong! I thought that was all over between you two long ago.'

'It was. It *is*.' Olivia glanced away across the green to where Joel's house was situated. 'I—well, his son's staying with him at the moment and I've promised to give Sean a lift to school.'

Brian regarded her curiously. 'You?' he said blankly. 'Why can't Joel take him himself?'

'Because I said I'd do it,' replied Olivia, not wanting to discuss Joel's schedule or her own. 'And I'd better get going. They're expecting me.'

Brian stepped back, spreading his arms dramatically. 'Well, don't let me hold you up,' he said, though she sensed he didn't approve. 'Perhaps I'll see you again—when you're visiting Millford,' he added pointedly. 'Give Joel my best, won't you? Tell him it's too long since he graced the doors of my church.'

'I will.'

Olivia smiled as she turned away, but she doubted Joel would appreciate the sentiment. He and Brian had never liked one another, due in no small part to the fact that Brian had been in her year at school. They had just been friends, but Brian had loved to rub Joel's nose in it, exaggerating their closeness and chiding him about baby-snatching when Olivia and Joel got together.

She was tempted to leave the car where it was, but that would have looked foolish, so she slipped behind the wheel and drove the few yards to Joel's house. However, as she shifted into neutral, Joel came out of the door and down the path, and she knew at once that he'd seen her talking to the other man.

'At last,' he said harshly, pulling her door open. 'I was beginning to wonder if you'd forgotten why you were here.'

'And good morning to you, too,' retorted Olivia, swinging her legs out of the car and getting to her feet. 'It's only five-past eight, Joel. I've got plenty of time.'

She met his brooding gaze with a defiance she was far from feeling, but for once Joel was the first to look away. 'OK,' he said. 'Perhaps that was unjustified. But before I go, I want to give you some—some information.'

'Don't you mean instructions?' Olivia taunted. 'Come on, Joel. I have looked after kids before. One of Bruce's business colleagues had twins and they didn't come to any harm when their parents left them with me.'

Joel sighed, allowing her to precede him into the house. 'If I've offended you, I'm sorry,' he said heavily, and she actually thought he meant it. 'But this situation is new to me, and I don't want anything to go wrong.'

'Like Louise finding out?' suggested Olivia, waiting for him to close the door and then following him across the hall and into the kitchen. 'Well, I'm sorry about that, but you should have warned me that Brian Webster was the vicar of All Saints Church.'

Joel grimaced. 'The vicar of All Saints,' he echoed. 'Why does that make me want to laugh?'

'You did see us, then?'

'Oh, yeah.' Joel heaved a sigh. 'I wasn't spying on you,' he added. 'I was in Sean's bedroom, trying to persuade him to get dressed, and I happened to look out of the window.' He shook his head. 'Brian Webster, preaching the good word to the people. After the things he said to me when you and I split up.'

Olivia wanted to ask him what Brian had said, but something else Joel had mentioned was more important. 'You were trying to persuade Sean to get dressed?' she asked, confused. 'Don't he and I have to leave in about ten minutes?'

'You do.' Joel was resigned. 'Oh, don't worry, he's had his breakfast. But he's decided that, as you're coming, he doesn't want to go to school.'

Olivia stared at him. 'But doesn't he know I'll be picking him up from school this afternoon?'

'Well, that won't be necessary today, actually,' said Joel apologetically. 'I'm free from two-thirty, so I can pick him up myself.'

Ridiculously, Olivia was disappointed. But what had she expected? That Joel would want her in his house any more often than was absolutely necessary? 'I see,' she said, trying not to let her feelings show. 'Well, you've got my number if you need it.'

'Yeah, right.'

Joel regarded her through narrowed eyes for a moment and now she was forced to look away. 'Was that all you wanted to tell me?' she asked, much too aware of how easily he could get under her skin. 'As you're picking him up—'

'These are for you,' Joel interrupted her, holding out a bunch of keys. 'You might as well have them. You'll need them tomorrow afternoon, anyway.'

Olivia's lips parted. 'These are for the house?'

'What else?'

'But—are you sure you want me to have them?' She moistened her lips nervously. 'I mean, you said—'

'I know what I said,' Joel told her harshly, not at all sure he was doing the right thing. But it was too late now. 'The situation's changed,' he added. 'And I won't be here when you are, will I?'

'Won't you?'

Not if I have any sense, thought Joel grimly, but he said, 'I'll go and give Sean a shout.'

However, before he reached the door, they both heard the boy's feet running down the stairs. Sean paused in the doorway, gazing at both of them with anxious eyes. 'I've changed my mind,' he said unnecessarily, though his shirt was buttoned unevenly and his tie was skewed. 'You're not sending Olivia away, are you?'

'Why would I do that?' Joel was impatient. What did Olivia have that caused both him and his son to make fools of themselves over her? 'Come here, kid. Let me put that tie straight.'

Sean beamed at Olivia as he did so. 'You're taking me to school,' he said, and she nodded. 'Cool!'

When Olivia got back to the farm, Martin and Andy were sitting at the kitchen table, tucking into bacon, eggs and sausages. She knew they sometimes came back for a proper breakfast, so she wasn't surprised. But when Linda turned from the stove, there was something less pleasant about her expression.

'Where've you been?' she asked, and, although Olivia resented her tone, she had the feeling her sister already knew.

'Um—Sean's staying with Joel at the moment and he needed someone to take him to school, so I—'

'Volunteered,' broke in Linda scornfully. 'Honestly, Livvy, I'd have thought you had more sense.'

'I didn't volunteer.' Olivia flushed in spite of herself. 'Joel asked me to do it. Didn't Dad explain?'

'Dad?' Her sister looked puzzled. 'Dad knew?'

Now Olivia looked doubtful. 'Well, yes, I thought—oh, was it Brian Webster?'

'Louise rang,' said Linda, scowling. 'One of the other mothers saw you delivering Sean to school and called her. She wants to speak to you about it. I told her I'd get you to give her a ring as soon as you got back.'

'Did you?' Olivia objected to Linda making any promises on her behalf. 'Well, don't worry. I'll go and see her. I want to know what kind of mother doesn't know—or care—if her son's missing.'

Linda blinked. 'Sean's not missing.'

'He was.' Immediately regretting the impulse to put Linda on the defensive, Olivia was forced to explain how she'd found Sean in the barn. 'And it wasn't the first time,' she declared defiantly. 'He doesn't want to live with his mother. He wants to live with Joel.'

Linda grimaced. 'I see.' She paused. 'And I suppose Joel can't look after the kid on his own.'

'No.'

'He could employ someone,' Linda said thoughtfully. 'Other people do.'

'Perhaps you should offer to look after the boy on a permanent basis,' suggested Martin surprisingly. 'I'm sure he'd be willing to pay you the going rate.'

'Oh, I don't think so…'

Olivia shook her head, but she had to admit it wasn't totally off the wall. After all, Joel had offered to pay her. But she was a trained estate agent, not a nanny.

'You should give it some thought,' Linda put in, after exchanging a glance with her husband. 'That way you wouldn't have to leave Bridgeford. I know you're worried about Dad and you'd like to stick around.'

Olivia was taken aback. 'Well, I had thought of getting a job in Newcastle,' she confessed, and Linda nodded eagerly.

'That's a great idea,' she agreed. 'Then you wouldn't need to buy an apartment. You could stay here with us.'

Olivia was getting the sense that she was missing something here. 'But—wouldn't that be an imposition?' she asked warily.

'Heck, no.' It was Martin who spoke now, wiping his mouth with the back of his hand. 'This is as much your home as ours. If you can put up with us.'

Olivia didn't know what to say. 'Well—thanks,' she said at last. 'I do appreciate it. But if I get a job in Newcastle, I'll buy an apartment there.' She took a breath. 'I'm sure you'll agree that one bathroom isn't enough for five of you, let alone six.'

'Dad can't get upstairs,' pointed out Linda at once.

'And we're thinking of dividing the main bedroom so

Linda and I can have an *en suite* shower room,' Martin added swiftly. 'Anyway, at least think about it, Livvy. We are your family. And I know Ben would be delighted if you stayed.'

Which was probably true, Olivia conceded, accepting a cup of tea from Linda but refusing anything else. She felt a little hollow inside, but she wasn't hungry. All of a sudden she had a family again, and she wished she didn't feel as if none of them was being quite sincere.

Church Close was, as Sean had said, a road of new mock-Tudor houses. Driving into the road later that morning, Olivia hoped she was doing the right thing. She had no idea if Joel would approve of what she was going to say to Louise really. But she had to put the woman straight about hers and Joel's relationship. The last thing she needed was more gossip about her and her ex-husband.

Belatedly, it occurred to her that Louise might not be at home now. Sean had said his mother had a job, and it was certainly true that most of the houses in the road looked unoccupied. There was a car parked on the drive of one house, but, although Olivia's spirits lifted, it was the house next door to the Barlows. Still, she was here now. It was worth taking a chance.

It was as she was locking the car that she looked up and saw Louise watching her. She was standing at the bedroom window, staring down at her visitor, as if she didn't quite believe her eyes.

Olivia didn't attempt a smile, but merely nodded before walking up the open-plan drive to the house. And, by the time she reached the door, Louise had it open, her expression mirroring the obvious agitation she was feeling.

'Well,' she said tersely. 'You've got a nerve!'

Olivia blew out a breath. 'May I come in, or do you want to discuss Sean out here?'

Louise's lips tightened. 'You'd better come in,' she said, albeit unwillingly. 'I just hope nobody recognises your car.'

'It's a rental,' said Olivia flatly, following the other woman across a narrow hall and into a pleasant sitting room. Then, noticing how pale Louise was looking, she added, 'I'm sorry if I've upset you, but Joel should have told you what he was going to do.'

'Yes, he should.' Louise nodded to a chair. 'You'd better sit down and tell me why he isn't looking after Sean himself.'

Olivia sighed. 'The tutor who was going to cover his lectures has broken his hip.'

'So why didn't he tell me he couldn't have Sean and been done with it?'

'You'll have to ask him that.' Olivia hesitated. 'I assume because he didn't want to disappoint the boy.'

'And I dare say he was glad of any excuse to ask you to help him out,' said Louise scathingly. 'If it wasn't so embarrassing, it would be pitiful!'

'Actually, it wasn't like that,' said Olivia, taking the seat she'd been offered and crossing her legs as if she was completely at her ease. 'Did he tell you I found Sean after he'd spent the night in our barn?'

Louise sagged a little, and then sank onto the sofa opposite. 'It was you who found him!' she exclaimed. 'No, I didn't know that. Joel just said someone had found him and Sean had insisted on being taken to Millford.'

'Well, it was me.' But Olivia was feeling concerned now. Louise did look incredibly white and exhausted. 'I— we—he did insist on speaking to his father. And I have to admit, I was pretty peeved that you apparently hadn't even noticed he was missing.'

Louise nodded. 'I suppose it did look bad,' she admitted in a much less confrontational tone. 'But he had run away just a few days before, and I've been feeling so—well, so sickly, I suppose I didn't give it the significance it deserved.'

Olivia frowned. 'You've been ill?'

'No.' Louise flushed. 'Just a bit under the weather, that's all.'

'And you assumed Sean had gone to Joel's again?'

'Yes.' Louise pushed weary hands through her tumbled dark hair and Olivia saw with some concern that she was sweating. 'I suppose you think I'm a bad mother. But Sean's not an easy kid to deal with. Not when he and Stewart don't get on.'

Olivia shook her head. 'It's nothing to do with me, Louise.'

'So you're not going to spread the fact that I neglect my child around the village?'

'No.' Olivia was horrified. 'I came here because I didn't want you to get the wrong impression about Joel and me. He was in a bind and I was—available.' *Oh, God!* 'There's no hidden agenda,' she added hurriedly. 'I'm not trying to cause trouble between you two.'

Louise regarded her curiously. 'You and Joel aren't getting back together, then?'

'Heavens, no!' Olivia was very definite about that.

But even as she said the words, she wondered at the pang of regret that stirred deep in her stomach. Was it possible to want a man you didn't like? She had to believe it was, or face the alternative. That these feelings she couldn't seem to control weren't going to go away.

'I wondered,' Louise was saying now, and Olivia found it very hard to remember their conversation. The other woman pulled a wry face. 'It took him a long time to get over you, you know.'

'Oh, I don't think—'

'It's true.' Louise had evidently decided to be generous now that her own position wasn't threatened. 'I've thought, since the divorce, that he only married me because he wanted to prove to himself—and all the gossips in the village—that he'd moved on; made a success of his life.'

Olivia shook her head. 'Well, thanks for that, but Joel isn't the reason I came here. You probably know, my dad had a stroke and I wanted to come home to see him.' If that wasn't quite the way it had happened, it served the purpose. 'I am thinking of staying on for a while, but just so I can be with the family.'

'All the same—'

'Louise, really, I'd rather you didn't say anything about Joel and me to anyone. You may not know it, but I only came back to England because my second marriage didn't work out either.' She paused, and then, realising she had to say something dramatic to wipe that smug look off Louise's face, she added, 'Bruce and I were together for much longer than Joel and me.'

Louise's eyes widened. 'So you're divorced again?'

'Afraid so.' Olivia got to her feet, trying to sound philosophic. 'Anyway, I'm glad we've had this talk, Louise. I think we understand one another now.'

CHAPTER TEN

OLIVIA parked her car above the dunes and turned off the engine. It was a beautiful evening. It had been an incredibly mild day for early May and, now that the sun was sinking in the west, the sky above Redes Bay was streaked in shades of red and orange and purple.

Reaching into the glove compartment, Olivia pulled out a scrunchie and tugged her hair into a high pony-tail. Then, thrusting open her door, she got out of the car.

She was dressed in just a khaki tank-top and running shorts, and, after checking that her trainers were safely tied, she tucked the car keys into her pocket and set off.

It was weeks since she'd run any distance. When she'd first returned to England she'd contented herself with exercising at the local gym, but there was nothing like running in the fresh air. And today, particularly, she'd needed to get out of the house.

It wasn't that either Linda or Martin had said anything to upset her. On the contrary, during the past week or so, since she'd been ferrying Sean about, they'd been very supportive. In Martin's case, amazingly so, but she still felt as if sooner or later the axe was going to fall.

She had talked to her father about Linda and Martin's ambitions for the farm. It was he who'd brought the subject up and she'd had to admit that she thought it had some merit. But Ben Foley was opposed to letting strangers have free use of his land, even if he could offer no other solution to the problem.

Nevertheless, Olivia enjoyed the time she spent with the old man. Unlike the rushed awkward encounters she had with Joel, she and her father had long conversations about everything under the sun. She'd even told him about Bruce and why he hadn't wanted her to leave him. And discovered that the pain of that betrayal no longer had the strength to hurt her.

Her relationship with her first husband did not progress so easily, however. Not that she saw a lot of Joel really. He was there to say goodbye to his son in the mornings. And on those occasions when she was obliged to stay with Sean until his father got home in the evenings, she'd usually got her coat on before he'd got out of the car. Their exchanges were brief and always subjective. They spoke of Sean, of any conversations she'd had with Sean's teachers, and little else.

On the other hand, she and Joel's son had become much closer. Indeed, she was dreading the time when he would have to go back to his mother. It was almost two weeks now, but talk of his return hadn't been mentioned yet, and Olivia was hoping that Joel would be granted a stay of execution.

Tonight she hadn't been needed, however. Sean had gained permission from his father to spend the night at his best friend's house. They were having a sleepover, Sean had told Olivia that morning, full of excitement at the thought of the midnight feast they were planning. She wouldn't be needed in the morning either, because the other boy's mother would take them both to school.

Now Olivia stopped at the edge of the dunes, doing some warm-up exercises before stepping down onto the sand. She intended to run along the shoreline where the sand was damp and firm. Then she might call in the pub for a cool drink before heading back.

Drawing one knee up to her chin and then the other, she felt a rising sense of anticipation. Running had always given her a feeling of freedom, of the confidence she could have in her own muscles, her own strength.

And then she saw him. He was doing what she had planned to do, running along the shoreline, pounding the sand in a steady pace, long strides stretching long, powerful legs.

Joel!

Olivia blew out an impatient breath. Wouldn't you know it? she asked herself. Two minds with but a single thought. Why hadn't she considered that he might take advantage of his freedom? Redes Bay had always been a favoured spot for both of them.

She would have turned away then, but he'd seen her. There was a moment when he faltered, when she was sure he would simply acknowledge her with a lift of his hand perhaps and go on. Contrarily, he didn't do either of those things. He stopped for a moment, and then jogged towards her. What now? she wondered uneasily. She hoped he didn't think she was following him.

For all that, she couldn't help watching him as he drew nearer. A grey tank-top clung damply to the contours of his chest and his arms bulged with muscle. Tight-fitting cycling shorts did nothing to hide his maleness, and with sweat beading his forehead he looked big and impressively virile.

'D'you want to join me?' he asked, surprising her. He was closer now, but remained on the damp sand, jogging on the spot, not allowing his body to cool down.

'I—well, if you don't mind,' said Olivia, stepping over the soft sand and testing the damp sand for its firmness. 'Do you often run here?'

'Why? So you can avoid it in future?' Joel asked drily, realising he had probably made a mistake by inviting her company. But the beach was free to all, for goodness' sake, and he'd sensed that if he hadn't spoken she'd have abandoned her run.

'No.'

Olivia's response was defensive, and, breaking away from him, she jogged away along the beach. She took it slowly at first, only increasing her pace when she felt the muscles in her legs loosen and the adrenalin started flowing through her body.

Joel let her go, let her get some distance ahead of him, knowing that in a few loping strides he'd overtake her. As he watched her, however, he felt his body tighten. In the skin-tight tank-top and running shorts, she was every man's wet dream come true and heaven knew he wasn't immune to her appeal.

She was so sexy, that was the problem. Long, slim arms and legs; hips that swelled into the provocative curve of her bottom. She might not have been aware that her breasts had puckered when he'd challenged her, but he was. Distinctly upturned, they'd pushed delicately against the cloth of her vest.

Hell!

He saw her glance back over her shoulder then and guessed she was wondering if he'd changed his mind about them running together. He should, he acknowledged grimly. But although his brain might protest his recklessness, his flesh was shamefully weak.

Picking up his pace, he went after her and seconds later he came alongside her. She was running smoothly now, taking long, ground-covering strides, her breasts bobbing rhythmically beneath the tank-top.

They ran in silence for a while, but then Joel saw the line of dampness appearing in the small of her back. 'Don't overdo it,' he warned, feeling obliged to remind her that, unless he was mistaken, she hadn't done any running since she'd come to Bridgeford.

'I'm OK.' Olivia spoke breathily. 'It's a beautiful evening, isn't it?'

'Beautiful,' agreed Joel, dragging his eyes away from her and looking towards the horizon. 'On evenings like these, it feels as if it's going to stay light forever.'

'I know what you mean.' Olivia was relieved that he seemed prepared to meet her halfway. 'At this time of year, you don't want to go to bed.'

Joel couldn't help himself. 'I suppose that depends who you're going to bed with,' he remarked wryly, and Olivia gave him an impatient look.

'You had to say that, didn't you?'

Joel arched mocking brows. 'Well, you asked for it.'

Olivia shook her head. 'Must you bring sexual innuendo into everything? Is that what comes of mixing with amorous adolescents like that girl I saw at your office?'

Joel stifled a laugh. 'Oh, Liv, have you any idea how prudish you sound?' He turned, running backward so he could see her face. 'For your information, Cheryl Brooks is twenty-four. She's already a graduate and working towards her second degree.'

'Bully for her.' Olivia resented the ease with which he was keeping up with her. 'In any case, she's too young for you.'

Joel gasped. 'Did I say she wasn't?'

'No, but as you were talking about taking women to bed—'

'I wasn't talking about any such thing.' Joel was indignant. 'You brought it up, Liv. Not me.'

'Whatever.'

Olivia could feel her legs beginning to tire. She'd passed the pain barrier some minutes ago, but now it was becoming a distinct effort to keep putting one foot in front of the other. However, she wasn't going to let Joel get the better of her in this as well as everything else, and, making an especial effort, she quickened her pace until she was actually pulling away from him.

The pain was excruciating, her knees burning as if they were on fire. But there was such satisfaction in besting him that she could actually numb her mind to the agony in her legs.

It didn't last. As soon as he realised what she was doing, Joel quickened his own pace and within seconds he'd caught up with her.

'Crazy woman!' he exclaimed, one look at her contorted face enough to tell him that she was in danger of doing some permanent damage to herself. He put a restraining hand on her arm, feeling the trembling muscles, the sweat that was streaming out of her. 'For heaven's sake, Liv, you're going to kill yourself!'

Olivia sagged. She couldn't help it. Even the warning touch of his hand was too much, and, stumbling, she fell to her knees on the sand.

'Liv, are you all right?'

Instantly abandoning any thought of continuing his own run, Joel came down on his haunches beside her, one hand on the back of her neck, the other gripping her upper arm, supporting her when she would have sunk onto the sand. Despite his own exertions his hands were cool and firm, and, unable to help herself, Olivia slumped against him.

'For pity's sake!'

Joel swore to himself, looking about him as if assistance was going to materialise by magic. But there was no one else on the beach. And they were some distance from where they'd left their cars. Part of the beauty of Redes Bay was its absence of human habitation. Apart from the pub, that was, but that was some distance away, too.

'I'll—I'll be all right in a minute.'

Olivia spoke faintly, still struggling to regulate her breathing. Her lungs burned and it was incredibly difficult to take the gulping breaths she knew she needed to recover. She was beginning to feel cold, too, the breeze off the North Sea picking up as night drew in.

She shivered and Joel felt it. Dammit, she was going to develop hypothermia if he didn't get her warm soon. There was no way she was going to be able to walk back to her car in her present condition. He was going to have to leave her here and go and get help on his own.

He hesitated a moment, aware that his tank-top was rank with his own sweat, but then he pulled it over his head and wrapped it about her shoulders like a shawl. 'Stay there,' he said, and when she tried to protest he held the top tighter about her. 'I won't be long,' he promised grimly. 'Please, Liv. Just stay here until I get back.'

'But—you'll get cold,' she protested, and he managed an ironic grin.

'I don't think so,' he said, getting to his feet in a swift, lithe movement. 'Baby, just looking at you burns me up. Now, be good. I won't be long.'

Olivia had managed to get to her feet and was taking several tentative steps across the sand when she saw the Lexus barrelling towards her. For the first time in her life, she appreciated the advantages of having a four-wheel-drive vehicle. Its huge tyres ate up the beach as if it was the smoothest highway, only the spray of sand behind showing its passing.

Joel braked beside her and sprang out. He'd evidently found a T-shirt to cover his bare chest that Olivia had admired so briefly and in his hands he carried a sheepskin jacket that he quickly exchanged for the ratty tank-top. Feeling the comfort of the jacket envelop her, Olivia began to feel warmth radiating inside her, the spasmodic shivers that had racked her fading swiftly with its heat.

'Come on.'

Not giving her a chance to object, Joel swung her up in his arms and carried her to the Lexus. Swinging open the passenger-side door, he lifted her into the seat, pausing long enough to secure the safely belt before circling the bonnet and getting in beside her.

'Better?' he asked, looking sideways at her, and she nodded her head.

'Much.' She moistened her lips. 'Thanks.'

Joel didn't make any response. He just held her gaze for a few moments longer and then, thrusting the Lexus into drive, he did a U-turn and drove back to where the vehicle had carved a path across the dunes.

However, when they were safely on the coast road again, he didn't take her back to where she'd left her car. Instead, he turned up the cliff road, negotiating the precipitous bends with admirable speed.

Olivia looked at him then, and, feeling her eyes on him, he said, 'You're not fit to drive yourself home right now. Your body's had a shock. You need to chill out before you get back behind the wheel of a car.'

'Perhaps so.' Olivia blew out a breath. 'But I am feeling much better now.'

'That's good.' Joel was approving. 'But you don't realise how exhausted you are. What you need is a long, hot shower and a cool glass of wine. That's my recommendation anyway.'

Olivia's lips tightened. 'Yeah, right,' she said drily, wondering what Linda would say if she used all the hot water. 'I'll—think about it.'

'We'll do better than that,' said Joel blandly, and, blinking, Olivia realised something that she should have noticed minutes ago. She was so used to driving to Millford these days that she hadn't questioned the route they were taking. But now comprehension dawned.

'This isn't the way to Bridgeford!' she exclaimed, her tongue adhering to the roof of her mouth. 'Joel, I can't go to your house.'

'Why not?' Joel was complacent. 'You spend a couple of hours there most days. You must be quite familiar with it by this time.'

Olivia shook her head. 'That's different.'

'I know. Sean's there. And he provides a chaperon. But that doesn't mean we need one, does it?'

Doesn't it? For a moment, Olivia thought she'd said the words out loud, but Joel hadn't responded so she knew she'd only been thinking them. But, dear God, going to Joel's house late in the evening, using his shower! Wasn't that just asking for trouble?

Joel parked the car at his gate and without waiting for his assistance Olivia thrust open her door. But her legs felt like jelly when she climbed down from the seat and she couldn't decide whether it was exhaustion or anticipation.

'Here, let me help you,' he said, but Olivia lifted a warning hand to keep him at arm's length.

'I can manage,' she said, with more confidence than she was feeling. But she could just imagine the Reverend Webster's reaction if he saw Joel carrying her into his house.

Joel opened the door and, unwillingly, Olivia stumbled up the path and into the house. It was all familiar, yet strangely unreal. For the first time since that afternoon in his office, they were alone together.

Joel closed the door with his foot and looked at her. Then, when Olivia evaded his gaze, he dropped the tank-top he'd been carrying onto the floor and walked across to the stairs. 'Can you make it?' he asked, indicating the climb, and Olivia took a deep breath.

'If you think that what we're doing is wise,' she said at

last, trudging across the floor. 'What if Louise finds out? Aren't you worried that she might use it against you?'

Joel rested one hand on the newel post at the foot of the staircase. 'The way I heard it, you apparently put her in her place. And why should she care what I do? It's not as if Sean's a witness to my depravity.' He regarded her impatiently. 'Come on, Liv. You're wasting time and I'm getting cold.'

'Oh—sorry.' Olivia made a helpless gesture, indicating that he should go first. Although she'd been upstairs before and had a pretty good idea where Joel's bedroom was, she had no intention of letting him know that. 'Go ahead.'

Despite her determination not to show any weakness, it was an effort going up the stairs. By the time she reached the landing, she was panting again and she had to acknowledge how out of condition she was. But to her relief Joel chose not to call her on it, and, walking across the gallery, he opened the door into one of the spare rooms.

'You can use the bathroom in here,' he said, his voice cool and objective. 'Take as long as you like. You'll find plenty of towels on the rack.'

'Thanks.'

Olivia moved past him into the bedroom, admiring the gold satin counterpane on the colonial-style bed. There were gold and green patterned curtains at the windows and a carved *armoire* where one could store clothes. The carpet underfoot was a cream shag pile, its softness evident even through her shoes.

She turned to say how much she liked his style of decoration, but Joel was gone. He'd closed the door silently and left her, and she beat back a sudden surge of disappointment. This was what she wanted, wasn't it? she asked herself: their relationship to remain on civil terms. She felt tonight had proved that friendship was out of the question. She was much too aware of the pitfalls she faced when she tried to be sociable with him.

The bathroom was delightful. A claw-footed tub flanked a glass-walled shower cubicle, with twin basins matching the low-level lavatory. A rack of towels occupied the wall beside the shower and Olivia didn't hesitate before stripping off her tank-top and shorts and stepping into the cubicle.

Unlike at the farm, it was a power shower, and, feeling the hot spray massaging her shoulders, pummelling her hips, shedding its heat all over her body, she felt her exhaustion easing into a healthy tiredness. It was so good to feel thoroughly warm again, inside as well as out, and, finding a tube of shampoo on a ribbed shelf inside the cubicle, she decided to wash her hair as well.

She left the shower with real regret. It had been so wonderful to wash herself without the ever-present prospect of being disturbed hanging over her head. And, although it was satisfying to feel clean again, she was sorry it was over.

She dried herself rapidly. There was no lock on the bathroom door and, though she doubted that Joel would intrude on her here, she was intensely aware of her nakedness.

That was why, when there was a knock at the bathroom door, there was a rather ungainly scramble to get the towel wrapped securely about her before she spoke.

CHAPTER ELEVEN

'YES?' she called, her voice sounding absurdly weak and thready. What could he possibly want?

'I've left a robe on the bed,' Joel responded equably. 'If you'd like to put it on and bring your running clothes downstairs, I'll put them in the washer with mine.'

'Oh.' Olivia swallowed, thinking hard. But, although she knew that accepting his offer would inevitably delay her departure, the idea of wearing dirty clothes when she felt so deliciously clean swung it for her. 'OK,' she agreed. 'I'll do that. Thanks again.'

'No problem.'

She waited until she heard the outer door close behind him before venturing a peek into the adjoining room. Sure enough, a white towelling bathrobe was lying on the bed, along with a pair of chunky white athletic socks she could wear instead of her trainers.

Giving her hair one last rub with the towel, Olivia combed it with her fingers before sliding her arms into the sleeves of the bathrobe. It was much too big. Joel's, she guessed, though she chose not to dwell on that. Fastening the belt tightly about her waist, she pulled on the socks, also too big, and collected her dirty clothes.

Even if she hadn't known the way to the kitchen, the delicious smell of food would have guided her. Someone, Joel obviously, was preparing his evening meal, and the mingled scents of frying meat and sautéed vegetables drifted up the stairs.

Her feet making no sound in the chunky socks, Olivia padded downstairs and across the hall. Joel was standing at the Aga, stir-frying the food in a rather professional-looking wok. Like her, he'd evidently had a shower, because there were droplets of water sparkling on his dark hair and trickling down into his collar at the back.

Her mouth drying at the sight of him in faded jeans, unbuttoned at the waist, and a short-sleeved shirt that was open down his chest, Olivia knew she had to say something before he caught her watching him. 'I didn't know you could cook,' she said, recalling her own early disasters in that direction. She crossed the tiled floor and peered over his shoulder. 'It certainly smells good.'

Joel started. He'd not been aware of her approach, and his eyes darkened at the picture she made in his robe and socks. Judging by the bundle of clothes in her arms, he was fairly sure she had nothing on under the terry-towelling, and the sudden urge to find out was hardly a surprise in his present mood.

'It's just steak and vegetables,' he said, his voice harsher than it should have been. 'Are you hungry?'

Olivia took a backward step away from him. She was realising that this was hardly keeping her distance, as she'd planned to do when she was upstairs. 'Oh—don't worry about me,' she mumbled awkwardly. 'I—er—I'll just wait until the clothes are dry and then I'll go.' She indicated the bundle in her arms. 'Shall I put these in the washer? It's in the utility room, isn't it?'

'Don't you know?'

Joel growled his answer, but he wasn't feeling particularly charitable right now. Earlier on, going into his spare bedroom, knowing she was naked in the next room, had left him with a hard-on he could do without. But, dammit, his body ached with the need to bury itself in her, the memory of how it used to be between them never totally fading away.

'I suppose I do,' she replied a little stiffly now, moving past him to the outer door. 'I assume you've put yours in already.'

'Yeah.'

Jake gave the stir-fry a vicious shake, unable to prevent his eyes from following her slim form. She'd been right, he thought irritably. This had not been the wisest move he'd ever made.

He heard her close the washer and then the unmistakable sound of running water as she turned the machine on. She came back into the kitchen, carefully averting her eyes as she shut the utility-room door, and his temper erupted. This was crazy, he thought angrily. They were acting as if they were strangers. Intimate strangers, perhaps, but with an atmosphere between them you could cut with a knife.

Taking the pan off the heat, he spun round to face her. 'What is it with you?' he asked savagely. 'I practically save you from pneumonia. I bring you here, to my house, give you free use of my bathroom, offer to wash your clothes and give you half my supper, and what do you do? You say, thanks, but no thanks. I'd rather sit on my own in the other room than share a meal with you!'

'That's not true!' But Olivia's face burned with embarrassment even so. 'I am grateful, truly I am.'

'Well, you have a bloody funny way of showing it.' He raked his nails across his chest where a triangle of dark hair grew between his pectoral muscles and arrowed down to his navel and beyond. 'What did I ever do to make you hate me, Liv?'

Olivia's eyes widened. 'I don't hate you, Joel.'

'What, then?' he demanded, something darker than frustration in his eyes. 'Come on, Liv, tell me what it is you want from me. Because God knows, I'm running out of ideas.'

Olivia shook her head. 'I don't know what you mean.'

'Sure you do.' He was relentless. 'We've tried hostile and neutral. And yes, there have been times when I've stepped over the line. But tonight, I was really trying to be civil. To show you another side to my nature, one you don't seem to believe is there.'

Olivia drew a breath. 'Well, I'm sorry—'

'Yeah, you should be.'

'But you weren't exactly jolly when I came downstairs.'

'You startled me.'

'Did I?' Olivia didn't know where this was going, but she refused to let him walk all over her. 'Or were you in a black mood because you regretted bringing me here? Come on, Joel. Be honest. You made it plain enough before that you didn't want me in your house.'

'*Before*.' Joel latched on to the word. 'That's the pivotal difference. As you've probably been in the house as much as I have the past couple of weeks, it would be freaking crazy to try and bar you from the place now.'

'Ah, but you weren't there when I was, and vice versa,' retorted Olivia at once. 'This isn't the same.'

Joel watched her balefully. She had no idea how he was feeling, he thought, or she wouldn't be standing there, trading put-downs with him. Without make-up of any kind, she was even more desirable than she'd been earlier, her cheeks flushed a becoming shade of pink, her green eyes sparkling with what she thought was a victory.

'You could be right,' he said at last, and although his words were innocent enough, she seemed to sense that he meant something different by it.

'You—you're agreeing with me?' she asked warily and Joel spread his hands.

'That being here alone with you is different from being with Sean? Hey, you'll get no argument from me.'

Olivia gnawed on her lower lip. 'Well—good.'

'No, this is much more interesting,' he said, lowering his arms and shoving his thumbs into his dipping waistband. 'Much more interesting, believe me.'

Olivia swallowed. He saw the jerky movement in her throat, saw the way she gathered a handful of the terry-towelling between her breasts. 'Joel,' she said nervously, her eyes flickering to the opening *V* of his jeans. 'Joel, I thought we understood one another.'

'What's to understand?' He looked at her from beneath lowered lids. 'I think we know one another well enough by now.'

She caught her breath. 'Joel,' she said again, but it was more of a plea now. 'Joel, we can't do this.'

'Can't do what?' He placed one bare foot in front of the other. 'What did I say?'

Olivia backed up a pace. 'You didn't have to say it,' she protested, and once again Joel spread his arms.

'I'm not a mind-reader, Liv,' he said, but this time when he lowered his hands he allowed one finger to hook the belt of the bathrobe. 'Perhaps you'd better lay it out for me.'

Olivia shook her head, aware that she'd have to loosen the belt to escape him. 'I think you know exactly what you're doing.'

'No.' Joel was very definite about that. 'No, you know, I don't. But, damn, I'm beginning not to care.'

'Joel—'

Her voice was plaintive, and Joel's mouth took on a sensual curve. 'Yeah,' he said, using the belt to pull her towards him. 'Yeah, say my name, Liv. Say it like you mean it, 'cos I know you do.'

Olivia tried to hang back, but it was a losing battle and she knew it. When he bent his head and covered her lips with his, she couldn't prevent herself from sinking into him. Joel's lips—Joel's tongue—her world suddenly seemed bounded by the sensual invasion of his kiss, and when he parted the robe and found her breasts her nipples thrust eagerly against his palms.

'Oh, baby,' he groaned, pushing his hips towards her, and, feeling the rough fabric of his jeans against her bare legs, she realised the bathrobe was now completely open. 'I knew you were naked,' he added hoarsely, looking down at her. His teeth nuzzled her ear. 'Do you wonder why I can't fasten my jeans?'

'It's not something I've thought about,' protested Olivia,

not altogether truthfully, and Joel regarded her with smouldering eyes.

'No?'

Olivia quivered. 'Why don't you tell me?' she found herself saying, her voice as unsteady as his. His words had been unbearably sexy and she wanted to prolong the moment. 'Do I—do I turn you on?'

'Why don't you find out for yourself?' he breathed, taking one of her hands and letting her feel the hard ridge that was threatening his zip. 'Do you have any idea how long it is since I was in danger of losing it completely?'

Olivia's tongue circled her lips almost consideringly. Then, averting her eyes, she deliberately loosened his zip so she could slip her hand inside his jeans. He wasn't wearing underwear and when her fingers closed around his thick shaft he bucked violently against her.

'Hell, baby, take it easy,' he groaned, drawing back from her and restoring himself to some semblance of dignity. 'D'you want me to come in your hands?'

'I wouldn't mind.' Olivia realised this had gone too far now for her to pretend. Lifting her hands, she cupped his face, not even thinking about her nakedness. 'But I'd rather you were inside me.' She nudged him provocatively. 'What about you?'

'God!' Joel stared down at her. 'Need you ask?'

'Good.' Without a shred of shame, Olivia tipped the robe off her shoulders, letting it fall in a soft heap about their feet. 'Is this better?'

Joel moved his head a little dazedly. But then the realisation that they were standing in a room that was lit by fluorescent tubes that ran beneath the wall units caused him to utter a muffled curse.

'Not here.' He gripped her waist and lifted her so that she was able to wind her legs about his hips. His voice thickened. 'Let's go upstairs.'

He crossed the hall and climbed the stairs without any visible effort on his part. On the landing, he made straight for his own bedroom. He could have taken her into either of the two spare rooms, but he didn't. He wanted her in his arms in his bed, and, as if she knew how he was feeling, Olivia spread herself invitingly as soon as he laid her on the slub silk coverlet.

'Why don't you lose the socks?' he suggested as he sloughed his shirt and kicked off his jeans and she turned onto her side and lifted first one leg and then the other, making the removal of the socks a deliberate provocation. Her breasts rested full and luscious against the coverlet, the curve of her hips as sleek and smooth as the rest of her.

'You weren't kidding,' she mocked him softly, admiring his erection. 'I do turn you on, don't I?'

'Baby, I've had a hard-on since I saw you doing those sexy moves on the beach,' he told her huskily. He knelt on the bed, rolling her onto her back so he could move over her. Supporting himself on his hands so he didn't crush her, he bent and bit one swollen nipple. 'Did you think I hadn't seen you? Or was it all for my benefit?'

Olivia's lips parted, half in protest, half in delicious pain. 'I was stretching, Joel.'

'And the rest.' Joel transferred his attentions to her other breast and sucked hungrily. 'You knew exactly what you were doing.'

'Yes. I was warming up,' she insisted, catching her

breath at the sudden heat between her legs. 'I didn't even see you at first.'

'Well, I saw you,' said Joel, moving lower to circle her navel with his tongue. 'I couldn't take my eyes off you.'

Olivia quivered, her nails digging into the coverlet at either side of her. 'I'd never have guessed.'

'Liar!'

'No, I mean it.' She took an uneven breath. 'Does that mean you liked what you saw?'

Joel's eyes flicked briefly to her face. 'What do you think?'

Olivia tried to reach for him then, but he evaded her hands, moving lower to part the soft brown curls at the apex of her legs. He watched her as he touched her there, his fingers discovering how wet she was before he bent and replaced them with his lips.

'Joel—'

She shifted feverishly, but Joel wouldn't let her get away. 'You taste incredible,' he said thickly. 'Shall I make you come? You want to. I can tell.'

'I want you,' whispered Olivia helplessly, and he lifted his head and met her tormented gaze.

'I think you do,' he said, his tongue making one last intimate invasion before he moved over her again. 'I want you, too, baby.' He lowered his body onto hers. 'Hmm, that feels so good.'

Olivia clutched his shoulders, winding her fingers into his hair, shifting restlessly beneath him. She parted her legs, trying to show him she was ready, but his sex continued to throb silkily against her thigh.

Joel understood how she was feeling. His body was aching with needs only she could satisfy. His mouth found hers, his breathing hoarse and unsteady. If things were moving too fast, he couldn't control them any longer, and, lifting her legs until her feet were flat against the cover, he pushed his hard length into her slick sheath.

He heard the moan she gave as he entered her, but it wasn't a moan of protest. Her legs were already lifting, winding around him, urging him so deeply inside her that he was sure he touched the vulnerability of her womb.

Then his own needs took over. As he moved, she tightened around him, showing him more clearly than in words how close to the edge she was. Her breasts were crushed against his chest as she arched her body against him, the sensual dance of their mating growing more and more intense.

Olivia's senses were spinning out of control, yet some coherent part of her brain knew that this was Joel she was with, Joel who was inside her; Joel, whose thrusting hips were causing her to experience the kind of wild abandon she hadn't known since the last time they were together.

Sweat was slicking their bodies, and Joel's mouth ravaged hers, his tongue plunging over and over in imitation of his lovemaking. And she clung to him as if she'd never let him go again, as if he was the only safe place in this furious storm of emotion.

When she felt her excitement was in danger of exploding, she tried to control it. She didn't want this to end, didn't want to lose the spiralling delight that Joel was giving her. But it was too hard to hold it back, too tantalising to be restrained by her trembling efforts. Like a fountain, it rose inside her, enveloping her in its heat and sensuality. And, when the peak was reached, she fell through mindless caverns into heavenly space...

Joel felt the racking tremors as they swept over her, knew the moment she climaxed and he was drenched in the heat of her release. It was all he needed to tip him over the edge and his body convulsed almost simultaneously. He spilled his seed helplessly, his limbs shaking long after he was spent. And knew if this was a mistake, it was a doozy. There was no way he could explain this to himself.

CHAPTER TWELVE

HE MUST have fallen asleep because Joel opened his eyes to find soft fingers stroking back his hair from his forehead, trailing down his roughening cheek to his chin. The same fingers continued on over his throat and the muscled contours of his upper chest to where his flat nipples received similar attention.

He didn't know if Olivia knew he was awake or not, but what she was doing was so pleasurable that he didn't want her to stop. He could feel himself hardening from the state of semi-arousal he'd awakened in, and wondered if she knew his jutting sex meant he was fully aware of her ministrations.

Whatever, she didn't look at him, concentrating instead on caressing the hair that grew low on his stomach. Fine and dark, it couldn't compare to the curly thatch that surrounded his erection, and he sucked in a breath when she bent her head and took his length into her mouth.

His blood pressure erupted. He'd thought he was totally spent but one touch of those tempting lips, of that sensuous tongue, and he was as hard as a ramrod. He clenched his fists when he felt her soft breasts swing against his thighs, and stifled a groan when she parted his legs so she could cup him in her hand.

'Oh, Liv,' he muttered then, the sucking motion of her mouth creating an explosive heat he wasn't sure he could contain. The temptation was to let her have her way with him, to pump whatever strength was left inside him into the liquid fire of her mouth.

He was shuddering with the effort of resisting this when she lifted her head and gave him a teasing look. 'Did I do something wrong?' she asked, continuing to caress him. And, when he would have grabbed her shoulders and rolled her over onto her back, she swiftly straddled him.

'My turn,' she said, deliberately lowering herself so that her wet heat burned his thighs. 'Is this what you want?'

'You know what I want,' muttered Joel hoarsely, his hands gripping her knees almost painfully. 'Liv—for pity's sake! Put me out of my misery.'

Olivia smiled then, and Joel was struck by how beautiful she was, more beautiful now than he had ever seen her. 'Oh, all right,' she said with assumed resignation. 'If I must.'

'You—must,' said Joel grimly, and with a toss of her head she lifted herself until the very tip of his shaft was brushing her core.

'Like this?' she asked, unable to deny the breath of satisfaction that issued from her as she impaled herself upon him. 'Yes?'

'Yes,' said Joel, thrusting his head back into the pillow. 'Yes, yes, yes.'

She rode him with a sensual expertise that had him reaching for her breasts, dragging her head down and savaging her mouth with his. And although once again

Olivia would have liked to prolong their pleasure, her body was too finely attuned to his. When he began to buck beneath her, the white-hot heat of her own desires swiftly swept her away.

However, when she sank onto his chest, Joel rolled her over onto her back, and she experienced another orgasm before he allowed himself to share her climax. Totally exhausted, she found she couldn't keep her eyes open, and the last thing she remembered was Joel's heavy weight slumping beside her.

She awakened feeling amazingly refreshed. She didn't know how long she'd been unconscious, but, although it was completely dark beyond the uncurtained windows, she felt as if she'd slept for hours.

She stirred and immediately the lamp was lit next to the bed. And now she saw that Joel was sitting beside her, a glass of white wine in his hand.

'Hey,' he said, leaning over to kiss her, and the hair on his chest tickled her bare breasts. It made her instantly conscious of her nakedness, though someone, Joel apparently, had removed the coverlet and covered her to the waist with a linen sheet.

'Hey,' she answered, responding to his kiss, but then almost immediately drawing away. 'What time is it?'

'About one.'

Joel spoke carelessly, but Olivia was horrified. 'One o'clock?' she echoed. 'In the morning?'

'Well, it looks like the middle of the night,' agreed Joel mildly. 'Here.' He reached for a second glass from the bedside cabinet. 'Have some Chardonnay.'

Olivia ignored the glass. 'I must have slept for hours.'

'A couple of hours,' he conceded, returning the second glass to the cabinet. 'Chill, baby. Linda knows where you are.'

Olivia's jaw dropped. 'She does?'

'Yeah.' Joel took a sip of his wine before continuing. 'I phoned her and explained you'd fallen asleep.' His mouth tilted. 'Of course, I didn't tell her where you'd fallen asleep exactly. I let her think we'd been having a drink after our run and you'd flaked out.'

'Well, thank you.' But Olivia didn't sound grateful. 'My God, Joel, what's my father going to think?'

Joel regarded her steadily. 'If I know Ben, he'll have guessed precisely what we've been doing. He may have had a stroke, Liv, but he's not a fool.'

'I know that.' Olivia levered herself up against the pillows, and then, seeing where his eyes were riveted, she hauled the sheet up to her chin. 'I've got to get back. I can't stay here. No one's going to believe I slept on your sofa all night.'

Joel's eyes darkened. 'Does it matter what anyone thinks?'

'Of course it matters.' Olivia looked anxiously about her. 'You may not care what anyone in Bridgeford thinks of you, but I've got to live there.'

Joel sighed and put his glass aside. 'Stop stressing,' he said, one hand sliding sensuously up her arm to her shoulder. 'Can't we talk about this in the morning?' He nuzzled her shoulder with his lips. 'There's so much I want to say to you.'

Olivia shook her head. 'You don't understand—'

'No, *you* don't understand,' said Joel huskily. 'Do you think you can share what we just shared and walk away?'

His hand curved along her cheek, turning her face towards him. 'I want you, Liv. Not just for one night, but for the rest of my life!'

Olivia sagged back against the pillow. 'You don't mean that.'

'I do.' His lips brushed the corner of her mouth as his hand slid familiarly beneath the sheet she was clutching to her with desperate hands. 'Oh, baby,' he breathed, cupping her breast. 'You must know I never stopped loving you.'

'Joel—'

'No, listen to me,' he persisted urgently. 'Louise knew I didn't love her. Not in the way I'd loved you, anyway. But by the time I'd discovered my mistake, she was expecting my baby. And however much I might regret my second marriage, I'll never regret having my son.'

Olivia moistened her lips. 'I can understand that.'

'Can you?' Joel's hand had found its way between her thighs and she gave a helpless little moan. 'Oh, God, Liv, you don't know how much I wished he was ours. When I first held him in my arms, I wanted him to be our son.'

'Oh, Joel…' Olivia could feel tears burning at the backs of her eyes. It had been such an emotional few hours and hearing him say how he'd felt when Sean was born really tore her apart. 'Thank you for saying that.'

'Don't thank me,' he muttered hoarsely, his mouth seeking hers. 'It's the truth.' He bit her lower lip. 'And maybe you were right to do what you did all those years ago. We were too young—'

'Wait!' Olivia's hand against his chest obviously surprised him, but it gave her the chance to scramble off the bed. Snatching up the silk coverlet, she wrapped it protectively about her. 'What are you saying, Joel? That after everything—everything that's happened, you still think I aborted our child?'

'Liv—'

But his persuasive tone cut no ice with her. 'Answer me, damn you,' she demanded. 'Do you still believe I murdered our baby?'

Joel slumped back against the pillows, resting one wrist across his forehead. 'Don't be melodramatic, Liv,' he said wearily. 'I didn't bring it up to hurt you. I wanted you to know that I've forgiven you—'

'Big of you!'

'—and that as far as I'm concerned that part of our lives is over and forgotten.'

'I haven't forgotten,' said Olivia bitterly. 'How could I forget something that almost destroyed me? *You* almost destroyed me, Joel. You left me, just when I needed you most.'

Joel's hand fell away and he regarded her through heavy-lidded eyes. 'And how do you think I felt when I discovered you'd run away to London rather than face me?'

'I had faced you, Joel.' Olivia was indignant. 'I didn't leave you, Joel. It was you who walked out.'

Joel pushed himself into a sitting position. 'And didn't it occur to you that I might need a little time to get over it?'

'So you went running home to Mummy and Daddy and I bet they didn't advise you to—how would they put it?— give me a second chance.'

'They were as shocked as I was,' retorted Joel, his temper rising. 'They'd thought they were going to be grandparents. How do you think they felt?'

'Well, they never liked me.'

'They thought we were too young to get married, that's all.'

'Then they should have been pleased that we'd split up.'

'Liv—' Once again, Joel tried to appeal to her. Swinging his legs out of bed, he got to his feet. 'We were too young. I accept that now. Can't you just meet me halfway?'

'No!' Olivia stared at him through suddenly tear-wet eyes. 'Joel, I've told you this before, but I'll tell you again. When I found out I was pregnant, I was frightened. Not of having the baby, but of what it might mean to us. You were twenty years old. OK, you were working at the farm, but I knew that wouldn't satisfy you forever. I needed to get a job, a decent job, if only to support you. How was I going to be able to do that with a baby we couldn't possibly afford?'

'Liv—' he tried again, but she wasn't finished.

'I didn't want to lose you,' she said painfully. 'I'd seen how Linda and Martin had had to struggle when they got married. It nearly drove them apart. It wasn't until Martin got that job at the garden centre that they could afford a home of their own.'

'They managed,' said Joel flatly.

'Well, I didn't want that for us. I didn't want us having to live at the farm for years and years. I wanted us to be independent, too. To have a home of our own.'

'So you decided to abort our baby.'

'No!' Olivia was desperate now. 'All right, I did make an appointment at the clinic in Chevingham. I've never denied that. But when I got there I cancelled the appointment. When it came to the point, I couldn't destroy something we'd made together. In love.'

Joel reached for his jeans and started pulling them on.

'I'll take you home,' he said flatly. 'Your clothes should be dry by now. I put them in the dryer when I got the wine.'

Olivia's shoulders sagged. 'You won't listen to reason, will you?'

'Oh, please.' Joel regarded her with scorn in his eyes. 'Your story is that you changed your mind and left the clinic without having the abortion—'

'Yes.'

'And that you had a miscarriage when you got home?'

'You know it is.'

'Bull,' said Joel succinctly. 'You didn't cancel the appointment; you went through with it. And then, when you got home, you cooked up this story about having a miscarriage while there was nobody in the house but you.'

'No!'

'Yes, Olivia. How do you think I found out about the abortion in the first place?' His face contorted. 'You must have thought you were so safe: patient's confidentiality and all that rubbish. You never thought that someone else might care enough to tell me I was being taken for a fool. I've never felt so shattered as I did that day, believe me.'

'But who—?'

'D'you think I'm going to tell you?' Joel shook his head. 'I'll get your clothes,' he said, making for the door. 'And by the way, Sean's going home tomorrow—or rather today. I was going to phone you and thank you for what you've done for him. But it looks like we're all out of explanations, doesn't it?'

CHAPTER THIRTEEN

THANKFULLY, Olivia had a key and when Joel dropped her off she could let herself into the house without waking anyone. But, as she started across the hall to the stairs, she thought she heard someone calling her name. It could only be her father, she thought, making a detour to his room. Pushing the door ajar, she put her head round it, and found Ben Foley propped up on his pillows, as wide awake as if it were the middle of the day.

'Dad!' she exclaimed, pausing a moment to check there was no suspicion of wetness on her cheeks. She sniffed, and moved further into the room. 'What are you doing? You're supposed to be asleep.'

'I sleep a good part of the day,' retorted the old man drily. 'What about you? I thought you were spending the night at Joel's.'

'Linda told you that, I suppose,' Olivia said tightly. 'No. I fell asleep, that's all. When I woke up, he brought me home.'

'So why did he have to bring you home? Where's your car?'

'I left it at the beach.' Olivia made a careless gesture. 'I'd overdone it—running, I mean—and Joel drove me back.'

'To his house.'

'Yes, to his house.'

'Is that why you're looking so tearful now?'

Olivia gasped, rubbing furiously at her eyes. 'I'm not looking tearful.'

'You've been crying,' declared her father steadily. 'You needn't bother to deny it. When a woman's eyes and nose are red, it's a dead giveaway.'

Olivia sniffed again. 'Well, all right. I've been crying. It's not a sin, is it?'

'No.' Ben Foley shook his head. 'But I'd like to know what young Armstrong's done to upset you.'

'Young Armstrong!' Olivia tried to force a laugh. 'Dad, Joel's thirty-five, not nineteen.'

'I'm aware of that.' Her father frowned. 'What's happened? Did you sleep with him?'

'Dad!'

'Don't look at me like that, Livvy. I may be old and crippled, but I'm not numb from the neck down.' He sighed. 'If that man's hurt you, I want to hear about it. He may be thirty-five, but he's not too old to feel the sharp edge of my tongue!'

'Oh, Dad!'

'Well, did you?'

To her dismay, Olivia could feel the tears running down her cheeks again and she fumbled for one of the tissues from the box on the table beside her father's bed. 'I don't want to talk about it, Dad,' she said, scrubbing her eyes again. 'It's late. I ought to get to bed myself.'

'So you did sleep with him,' remarked the old man resignedly. 'I knew you would. Sooner or later. But obviously it didn't work out.'

'Dad!'

'Stop saying "Dad" as if I was a juvenile. You forget, Livvy. I was both mother and father to you for years after Elizabeth died. All right, it's been some time since we spent any time together, but I haven't forgotten one small thing about you. You'll always be my baby, Livvy. The little girl I had such high hopes for.'

Olivia gripped his hand lying on the duvet beside her. 'Linda told me you had to scrape and save to keep me at school until I was eighteen,' she said. 'Is that true?'

'Linda had no right telling you any such thing. I was happy to do what I could. And I'm proud of the way you've turned out, although you may not believe me. You're a good woman, Livvy. Caring and generous and too honest for your own good.'

'What do you mean?' Olivia frowned.

'I mean, all those years ago, telling Joel you'd arranged to have an abortion. If you hadn't told him that, no one would have been any the wiser. Miscarriages happen all the time. Your mother lost a baby just after we got married. Then we had Linda, without any bother at all.'

Olivia stared at him. 'I didn't know that.'

'Why should you? It's not something most people brag about. Your mother was very upset, but we got over it. Things happen!'

Olivia felt a smile tugging at her lips. 'Thanks, Dad,' she said. 'You've made me feel so much better.' She sniffed again. 'Is there anything I can do for you before I go?'

'Yes.' Ben Foley's brows drew together. 'You can tell

Linda I've decided to ask the bank for a loan.' He paused. 'Talking to you, being with you, has made me see there's more to life than lying here, waiting for the devil to come and get me. Martin's right. I'm never going to be able to run this place again. Why should I stand in their way? I've got better things to do.'

Olivia caught her breath. 'Like what?'

'Like getting out of this bed, for one thing,' declared her father grimly. 'I'm going to get myself one of those electric wheelchairs, so I can get about by myself. Having that beer the other day reminded me of how long it's been since I had a drink in The Bay Horse. Who knows, maybe some of my old pals won't have forgotten me?'

The following week dragged. Olivia felt emotionally drained, robbed of any sense of optimism about the future. And, although the atmosphere in the house was infinitely more cheerful, now that her father had agreed to approach the bank for a loan, Olivia couldn't see herself staying there any longer than it took to find a place of her own.

It was a situation that had been reinforced by the conversation she'd accidentally overheard Linda and Martin having one evening after they'd thought she'd gone to bed. But she'd been thirsty, and when she'd gone downstairs for a drink she'd heard Martin mention her name.

She hadn't intended to listen. She knew eavesdroppers seldom heard good of themselves. But what she had heard had confirmed her earlier suspicions about her brother-in-law's apparent change of heart where she was concerned.

Martin hadn't changed his mind about her. He hadn't wanted her to stay on at the farm because she was family.

It appeared he'd invited her to stay because he'd been hoping to persuade her to use what little money she had to finance the redevelopment of the cottages, after all. He'd reasoned that without the expense of an apartment, she'd have had no excuse for needing extra funds.

What hurt Olivia the most was that Linda had gone along with it. Obviously her father hadn't known anything abut Martin's manipulations, but Linda had been party to his plans all along. If it hadn't been for her father, Olivia was sure she'd have packed up and gone back to London, the sense of betrayal Joel had awakened only strengthened by her sister's deception.

That was why, a few days later, she found herself in Newcastle again, checking out the estate agents. It served the dual purpose of pricing possible apartments and asking about job vacancies.

She didn't have her CV with her, of course, and it was a very unorthodox way of introducing herself to possible employers. But her experiences in London had taught her that having confidence in her abilities was worth a handful of good references.

Even so, the day was a bit of a disappointment as far as finding herself an apartment was concerned. Those she did view were usually too small or too expensive. The one she did like on the riverside was already spoken for, and she'd had to content herself with leaving her name and phone number just in case the present buyer pulled out of the deal.

Still, she did have a couple of interviews lined up for the following week. She'd have to take a trip to London before that to arrange to have the rest of her belongings couriered north. She'd also check out of the small hotel where she'd stayed when she'd first returned to England. The manager there had offered to keep a room free for her until her return.

On impulse, when she left Newcastle she drove back to Bridgeford via Millford. She assured herself she wanted to see the village again, but the truth was she wanted to drive past Joel's house one more time. She didn't expect to see him. It was the middle of the afternoon and he'd probably be lecturing. In any case, there was no point in pursuing their relationship. Whatever excuses he came up with, she'd never forgive him for not believing her.

She slowed as she reached the green. If Joel's car was at his gate, she was prepared to do a U-turn. But it wasn't. As anticipated, the house looked deserted. Well, what had she expected? But it proved how much she was deceiving herself.

She was driving round the green when she saw Sean. He wasn't on his own. He was walking beside a tall, lanky individual who, despite the fact that he wasn't wearing his cassock, was unmistakably the vicar of All Saints Church.

Olivia hesitated, slowing behind them, not sure what she intended to do until she'd pulled alongside. Then, rolling down her window, she said, 'Hi there,' including them both in her deceptively casual greeting.

'Olivia!' Sean recognised her at once, leaving his relative's side to put both hands on the rim of the open window. He gave her a wistful look. 'I've missed you, Olivia. Have you missed me?'

Olivia wasn't sure how to answer that one. Of course she'd missed the boy, but saying so wasn't going to help anyone. However, Brian Webster saved her the dilemma.

'Oh, it's you, Livvy,' he said without enthusiasm. 'What are you doing in Millford? Joel's not here.'

Olivia could have said that she hadn't come to see Joel, but she didn't. Instead, she turned her attention to the boy. 'Does your mother know you're here, Sean?' she asked, with a swift glance at Brian. 'I thought it was only weekends that you spent with your dad.'

'You're right. He shouldn't be here,' agreed Brian, without giving the boy time to reply. 'He evidently expected to find Joel at home, but he was disappointed. Fortunately, I'd seen him getting off the bus, so I intercepted him before he found somewhere to hide.' He sighed. 'I mean, he could have been hanging about for hours.'

'That's true,' said Olivia, giving Sean a disapproving look. She was remembering what had happened the last time he'd run away and she knew Joel wouldn't be pleased at his reckless disregard of his mother's feelings.

'Well, it is Thursday,' Sean protested. 'And I am supposed to be spending the weekend with Dad. What does it matter if I come a day early?'

Olivia and Brian exchanged glances, and then she said, 'You know the answer to that as well as I do. You're supposed to wait until Friday so your dad can collect you.'

'And let's not forget your mother!' exclaimed Brian. 'She must be out of her mind with worry by now. I'm going to go straight into the vicarage and ring her to let her know where you are. Then I suppose I'll have to drive you home.'

'I don't want to go home,' muttered Sean stubbornly, but Olivia steeled her heart against him.

'I can take him back,' she said instead, immediately regretting the impulse to get involved again.

'Oh, could you?' Brian's face cleared for the first time since she'd met them. 'That is kind of you, Livvy. I've got a wedding rehearsal at five o'clock and I was thinking I'd have to put them off.'

'But I don't want to go home,' said Sean again; however, Brian had no sympathy.

'You don't have a choice,' he said briskly. 'Come along. Get into the car.'

Sean looked sulky. 'I don't have to. Mum says I should never get into a car with a stranger. I can get the bus back. I'm old enough.'

'Get in,' said Olivia warningly, leaning across the passenger seat and pushing the door open. 'Now.'

Heaving a sigh, Sean obeyed her, flopping into the seat beside her with evident ill grace. Brian slammed the door, raising his hand to both of them, and then Olivia put the car in gear and drove away.

'Dad isn't going to like this,' said Sean eventually, apparently deciding to take a different approach. 'He said we wouldn't be seeing you again. Ever. I think he's angry with you. Have you done something to upset him? He wasn't in a good mood all last weekend.'

Olivia gave a brief shrug of her shoulders. 'I'm sure in this instance he'll be glad you're not spending another night in the barn, don't you?'

'I wasn't going to spend the night in the barn.' Sean was indignant. 'I was just going to go and play football on the lawn until Dad got home.'

'And what about your mother?'

Sean sniffed. 'Dad would have rung her when he got back.'

'But what if he had an evening lecture? It could have

been eight or nine before he came home. Your mother would have been frantic by then.'

'No, she wouldn't.'

'Yes, she would.'

'She wasn't before.'

'That was different. She thought you were at your Dad's.'

'But I wasn't.'

'No. But she didn't know that. And as that's where you'd gone before...' Olivia sighed. 'You know I'm right, Sean. You can't keep running away like this.'

Sean hunched his shoulders. 'I wish I could live with Dad.'

'Yes, I think we all know that. But you can't.'

'Why can't I?'

'Because your father isn't married. He doesn't have a wife to look after you when he's not there.' She took a breath. 'If he was married, it would be different. But he's not.'

Sean looked thoughtful. 'You like my dad, don't you?'

Olivia knew where this was going. 'Yes. But I don't want to marry him.'

And how true was that?

'Why not?'

She hesitated, and then, deciding it was now or never, she said, 'Because I was married to him years ago. Before I went to America.' She gave him a rueful smile. 'It didn't work out.'

Sean gazed at her in amazement. 'You were married to Dad,' he said incredulously. 'He didn't tell me that.'

'No, and probably I shouldn't either,' murmured Olivia uneasily. 'But—well, it's not a secret.'

Sean was thinking hard. 'So you must have liked him once,' he said at last, and Olivia stifled a groan.

'It was all a long time ago,' she said quellingly. 'I'd rather talk about why you keep running away from home.' She paused. 'What's wrong? Jo—your dad said you seemed happy enough in the beginning.'

Sean shifted in his seat. 'It was all right, before—'

He broke off and Olivia glanced quickly at him. They'd been here before, too. 'Before—what?' she prompted. 'Go on.'

Sean cast her a look out of the corners of his eyes and then he seemed to slump lower in his seat. 'Before—before the hulk told me they were going to have a baby,' he muttered in a low voice, and suddenly everything he had done made a peculiar kind of sense.

Olivia sought for an answer. 'Well—that's wonderful,' she said at length. 'You're going to have a brother or sister. You should be pleased.'

'So why hasn't Mum told me?' demanded Sean, startling her by his vehemence. 'She hasn't even mentioned it and I don't know if Stewart's lying or not.'

Olivia was beginning to understand a little more. 'Oh, I think it's true,' she ventured gently, remembering Louise's sickness and how pale she'd looked that morning Olivia had called at the house. 'Perhaps she doesn't know how to tell you. Perhaps she's afraid you'll be angry. And what with you running away and all, she probably thinks it's the last thing you want to hear.'

'But—' Sean stared at her. 'But that's why I've been running away. Well, partly, anyway. I'd still rather live with my dad, but that's not going to happen, is it?'

'Not yet,' said Olivia, forcing a smile, wondering how she'd feel if Joel found someone else. Hearing about his marriage to Louise had been painful enough, but at least she hadn't been around to witness it.

Sean frowned. 'So—do you think if I told her I knew she'd be pleased?' he asked consideringly.

'I'm sure of it.' Olivia spoke firmly, wishing her own problems could be solved so easily. 'I think you've got to be grown-up about this, Sean. You're not a baby, are you?'

'No.'

'So, show your mum that you love her; that you'll go on loving her even if she has half a dozen babies!'

The following morning, Olivia was in her father's room, helping him into his wheelchair preparatory to wheeling him to the car, when Linda appeared in the doorway.

'You've got a visitor,' she said without preamble. 'Can you come?'

'A visitor?'

For a heart-stopping moment Olivia wondered if it was Joel, come to thank her for taking Sean home, but Linda soon disillusioned her. 'It's Louise Web—I mean, Barlow,' she said irritably. 'Do you know what she wants?'

Olivia could guess, but she only shook her head. She'd dropped Sean at the end of the road, allowing him to explain where he'd been to his mother if he wanted to. She'd thought it would be easier if he wasn't forced to say what he'd been doing, but if Louise was here it looked as though he'd told her the truth.

'I won't be a minute, Dad,' she said, settling the old man in his chair with an apologetic grimace. 'You can come through, if you like.'

'No, you go and talk to her, Livvy. I'll have another look

at the crossword. And don't worry about me,' he warned her. 'If there's one thing being confined to a bed teaches you, it's patience.'

Linda had put Louise in the living room, and, although she hovered in the doorway for a moment as if she'd have liked to know what the woman wanted, eventually common courtesy forced her to withdraw.

Olivia looked at Louise a little warily when they were alone. 'Linda said you wanted to see me,' she said, gesturing towards the sofa. 'Why don't you sit down?'

As she did so, Olivia noticed that Louise looked much better this morning. There was colour in her cheeks so whatever this was about, it couldn't be all bad.

'I hope you don't mind me coming here,' she said, apparently understanding the situation with Linda. She waited until Olivia had seated herself on the armchair opposite, before she continued, 'First of all, I want to thank you for bringing Sean home yesterday afternoon.'

'That's OK.' Olivia was relieved. 'I'm glad he told you.'

'He had to anyway.' Louise pulled a wry face. 'Brian called me just after you left Millford.'

'Ah.'

'But that wasn't all he told me,' Louise went on, smoothing a hand over the knee of her trousers. 'He told me he knew about the baby; that Stewart had told him without mentioning it to me.'

Olivia nodded. 'I see.'

'It was because he'd talked it over with you, wasn't it? Why is it that he always seems to find it easier to talk to someone else and not to me?' She sighed. 'Still, I suppose I have been pretty wrapped up in myself since I started this morning sickness. I didn't have any with Sean, you see, so I've taken badly to it.'

Olivia didn't know what to say. She and Louise were hardly likely to be friends. 'And was he pleased?' she asked, choosing the least controversial option. She didn't even want to think about how it was when Louise was expecting Sean. That was much too much information.

'I think he is pleased, yes,' Louise said now. 'He thought I didn't want him to know.'

'Well, I'm glad it's turned out so well,' said Olivia, wincing at her choice of vocabulary. 'He's a really nice boy. And a credit to you.'

'Yes, he is. A nice boy, I mean.' Louise blew out a breath. 'Does Joel know? About the baby?'

'Not from me,' said Olivia flatly.

'You don't think Sean might have confided in his father?'

'I think he was worried about you,' said Olivia carefully. 'Staying with his father allowed him to put it out of his head.'

'Well, I appreciate what you did.' Louise bent her head. 'Particularly after the way I behaved.'

'Like you said, you had other things on your mind,' said Olivia, wishing this conversation was over. She made to get to her feet. 'But now, if you don't mind—'

'Wait!' Louise put out a hand, making Olivia stay in her seat. 'I haven't finished.' She wet her lips. 'When I said after what I'd done, I wasn't talking about Sean, Livvy. I was talking about Joel.'

'Joel?'

Olivia was totally confused. What on earth was Louise saying? Unless… The bile rose in the back of her throat.

Unless Louise was about to tell her that the child she was expecting was Joel's.

'I'm not explaining myself very well,' Louise went on uncomfortably. 'But this isn't easy, Livvy.'

Olivia frowned. 'What isn't easy?'

'It was me,' said Louise quickly. 'I was the one who told Joel you'd had the abortion. Maureen—my cousin Maureen, that is—used to work at the clinic in Chevingham. She knew how I felt about Joel, how jealous I'd always been of you. She couldn't wait to tell me that you'd made an appointment and then changed your mind at the last minute.'

Olivia's throat felt dry. 'But you knew I hadn't gone through with it.'

'Yes, but when I heard about your miscarriage, I told Joel that you had.' She hurried on, trying to excuse herself. 'I hated myself afterwards, Livvy. When you two split up and everything. But it was too late then.'

Olivia blinked. 'You destroyed my life because you were jealous!'

'I was totally, totally ashamed of what I'd done.'

'But that didn't stop you from marrying Joel when he came back to Bridgeford, did it?' exclaimed Olivia bitterly. 'My God, Louise, I don't know how you could do such a thing.'

Louise sniffed. 'I know, I know. I was a bitch. And I've paid for it. But—well, I didn't have to tell you,' she added defensively. 'And like I said before, Joel still loved you. So lying to him didn't do me a bit of good.'

CHAPTER FOURTEEN

JOEL emptied his glass and reached for the bottle sitting on the low table in front of him. He upended it into the glass and then scowled when only a few drops of the amber liquid emerged to cover the base of the crystal tumbler. The whisky was all gone. He'd swallowed almost half a bottle of the stuff. Even so, he thought irritably, he should have called at the pub on his way home and bought another. But at that point, he'd still been kidding himself that this wasn't going to be another lousy night.

He flung himself back against the cushions of the sofa, staring unseeingly into the empty grate. It wasn't cold enough to need a fire, but right now he could have done with one. He felt chilled, through and through.

He'd been feeling this way for days, ever since he'd had that phone call from Louise. He'd suspected something was wrong when he'd gone to pick up Sean on Friday afternoon, but he'd assumed she and Stewart had had a row. And then Sean had told him that his mother was expecting a baby, which had seemed to explain her agitation. He knew from the first time she was pregnant that Louise didn't take kindly to losing her figure.

But the call that had come on Sunday evening had been totally out of the blue. After all, it had only been a couple of hours since he'd dropped Sean off, and his first concern had been that there was something wrong with his son. But it had soon become apparent that the reason for Louise phoning him had nothing to do with Sean. What Louise had to say, she hadn't had the nerve to reveal to his face.

To say Joel was devastated by her confession would have been an understatement. He'd wanted to get in his car and drive to Bridgeford and confront Louise personally with her lies. Only the knowledge that Sean would be there, that he might be frightened and not understand his father's anger, had kept Joel from making a scene that night.

However, he had gone to see Louise the following morning. He'd cancelled a lecture and driven straight to his ex-wife's house. He'd been so angry, but she'd been tearful—even though he knew she could turn them on to order—and pregnant, and although he could blame her, the person who was really to blame was himself.

He'd been so stupid. Accepting Louise Webster's story instead of believing his wife. No wonder she'd run away to London. She'd had to suffer the after-effects of the miscarriage without anyone to support her. They'd all believed she was lying. Even her father.

And now, he'd only compounded the offence by showing he still believed she'd had an abortion. That evening they'd spent together had been so perfect until he'd opened his big mouth. He'd thought that by telling her he'd forgiven her, she would be grateful. Instead of which, he'd destroyed their relationship all over again.

He had gone to the farm after seeing Louise, hoping

against hope that Olivia would agree to talk to him. But she hadn't been there. Linda had said her sister had gone to London and she didn't know when—or even if—she'd be back. She had been looking for an apartment in Newcastle, she'd added, but Olivia hadn't found anything she liked.

Which had been the final straw. Joel hadn't slept the night Louise phoned him and he hadn't had a good night's sleep since then. His smug little world had been shattered and he was afraid it was going to take more than a university degree to put it right this time.

When the phone rang, he practically leapt from the sofa to answer it. It might be Olivia, he thought. She could be back from London and Linda would have told her he'd called at the farm.

But it wasn't Olivia. It was his mother, calling from the airport in Newcastle. 'Can you come and pick us up, darling?' she asked. 'The plane was delayed or I'd have rung you earlier. But we wanted it to be a surprise.'

Joel stifled a groan. 'I can't, Mum.'

'You can't?' Diana Armstrong sounded put out.

'No. I'm afraid I've been drinking,' Joel admitted, knowing how that would be received. 'Sorry, Mum. It's good to hear from you, but you should have warned me you were coming.'

Diana mumbled something about thoughtless sons, and then Patrick Armstrong came on the line. 'It's OK, Joel,' he said. 'We can easily take a taxi. It was your mother's idea to ring you. I guessed you might have company tonight.'

Joel frowned. 'Company?'

'What your father's trying so unsubtly to say is that we heard Olivia was back home again,' put in his mother tersely. 'She's not there with you, is she?'

'No.' Joel's tone was cooler now. 'More's the pity. She's not even staying in Bridgeford any longer. Her sister told me she's gone back to London.'

'Well—' Diana was obviously trying not to sound too delighted. 'Well, it's probably all for the best, Joel. After what she did.'

'But that's the point,' said Joel grimly. 'She didn't *do* anything. Louise told me a couple of days ago that she'd been lying when she said Liv had had an abortion. She hadn't. She really had had a miscarriage. And nobody— but especially me—would listen.'

He thought he might feel better when he got off the phone, but he didn't. He'd thought that telling his mother she'd been wrong about Olivia all along would give him some relief. But he was mistaken. The hollowness inside him seemed greater if anything. A great gaping hole of nothingness where once he'd had a heart.

He was in the kitchen, checking for beers in the fridge, when the doorbell rang. He'd just discovered he had two bottles of a German brew and he put them down on the counter with a distinct lack of patience. What now? he thought. Someone selling double-glazing? Or perhaps Sean had run away again. Surely not, now that he knew why his mother had been feeling so unwell.

He hoped it wasn't anyone from the university. He was only wearing drawstring black sweatpants and a black T-shirt. He'd intended to go for a run earlier, but intermittent rain and the bleakness of his mood had deterred him.

It was still light out and when he pulled open the door, he had no difficulty in identifying his caller. Olivia stood outside, slim and beautiful in a red slip dress and incredibly high heels, a loose wrap of some gauzy material floating about her bare shoulders.

'Hi,' she said, sheltering under the lee of the overhang. 'Are you going to invite me in?'

Joel stepped back abruptly, almost losing his balance in his haste to get out of her way. And then, still staring at her as if he couldn't quite believe his eyes, he said stupidly, 'I thought you went back to London.'

'I did.' Olivia moved into the hall, shedding her wrap into his startled hands. Then, glancing thoughtfully at him, she said, 'Are you drunk?'

Joel was taken aback. 'Me?' he said. 'Drunk?'

'You're acting as if you are,' she declared, sauntering past him into the sitting room. Then, turning, she pressed one finger delicately to her nose. 'It smells like a distillery in here.'

Joel tried to pull himself together. 'You're exaggerating,' he said, following her into the room and snatching up the empty bottle and his glass, stowing them away in the drinks cabinet. 'I was having a quiet drink, that's all.'

'A quiet drink?' Olivia faced him, her hips lodged carelessly against the back of the sofa. 'All alone?'

'No, my harem dashed upstairs as soon as you rang the bell,' said Joel shortly. And then, just in case she thought he was serious, 'Of course alone. Who else would I be with?'

Olivia moistened her lips. 'I don't know. What was that girl's name? Cheryl something or other. You could have been with her.'

'No, I couldn't.' Joel took a steadying breath. 'Why are you here, Liv? Have you come to say goodbye?'

'Goodbye?'

'Linda said you might stay in London.'

'Did she? Well, actually, I was arranging to have the rest of my belongings sent to the farm.' She paused. 'Sorry to disappoint you.'

Joel swore. 'That doesn't disappoint me, for God's sake! But what was I supposed to think?'

'Oh, I don't know.' Olivia shifted and the silky bodice moved sensuously against her body. 'You could say you were glad to see me.' She paused. 'You could even say you like my dress.'

Joel groaned. 'You look—fantastic,' he muttered shortly. 'But what is this, Liv? A crucifying mission? Have you come to see how much more pain I can take?'

'No.' Olivia turned then, walking around the sofa, trailing long nails that matched her dress over the soft leather. 'Why should I want to hurt you, Joel? Haven't we hurt one another enough?'

Joel sucked in a breath. 'Then you know—'

'About the lies? Yes, Louise told me.' She glanced his way. 'I assume she's told you?'

Joel nodded.

Olivia moistened her lips. 'And how did that make you feel?'

'Stupid! Devastated! Angry!' Joel raked back his hair with a hand that shook a little. 'God, Liv, I knew Maureen Webster worked at that clinic. And I had no reason to suspect that Louise might be lying.'

'Except that I'd told you it wasn't true!' exclaimed Olivia unsteadily. 'It never occurred to you that I might be telling the truth, did it?'

'Of course it did.' Joel swore again. 'Didn't she tell

you? I phoned the clinic. I wanted proof that you'd actually had an abortion.'

Olivia stared at him. 'And what happened?'

'I got some empty-headed receptionist who said she couldn't give out confidential information about the patients.' He groaned. 'All she would tell me was that, yes, you had had an appointment. She said nothing about you cancelling it.'

'Oh, Joel!' Olivia trembled. 'You should have had more faith in me.'

Joel shook his head. 'Do you think I haven't tormented myself with that ever since Louise decided to tell me?' he demanded. 'I've gone over every minute of those days with a fine-tooth comb and, whatever I do, I can't forgive myself for being such a fool. I should have listened to you. I should have realised you wouldn't have been so upset if it was what you'd wanted. Instead, I could hear the recep- tionist telling me that you had made the appointment in one ear and Louise whispering that you'd never wanted my baby in the other.'

'Oh, God, Joel—'

'No. Don't feel sorry for me, Liv. I was twenty years old. I should have known better.'

'We were both just kids,' said Olivia huskily, gazing up at him with brimming eyes. 'I wonder if I hadn't run away if we might have learned the truth.'

Joel made a helpless gesture. 'Do you think I haven't considered that, too?' He sighed. 'It would be so easy for me to say that you running away settled the matter. That it proved you'd been lying all along. But I was the real culprit, Liv. I blame myself totally. I moved out of the farm. I let you think that, as far as I was concerned, our marriage was over.'

'Our marriage *was* over,' whispered Olivia, but Joel only shook his head again, coming towards her, his face dark with emotion.

'Do you honestly think that if you'd stayed in Bridgeford, I'd have been able to keep away from you?' he asked hoarsely. 'For God's sake, Liv, I love you. I've never stopped loving you, dammit. Louise knows that. Maybe that was why she decided to be generous for once in her life.'

Olivia's lips parted, but, although she was tempted to tell him why Louise had had a change of heart, she decided that could wait. Evidently his ex-wife hadn't told him the whole story and Sean wouldn't be too eager to confess that he'd run away again.

'So—what are you saying?' she breathed, running the tip of her finger along the roughened edge of his jawline.

Joel flinched at her touch, but he didn't move away. 'Look at me,' he said instead, gripping the back of his neck with agitated hands. 'You've been back—what? Barely a month. And already I'm a nervous wreck. I can't eat; I can't sleep. And any illusions I had that I was content with my life have all crashed and burned. Does that answer your question?'

Olivia gazed at him. 'You mean that, don't you?'

'Damn right, I mean it,' he declared savagely, and, abandoning any further attempt to restrain his actions, he slid his hands over her shoulders and pulled her against him. 'You know I love you,' he said huskily. 'You must know I want to be with you.' His eyes darkened. 'Does your being here mean that you might forgive me, after all?'

Olivia uttered a breathy little laugh. 'It might,' she said tremulously. 'I'm thinking about it.'

'Well, don't take too long,' said Joel unsteadily, burying his face in the scented hollow of her throat, and Olivia trembled all over.

Her fingers clung to his shoulders, glorying in the taut strength of the arms that encircled her so possessively. Even now, it was hard to let herself believe this was actually happening. She'd been so depressed when she went to London, so unsure of what to think, what to do.

But this was Joel, she thought incredulously, the man she loved and who loved her. Had loved her for fifteen long years, years they'd wasted because of a jealous woman's lies.

And like a dam breaking, emotion flooded her body. There was no need to keep him in suspense. She loved him too much to let this moment slip away. 'I've thunk,' she said huskily, pressing herself against his hard body. 'The answer's yes.'

Their journey up the stairs was only punctuated by moments when Joel divested himself and Olivia of what they were wearing. Her shoes barely made it past the first stair and her dress slipped silkily off her shoulders a few moments later.

The fact that she wasn't wearing a bra caused a few minutes' delay as Joel's hands found her breasts and stroked them into painful arousal. But when she slid her hands beneath his T-shirt, he was compelled to discard it and go on.

She found the drawstring of his sweats only seconds later. The soft fabric skimmed down his narrow hips and he had to kick himself free of them before he tripped. However, her lacy thong did make it to the landing, where it adorned the newel post, like some erotic symbol of their desire.

Their lovemaking was hot and urgent at first. They were hungry for one another and there was no time for foreplay before Joel spread her legs and plunged into her slick sheath. Her moan of satisfaction was stifled by his mouth, and Joel's head was swimming as the blood rushed wildly into his groin.

He felt Olivia climax only moments before his own release, the instinctive tightening of her body engulfing him in flames. 'God, I love you,' he groaned, when he lay shuddering in her arms, and Olivia stroked the damp hair back from his temple with a trembling hand.

'I love you, too,' she whispered. 'So much. As soon as I saw you again, I knew I'd just been kidding myself that I'd got you out of my life.'

They made love again then, gently this time, sharing every delicious moment, stroking and caressing each other in an emotional demonstration of their love and renewal.

But then, Joel propped himself up on one elbow and looked down at her. 'Tell me about Garvey,' he said, not wanting to spoil the moment but he had to know. 'Did you love him?'

Olivia gave a rueful smile. 'Yes, I loved him,' she said. 'But not like I love you,' she added huskily. 'I couldn't understand why at first. He was young and very good-looking and I don't deny I was flattered when he asked me to marry him and move to New York, but there was no real—connection, if you know what I mean?'

'I'm trying to,' said Joel gruffly, and Olivia giggled.

'You've no need to be jealous,' she assured him gently. 'Our relationship was anything but passionate.' She paused. 'I must be incredibly naïve. When he insisted on waiting until we were married before consummating our relationship, I thought he was doing it for me, because he knew I'd had one disastrous relationship—ours—and he thought I wasn't ready for another.'

Joel's brows drew together. 'What are you telling me? That he was—gay?'

'See, you got it in one,' said Olivia ruefully. 'Yes, he was gay. But it took me months before I found out. And because he convinced me that we were good for one another, that it wasn't necessary for a relationship to be a sexual one to work, I went along with it. For what seems like such a long time now.'

Joel turned her face towards him. 'God, Liv, if he hurt you—'

'He didn't.' Olivia sighed. 'I hurt him, I think. But it took me some time to realise that, although I was living this celibate life, Bruce wasn't. I was just his cover, the wife he could escort to functions and display on any occasion when a wife was needed.'

'Hell!'

Joel stared down at her with impassioned eyes and she reached up to press her lips to his. 'Don't look like that, darling. It wasn't all bad. Bruce was a generous man. He was kind. Selfish, perhaps, but kind. I had my own bank account, a string of credit cards. He liked me to spend his money. He encouraged me to fill my wardrobe with expensive clothes, expensive accessories. There was nothing I couldn't have—financially, at least.'

'And then?'

'And then I discovered that he was leading a double life. The nights he was supposed to be working late—he was a merchant banker and they often work late into the evening—he was visiting his lover. Well, a series of lovers, actually,' she appended, her cheeks turning pink. 'He was a member of this club and—'

Joel laid his finger across her lips. 'You don't have to go on,' he said. 'I get the picture.' He paused. 'So you told him you wanted a divorce?'

'Mmm.' Olivia's lids drooped. 'He wasn't pleased.'

'I can believe it.' Joel snorted. 'You were in danger of exposing his deception.'

'Right. And all our friends—*his* friends, and work colleagues, all thought we had an ideal marriage.'

Joel nuzzled her cheek. 'So, what happened?'

'I moved out of our apartment. I got myself a small walk-up in Brooklyn and started divorce proceedings.'

'I gather they took some time?'

'You better believe it.' Olivia nodded. 'Bruce fought me every step of the way.' She bit her lip. 'He—he even went so far as to tell anyone who'd listen that I'd moved out because he wanted children and I didn't. I'd been stupid enough to tell him about—about the miscarriage, and he chose to use that against me, too.'

'But God, you could have made him suffer. Not to mention taking him for every penny he had.'

'I didn't want his money. I didn't want anything from him. OK, maybe I was stupid, but I just wanted to be free.'

'Oh, Liv!' Joel gazed at her with agony in his eyes. 'I wish I could take back every one of those years and make it up to you.'

Olivia looked up then, a smile tilting the corners of her mouth. 'Hey, this is going a long way to achieving it,' she assured him huskily. 'We all make mistakes, Joel. Me more than most.'

'And now?'

She wet her lips with a nervous tongue. 'I suppose that's up to you.'

'OK.' Joel didn't hesitate. Getting up onto his knees beside her, he said, 'Marry me. Marry me, Liv. Again. As soon as I can get a licence.'

'You really want to marry me again?'

'How can you doubt it?' Joel groaned, taking one of her hands and raising her palm to his lips. 'I'm crazy about you, Liv. Say you'll give me a second chance.'

Olivia didn't hesitate either. She wound her arms around his neck and pulled him down to her. 'Oh, I'll give you another chance,' she whispered. 'And I will marry you. Whenever it can be arranged.' She hesitated. 'I want to have your baby, Joel. We can't replace the one we lost, but we can ensure that Sean has more than one brother or sister, hmm?'

They were both sound asleep when the doorbell rang.

Olivia, her bottom curled spoon-like into the curve of Joel's thighs, was the first to hear it. The sound echoed unpleasantly through her subconscious, and, although she didn't want to move, she was obliged to open her eyes and shift a little restlessly against him.

Joel, getting exactly the wrong impression, pressed closer, and she felt the unmistakable stirring of his erection. 'Hey, you're insatiable,' he muttered huskily, parting her thighs, but Olivia pulled away from him, turning onto her back as the doorbell rang again.

'Hear that?' she said, unable to prevent the smile that

touched her lips at Joel's obvious disappointment. 'You've got a visitor.'

'Shit!'

Joel scowled, but when the bell rang for a third time, he had no choice but to slide out of bed and reach for the dressing gown hanging on the back of the bedroom door.

As he wrapped its folds about him, Olivia pushed herself up against the pillows. 'Who do you think it is?' she asked, unknowingly exposing dusky pink nipples to his urgent gaze, and Joel groaned.

'My mother and father?' he suggested flatly, seeing the look of dismay that crossed her face at his words. 'They phoned from the airport earlier. They wanted me to go and pick them up, but, as you know, I'd been drinking. I had to refuse.'

'I'm glad you did,' she murmured, barely audibly, but Joel had heard her.

'So'm I,' he said, pausing to bestow a lingering kiss at the corner of her mouth. 'Hold that thought, baby. I won't be long.'

The bell rang again, more insistently this time, as he went down the stairs, and, although he'd been attempting to pick up all the items of clothing strewn around, the summons was too urgent to ignore. Abandoning his efforts, he dropped the clothes he had rescued onto the chest at the foot of the stairs and strode barefoot to the door.

'Are you aware that it's raining, Joel?' demanded his mother, brushing past him into the hall. 'So much for us being concerned about you. You certainly took your time answering the door.'

'Are you aware that I was in bed, asleep?' retorted Joel,

giving his father an apologetic look as he followed his wife inside.

'In bed?' Diana Armstrong took off her jacket and shook a spray of water over the floor. 'It's barely ten o'clock, Joel. How much have you been drinking, for heaven's sake?'

'It's none of your—'

He didn't finish. His mother had been about to deposit her coat on the chest when she saw the jumble of clothes Joel had dropped there. Without hesitation, she picked them up, saying with obvious distaste, 'You've got a woman here, haven't you? Your father was right.'

Joel took the garments out of his mother's hands and returned them to the chest. 'Not *a* woman,' he said tersely. *'The* woman. Liv arrived just after you'd called. Does that explain the situation?'

Diana's mouth dropped open in disbelief, but Patrick Armstrong was much less perturbed. 'I wondered how long it would be before you two got together again,' he said warmly. 'I hope it works out this time, son. I really do.'

'Thanks, Dad.'

Joel shook the hand his father offered, but Diana wasn't finding it so easy to come to terms with what she'd heard. 'You mean—you were in bed with Olivia Foley?' she said incredulously. 'Oh, Joel, is that wise? What if—what if she hurts you again?'

'I won't.'

The voice came from above their heads and Joel turned to find Olivia coming down the stairs towards them. She was wearing an old rugby shirt of his that barely covered her thighs, a momentary peek of scarlet lace proving she'd rescued her thong from its perch.

His heart leapt into his chest as he went to meet her. She was so adorable, so beautiful, and she was his. He could hardly believe that fate was being kind to him at last. He wanted to take her in his arms and howl his satisfaction to the moon.

'Olivia!' Diana recovered quickly, moving towards the pair of them with a practised smile on her face. 'You must forgive me for being anxious. It's a mother's privilege, you know?'

'Well, it's a wife's privilege to defend herself, Diana,' responded Olivia smoothly, realising that the intimidation Joel's mother had once represented was all gone. 'Hello, Patrick,' she added, accepting his warm hug. 'Did you have a good flight?'

'Well, it was delayed—' Joel's father was beginning, when Diana broke in.

'What did you say?' she demanded. 'A *wife's* privilege?' She turned blankly to her son. 'You two haven't got married again while we were away, have you?'

'Not yet, Mum,' said Joel comfortably, putting a possessive arm about Olivia's shoulders and pulling her close. 'But it's only a matter of time. I've asked Liv to marry me and she's said yes.'

'Well, congratulations!' Once again, it was Patrick Armstrong who made the first move. 'It's long overdue, if you ask me. There should never have been a divorce.'

'I agree.' Joel bent and bestowed a warm kiss on the top of Olivia's head, and no one watching them could be left in any doubt that he meant it. He looked at his mother. 'Aren't you going to give us your blessing, Mum?'

Diana's lips tightened for a moment, but then, as if the

realisation that she couldn't fight against her whole family occurred to her, she came to give them both a kiss. 'What can I say?' she exclaimed, and there was reluctant defeat in her eyes. 'I hope you'll both find the happiness you deserve.'

EPILOGUE

'CAN I go in the pool again, *please*?'

Sean dragged the word out and his father and step-mother exchanged a knowing glance.

'You've spent half the afternoon in the pool,' Olivia pointed out, deciding to play the bad cop for a change. 'Didn't your father suggest you needed a rest? If you want to come with us this evening, you need to have a sleep.'

'Well, just five minutes more,' said Sean wheedlingly. 'Then I'll go and rest for a while, I promise.' He gave Olivia a beaming smile. 'I know you don't mind, really. And after all, in a year or so you'll be wanting me to teach Natalie to swim.'

Olivia patted the baby digesting her feed on her shoulder and pulled a wry face at Joel. 'That is true,' she conceded, feeling a quiver in her insides when she met his disturbing gaze. She knew what that look meant and he was getting impatient.

'OK,' Joel said abruptly. 'Five minutes, and then you go to your room. And I don't want to hear you playing that electronic game when you're supposed to be resting. Or you'll be keeping Marsha company tonight.'

'OK, Dad.'

Sean grinned at both his parents and then dived smoothly into the water. Since coming to the United States, his swimming skills had improved tremendously. But then, having a private pool in their garden was such an advantage. Something they would seriously have to consider when they got back home.

It was just over a year since Olivia and Joel had married again, and so much had happened in those twelve short months.

Their wedding had been a quiet affair, with just their families present. Olivia had worn an oyster silk dress, which swirled about her knees, and carried a bouquet of roses and white baby's breath, that had proved to be quite prophetic in the circumstances.

Sean had acted as both pageboy and best man, his own delight enhanced by the new arrangements that had been made for his care. His mother and father had agreed to share custody from now on, Louise admitting she'd be grateful for a little time to get used to having their new baby.

Meanwhile, Olivia had found part-time employment with an estate agency in Chevingham. It meant she didn't have so far to travel and she could easily collect Sean in the afternoons when he was living with them. It worked really well, satisfying both her need to do something useful and her desire for motherhood.

The fact that Sean got on so well with his stepmother was an added bonus. And Joel, who'd been accustomed to working late into the evenings when he was living alone, found himself leaving the university as early as possible, eager to spend time with his new wife and family.

Then, towards the end of the summer, Joel had been offered a year's sabbatical in the United States. He'd be attached to a prestigious American university, and it would enable him to study their technology as well as giving him the opportunity to lecture to a different student faculty.

It had been a wonderful offer, and Olivia hadn't hesitated before encouraging him to take it. His wife and family were expected to accompany him, of course, and a house in a small town just outside Boston had been put at their disposal for the duration of their stay.

Naturally, Sean had wanted to go with them, but Joel had explained that it wouldn't be fair to his mother to take him away for so long. However, a compromise had been reached: Sean had joined them at Easter, flying the Atlantic on his own, to the envy of all his friends.

Olivia's own news had had to wait until they were settled in Massachusetts. The revelation that she was expecting a baby had filled them both with excitement and apprehension. But, in the event, their fears were groundless. Olivia had had a perfectly normal pregnancy. Their baby daughter, whom they'd called Natalie, had been born in the hospital in North Plains, instantly gaining the love and attention of both her parents and her brother.

Their year in the United States would be over in October, and, although Olivia would be sorry to leave, she was looking forward to going home. They had still to show off baby Natalie to both her grandparents and her aunt and uncle, and, despite Sean's dismay at leaving the swimming pool and the friends he'd made at his school in North Plains, he was full of excitement at the thought of telling all his English friends of the experiences he'd had and the places he'd seen.

His swim over, Sean went to take his shower and to have a nap, and Joel lifted Natalie out of his wife's arms and cradled the little girl against his chest. Natalie was three months old and thriving, and Joel had just watched Olivia feeding her, an experience he found both distracting and stimulating.

The baby reached for the finger he held in front of her, gripping it with amazing strength for her age. 'You must be tired,' he said, touching her soft cheek with amazing gentleness. 'Your mother's fed you and changed you, and you should be ready to give us a few minutes' peace.'

'Babies are unpredictable,' said Olivia, with the knowledge gained from mixing with other mothers at the baby clinic. Her eyes twinkled. 'Perhaps you ought to be honest with her and tell her you want to take her mother to bed.'

'Is it that obvious?' Joel grinned, his teeth very white against the tan that had deepened all summer long. It was much hotter in Massachusetts than it was in the north-east of England. Olivia thought he looked well-nigh irresistible in a black vest and cargo shorts, and she couldn't wait until they were alone together either.

Half an hour later, Joel rolled onto his back beside her, giving a groan of satisfaction that Olivia shared. 'I wish we weren't going out tonight,' he said regretfully. 'I'd rather stay here with you. Alone.'

Olivia looped one hand behind her head. Her hair was damp from the humidity in the atmosphere and she had no idea how tempting she looked to her husband at that moment. 'We have to go,' she said. 'Or you do, anyway. They're giving the dinner in your honour. A kind of send-off to say they'll be sorry to see you leave.'

Joel turned onto his side to face her, his fingers stroking one swollen nipple into an instantaneous peak. 'I know,' he said, his voice thickening as he bent to suckle from her breast. 'I guess I'm just feeling possessive, that's all. When we go home, I'm going to have to share you with your family again.'

Olivia tried to steel herself against what he was doing. 'I'm looking forward to seeing Dad,' she said a little breathlessly. 'According to Linda, he gets about in his new wheelchair a lot. He's even talking about getting a car with hand controls only. It's wonderful that he's feeling so much better about himself.'

'Thanks to you,' said Joel, his fingers straying down over her ribcage to her navel. His hand dipped between her legs and Olivia felt the sympathetic flood of heat his tongue and lips had engendered. 'Your coming home was the best thing that happened to all of us. Me, particularly. I can't imagine what my life was like before you came.'

'Well, I suppose I have Linda to thank for that,' she murmured weakly. And then, trying to be sensible, 'I must remember to leave a bottle of milk for Marsha to give Natalie if she wakes up while we're gone.'

Marsha had proved to be a godsend. An elderly black woman, she'd answered their ad for a housekeeper when they first arrived. Olivia had been grateful to her for so many things, not least being there when she'd gone into labour. It was Marsha who'd driven her to the hospital and made sure Joel was there when their baby was born.

'Marsha's had half a dozen children of her own. I think you can rely on her to know what to do in all circumstances,' said Joel drily. His mouth sought hers and Olivia gave up the fight to keep her head.

With a little moan, she turned onto her side and wrapped one leg over his hips, bringing his semi-aroused sex close to her throbbing core. 'OK,' she said, 'I'll stop talking. But you're wasting time now. We've only got about twenty minutes before Sean will start wondering where we are…'